ELEMENTS OF SERVOMECHANISM THEORY

McGraw-Hill Electrical and Electronic Engineering Series

FREDERICK EMMONS TERMAN, *Consulting Editor*

W. W. HARMAN and J. G. TRUXAL, *Associate Consulting Editors*

Bailey and Gault · ALTERNATING-CURRENT MACHINERY
Beranek · ACOUSTICS
Bruns and Saunders · ANALYSIS OF FEEDBACK CONTROL SYSTEMS
Cage · THEORY AND APPLICATION OF INDUSTRIAL ELECTRONICS
Cauer · SYNTHESIS OF LINEAR COMMUNICATION NETWORKS, VOLS. I AND II
Cuccia · HARMONICS, SIDEBANDS, AND TRANSIENTS IN COMMUNICATION
  ENGINEERING
Cunningham · INTRODUCTION TO NONLINEAR ANALYSIS
Eastman · FUNDAMENTALS OF VACUUM TUBES
Evans · CONTROL-SYSTEM DYNAMICS
Feinstein · FOUNDATIONS OF INFORMATION THEORY
Fitzgerald and Higginbotham · BASIC ELECTRICAL ENGINEERING
Fitzgerald and Kingsley · ELECTRIC MACHINERY
Geppert · BASIC ELECTRON TUBES
Glasford · FUNDAMENTALS OF TELEVISION ENGINEERING
Happell and Hesselberth · ENGINEERING ELECTRONICS
Harman · FUNDAMENTALS OF ELECTRONIC MOTION
Harrington · INTRODUCTION TO ELECTROMAGNETIC ENGINEERING
Hayt · ENGINEERING ELECTROMAGNETICS
Hessler and Carey · FUNDAMENTALS OF ELECTRICAL ENGINEERING
Hill · ELECTRONICS IN ENGINEERING
Johnson · TRANSMISSION LINES AND NETWORKS
Kraus · ANTENNAS
Kraus · ELECTROMAGNETICS
LePage · ANALYSIS OF ALTERNATING-CURRENT CIRCUITS
LePage and Seely · GENERAL NETWORK ANALYSIS
Millman and Seely · ELECTRONICS
Millman and Taub · PULSE AND DIGITAL CIRCUITS
Rodgers · INTRODUCTION TO ELECTRIC FIELDS
Rüdenberg · TRANSIENT PERFORMANCE OF ELECTRIC POWER SYSTEMS
Ryder · ENGINEERING ELECTRONICS
Seely · ELECTRON-TUBE CIRCUITS
Seely · ELECTRONIC ENGINEERING
Seely · INTRODUCTION TO ELECTROMAGNETIC FIELDS
Seely · RADIO ELECTRONICS
Siskind · DIRECT-CURRENT MACHINERY
Skilling · ELECTRIC TRANSMISSION LINES
Skilling · TRANSIENT ELECTRIC CURRENTS
Spangenberg · FUNDAMENTALS OF ELECTRON DEVICES
Spangenberg · VACUUM TUBES
Stevenson · ELEMENTS OF POWER SYSTEM ANALYSIS
Storer · PASSIVE NETWORK SYNTHESIS
Terman · ELECTRONIC AND RADIO ENGINEERING
Terman and Pettit · ELECTRONIC MEASUREMENTS
Thaler · ELEMENTS OF SERVOMECHANISM THEORY
Thaler and Brown · SERVOMECHANISM ANALYSIS
Thompson · ALTERNATING-CURRENT AND TRANSIENT CIRCUIT ANALYSIS
Truxal · AUTOMATIC FEEDBACK CONTROL SYSTEM SYNTHESIS

Elements of Servomechanism Theory

GEORGE J. THALER, DR. ENG.

Professor of Electrical Engineering
U. S. Naval Postgraduate School

McGRAW-HILL BOOK COMPANY, INC.

New York   Toronto   London

1955

ELEMENTS OF SERVOMECHANISM THEORY

Library of Congress Catalog Card Number 54-10647

VII

63880

THE MAPLE PRESS COMPANY, YORK, PA.

PREFACE

The material in this text is intended for a one-semester senior under-graduate course. It has been used successfully at this level in a course given at the University of Notre Dame, and the bulk of the material has been used in a number of servomechanism courses given at the U.S. Naval Postgraduate School over a three-year period. The first 10 chapters are intended for classroom presentation; Chaps. 11 and 12 merely introduce advanced topics for the interested student.

This text was written with a threefold purpose:

1. It was desired to present the basic theory without using operational calculus or complex-variable theory, since these subjects are not normally given in an undergraduate engineering program.

2. The frequency-response methods were to be emphasized, since these are commonly used in practical engineering.

3. The polar and logarithmic approaches to analysis and design were to be integrated and compared.

The author feels that these purposes have been accomplished, except that the discussion of the Nyquist criterion is not rigorous. It does not seem possible to discuss this subject rigorously without using complex variable theory.

In order to integrate and compare the polar and logarithmic methods, both are introduced at the same point, Chap. 5, where the basic graphical plots are defined and explained. In the chapters following, each topic discussed is considered in terms of both the polar plot and the logarithmic plot, as far as this is possible. In Chaps. 8, 9, and 10, this procedure is extended to numerical illustrations; in fact, these chapters consist principally of worked problems. A number of closed-loop systems are postulated, numerical values are given for the components, and a desired performance characteristic is specified. The adjustment or compensation required to meet the specifications is then computed, using both loga-rithmic and polar methods. Each step in the computation is given, together with reasons for using that specific procedure. This method enables the student to acquire an elementary working knowledge of the subject as well as a sound theoretical background. Student response to this approach has been even better than the author anticipated.

A word of caution seems advisable concerning the problems at the ends of the chapters. Many of the problems for Chaps. 3, 9, and 10 require considerable computation time, often from 15 to 30 hours for a competent student. Also, some of the problems in other chapters may require a similar computation time unless numerical results from a corresponding problem in Chap. 3 are available. In order to minimize the over-all computation time for a semester's work, and also in order to show the effects of gain adjustment and compensation on a given system, the author has utilized the problems at the end of Chap. 3 in setting up problems for later chapters. It is possible to set up an assignment schedule so that a given student works with one or two specific systems, obtaining the transient solution, the transfer function, the polar and logarithmic plots, and then adjusts the gain and compensates the system. If this is done, the student can use the results of previous work on each succeeding problem, which considerably reduces the over-all computation time.

In conclusion, the author wishes to thank J. A. Northcott, head of the Electrical Engineering Department, University of Notre Dame, for his encouragement in the initial phases of the undertaking; Dr. W. A. Stein and Dr. C. B. Oler of the U. S. Naval Postgraduate School for their assistance in polishing the manuscript; A. J. White for his help in obtaining the families of transient-response curves in Chap. 3 and the phase-plane plots in Chap. 12; and Mrs. Helene Johnson for the typing of the manuscript.

GEORGE J. THALER

CONTENTS

ELEMENTS OF SERVOMECHANISM THEORY

CHAPTER 1

INTRODUCTION

1-1. The Problem of Automatic Control. The word *servomechanisms* was originally defined by Hazen with reference to a specific type of automatic-control system. Present usage of the term has departed considerably from the original definition, and a variety of meanings are associated with the word; all of them, fortunately, refer to automatic-control systems.

The definition recommended by the Feedback Control Committee of the American Institute of Electrical Engineers is: "A servomechanism is a feedback control system in which the controlled variable is mechanical position." Mathematical considerations indicate that the equation (or equations) of a position-control system may be obtained as a special case from a much more general class of equations. This general class of equations includes those of other types of control systems, and a much broader understanding may be obtained by considering the general case. This text emphasizes the servomechanism, or closed-loop automatic position control, but includes considerable material (mathematical and illustrative) which is aimed at developing a broader concept of the automatic-control problem.

Modern technology finds automatic control both necessary and desirable. It is being incorporated in every field of endeavor—from the military machine through the maze of industrial manufacturing plants to the laboratory of basic scientific research. A number of automatic-control applications are listed below. Many of these are, in themselves,

Applications of Automatic Controls

1. Temperature regulators
2. Pressure regulators
3. Fluid-flow controls
4. Liquid-level controls
5. Speed regulators
6. Tension control in paper mills
7. pH controls
8. Generator voltage regulators
9. Frequency regulators
10. Gun directors

11. Search radar-antenna control
12. Computers for gun directors
13. Analogue computers
14. Automatic pilots
15. Atomic reactors
16. Guided missiles
17. Telescope-tracking controls
18. Automatic-tuning Controls
19. Automatic-combustion Controls
20. Automatic milling machines

1

servomechanism systems; others may incorporate one or more servo-mechanism systems as portions of a complex process.

In practically all the applications there is a desired output condition that the system is to produce. The system is told what to do by some sort of command signal, and the various components between this command input and the output serve to control the energy supplied to the output in such fashion that the desired output condition is obtained. Regulatory systems normally are designed to maintain a constant output which may be preset at some calibrated command station, i. e., the input to a regulator is usually constant for long periods of time, and the system is designed to compensate for changes in load. The command signal to other types of automatic-control systems is, in general, variable in magnitude and direction. The output must then vary in some fashion, owing to this command signal. In many cases the output is expected to duplicate the input variation, but in other applications the output must vary as some function of the input signal.

Many systems which are to respond to a variable input operate with constant-load conditions, so that the property of good regulation during load changes is not necessary. Other systems are subject to load variations and must be good regulators in addition to satisfying the basic requirements of their specific control problem.

In order to ensure accurate and satisfactory control, certain features are desirable. The system output must be measured in order to determine existing conditions. This output must then be compared with the desired output in order to find the magnitude and direction of any error. This comparison can almost always be accomplished by some device producing a usable signal indicative of the error. If the system itself is made sensitive to this error, i. e., if the presence of an error signal causes the release of energy to the output in a direction to reduce the error, the system has a feedback loop and may be called an automatic-control system. If a control system does not measure the output quantity and utilize this measurement to reduce errors, the system is said to be an "open-loop" or "open-cycle" system.

1-2. Block Diagram of an Automatic-control System. The basic characteristics of an automatic-control system may be illustrated qualitatively by a block diagram, such as Fig. 1-1. This diagram is functional, rather than physical, in the sense that the blocks represent things that have to be done rather than pieces of equipment. The operation of a simple servomechanism may be explained from the block diagram as follows: A command signal is applied to the input and compared with the position of the instantaneous output. The result of this comparison, E, is amplified (raised to a higher power level), and this amplified signal is used to control a power device. The power device amplifies the signal supplied to it in the sense that it supplies still larger amounts of power to the output, or load, which the servo system is controlling. This output may in itself be a desired end result, or it may simply be used as the input to still another system.

From the preceding discussion it may readily be seen that the specific blocks in Fig. 1-1 may not exist as separate units, or, as another extreme, each block may contain a large number of distinct components. For example, the comparison device (or error detector), the controller, and the power device might easily be stages of a single electronic amplifier built on one chassis, thus combining three blocks into a single physical device. On the other hand, the output-measuring device and the comparison device might consist of several gear trains with two or more

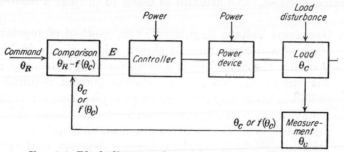

Fig. 1-1. Block diagram of an automatic-control system.

synchro units; the controller might be an electronic amplifier and a multistage amplidyne generator; and the power device might be a d-c motor and gear train. In such a system, there are several components in each block.

The block diagram of Fig. 1-1 is that of a simple, or single-loop, automatic-control system. It is not uncommon to have several measuring devices which determine instantaneous conditions at various places in the system and feed signals from these locations back to some point which is at a lower power level. Occasionally, but rarely, a signal may be fed to a high power level. Such systems are called multiloop systems. A detailed study of multiloop systems is beyond the scope of this text, although some elementary aspects are presented in a later chapter.

1-3. Qualitative Discussion of Specific Systems. In order to crystallize the concept of the block diagram, and at the same time provide some physical concept of systems, components, and general operation, it is desirable to explain in some detail the operation of specific systems. For this purpose, four different types of systems have been chosen: a generator voltage regulator, a hydraulic positioning servo, a tension control for a paper-reel drive, and a gun-director servo. These were selected for the following reasons:

1. They are relatively simple, and a physical explanation of their operation is not too involved.

2. They are dissimilar and thus indicate to some extent the diversity of problems to which automatic control can be applied and the diversity of methods and equipment which can be used to obtain satisfactory control.

3. Each is readily reduced to a functional block diagram.

In discussing each of the illustrative systems, the physical explanation of the purpose of each component is given, as well as a reasonably detailed outline of system performance. These explanations are intended to give the reader some background in the physical principles involved. The reasoning applied to obtain the block diagram is also explained, and for the same purpose. No attempt is made to present a mathematical analysis.

1-4. A Generator Voltage Regulator. One method of regulating the output voltage of a d-c generator is shown schematically in Fig. 1-2a. It is assumed that the generator is a large machine driven by a steam turbine. For such a machine, the excitation current required by the field is large and is frequently supplied by an exciter generator, as shown. The exciter may be built on the same shaft as the generator, or it may be geared to that shaft, or it may be driven by a different prime mover. In any event, the output voltage of the generator depends on the generator field current and thus on the armature voltage of the exciter.

If the output voltage of the generator is to be regulated, i. e., kept constant despite fluctuations in load current or turbine speed, then the generator field current must change to counteract such fluctuations. Since the generator field current is due to the exciter voltage, and this in turn is due to the exciter field current, it is apparent that the generator output voltage can be regulated by varying the exciter field current to counteract the effects of load and speed changes. These variations in the exciter field current must be automatic and must be caused by the output changes.

One method of automatically varying the exciter field current is to use a potentiometer *error-detection* system, as shown in the schematic diagram. One potentiometer is excited by a separate source of d-c voltage. The second potentiometer is connected across the generator output. The negative terminals of the two potentiometers are connected. The variable taps are then connected to the two ends of the exciter field. The difference in potential between the two taps drives current through the exciter field. For proper operation, the size and current capacity of the reference voltage and the potentiometers must be selected with due regard to the ratings of the exciter field, and the positions of the potentiometer taps must be adjusted.

Assuming that the system has been properly designed, its performance may be explained qualitatively as follows: A decrease in output voltage *increases* the potential difference between the potentiometer taps; this increases the exciter field current, which increases the exciter voltage, the generator field current, and the generator output voltage. Conversely, an increase in output voltage reduces the potential difference between taps, thus reducing the exciter field current, etc.

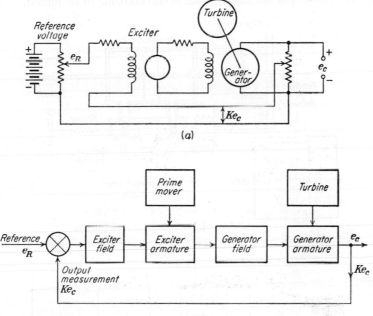

Fig. 1-2. (*a*) Generator voltage regulator. (*b*) Block diagram of a generator voltage regulator.

The block diagram of the system is shown in Fig. 1-2*b*. The use of separate blocks for the turbine, generator armature, generator field, prime mover for the exciter, exciter armature, and exciter field is fairly obvious. It is equally correct to use a single block for the generator unit and another single block for the exciter unit. This would be done in practice, but the separate blocks are shown here to emphasize the fact that physical units frequently require more than one block to show their characteristics on a block diagram. The output-voltage measurement is shown simply as a feedback line, and the reference voltage is shown in like manner. The error detection is shown symbolically as a subtractor into which the reference and output are fed, and from which comes a difference in voltage. Note that all blocks are interconnected by single lines, and the arrowheads on the lines indicate the direction in which the energy is

being fed.   Note also that there is a feedback of energy from output to
input; this makes a closed-loop system.

1-5. A Hydraulic Positioning Servo.   A hydraulic positioning servo
is shown in Fig. 1-3a.   The purpose of the mechanism is to position the
load accurately and to vary this position in accordance with some command signal.   An example of its use is positioning the cutting tool of a
profile milling machine.   In such a case, the load is the cutting tool, tool
holder, etc., and the command signal is the contour to be milled.

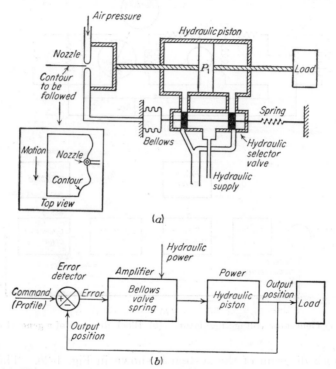

(a)

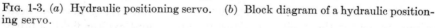

(b)

Fig. 1-3. (a) Hydraulic positioning servo.   (b) Block diagram of a hydraulic positioning servo.

The motor part of this device is the hydraulic piston, or ram, P_1.
This piston may be moved to the left or to the right by applying hydraulic
pressure to the proper port.   Control of this hydraulic pressure is obtained
with a selector valve.   This valve connects the hydraulic pressure line
to the proper port for a desired motion, and simultaneously connects the
other port to a hydraulic return line so that the fluid displaced by the
moving piston can escape.

The position of the selector valve is controlled in turn by the equilibrium position of a mechanical-spring–pneumatic-bellows combination.
The bellows is metallic, of course, and has a spring action of its own.

The spring and bellows are both set in compression, and air pressure is fed to the bellows.   Fluctuations in air pressure move the selector valve, causing the hydraulic ram to operate.

The fluctuations in air pressure that operate the power system are provided by the error-detection device.   The error detector consists of two nozzles rigidly supported in an axial line and mechanically connected to the main power piston.   The nozzle openings face each other and are as close together (in an axial direction) as is practical.   A constant-pressure air supply is connected to one nozzle, and the other nozzle is connected to the bellows.   When no obstruction is placed between the nozzle openings, maximum pressure is developed in the bellows.   The spring-bellows combination is set for equilibrium at about half of this maximum pressure.   The edge of the profile is inserted between the nozzles so as to interrupt the air flow, thus reducing the bellows pressure from the maximum.   Equilibrium is obtained when this obstruction reduces the bellows air pressure to the predetermined value.

Having obtained the equilibrium setting, the profile is moved past the nozzles.   If this motion tends to remove the edge from between the nozzles, the air pressure to the bellows increases, the selector valve is moved and supplies hydraulic pressure to the right-hand piston chamber, and the power piston is moved to the left to reestablish equilibrium. Conversely, if the profile motion moves the edge into the air stream, the bellows pressure is reduced, the selector valve is moved and supplies hydraulic pressure to the left-hand piston chamber, and the power piston is moved to the right to reestablish equilibrium.   Accuracies of 0.001 in. are readily obtained with such a system.

The block diagram of the system is shown in Fig. 1-3b.   The hydraulic piston is the power device and is represented by a block; the bellows–spring–selector-valve combination acts as an amplifier and is represented by a second block.   The output position is measured by the nozzle combination, and the command is the profile edge.   The error detection, resulting in a change in pressure to the bellows, involves the action of the bellows and physically is not separable into a distinct error-detector unit.   Thus the error-detector block is a symbolic, or functional, representation.   Note that the output measurement feeds back energy to the input, and makes the system a closed-loop system.

1-6. A Tension Control for a Paper-reel Drive.   In the manufacture of many types of paper, the paper sheet is continuous and must be rolled on a central tube.   To obtain a compact, uniform result, the paper must be pulled onto the reel at constant tension.   If the tension increases, the paper tears, while reduced tension produces a loose roll.   Thus, control of the tension is necessary.

As layers of paper are run onto the reel, the diameter of the roll is increased.   If the reel speed remained constant, the linear velocity of the paper would increase; this would increase the tension.   Thus, tension control may be obtained by varying the reel speed.

Figure 1-4a shows, in simplified form, a scheme which is commonly used.   The desired tension is set by means of a rider roll under which the paper strip passes.   The rider is constrained to vertical motion only, and the magnitude of the tension depends on the weight of the rider roll and on any spring loading which may be used in addition.   Since the paper tension effectively supports the rider, any change in tension moves the

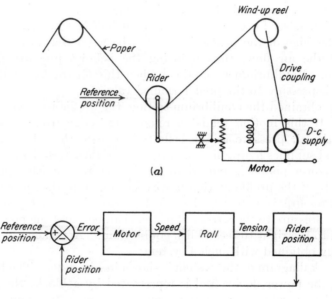

FIG. 1-4. (a) Tension control for a paper-reel drive.   (b) Block diagram for a tension control.

rider in a vertical direction, upward for increased tension and downward for decreased tension.

The vertical movement of the rider is used to control the speed of the d-c drive motor by changing the field current, and this change in motor speed adjusts the tension.   For example, if the tension in the paper increases beyond the desired limit, this raises the rider.   A lever connection (other means may be used) then reduces the resistance in the motor field.   The motor field current increases, and the motor speed decreases, which decreases the paper tension.

The block diagram of the tension control is shown in Fig. 1-4b.   The motor may be considered as a single device and a single block, or the motor field and armature may be thought of as separate parts of the system and two blocks may be used. The first scheme is used here. The output of the system is shown as three blocks instead of one, because this procedure seems more readily understood. The reference position is the desired rider position, and the feedback signal is the actual rider position. The error detector is the mechanical linkage between rider and field rheostat, and the error is the mechanical displacement produced by this linkage. Note that there is a feedback of energy from output to input; this makes the system a closed-loop system.

1-7. Gun-director Servos. The final result of an antiaircraft fire-control system is the alignment of the gun barrel. In order to point the gun in some desired direction, it is necessary to rotate the entire gun mount in the horizontal plane as well as to elevate or depress the gun barrel. Since both must be done simultaneously and automatically, two separate servomechanisms are required, one for rotation and the other for elevation. These are true servomechanisms because they control the position of the output.

The load of the rotation servo is the entire gun mount, which is a rather large inertia with appreciable friction. The load of the elevation servo is essentially the gun barrel, a smaller inertia with less friction. Thus, the two servomechanisms need not be identical, because the loads are different in magnitude. However, rotational motion is required in both cases, and d-c motors (of different sizes) might be used as power devices. The remainder of the systems would normally be quite similar, and so the following discussion is limited to the rotation servo.

The motor is connected to the gun mount through a reduction gear train because the normal speed rating of a d-c motor is much higher than the maximum permissible rotating speed of the gun mount. The size of the motor is determined by several factors:

1. The torque required by the maximum specified acceleration of the gun mount

2. The maximum power demanded during acceleration

3. The normal power required when the mount is rotating at some specified angular velocity

These factors arise from conditions inherent in the job which is to be done. When the gun-director servo receives a command to track a plane, the gun may be pointed in an entirely different direction. It is then necessary to get "on target" rapidly. The motor must therefore accelerate the gun mount and swing it into position. The maximum permissible acceleration is determined by allowable stresses in the gun mount, by personnel safety, etc. During such acceleration periods, a large torque and large amounts of power are obviously required and must be considered in selecting the motor. Since aircraft move at high velocities, the gun must move continuously to remain "on target." This continuous rotation is not necessarily at constant velocity, but a representative value for the expected gun velocity is determined and used in selecting the motor.

Assuming that a d-c motor is used, d-c power must be made available and must be controlled in such a way as to permit both position control and velocity control of the gun mount. It might be possible to use relays for such a purpose but, in general, better control is provided by using a separate generator to supply the motor armature. The Ward Leonard connection is normally used, but the generator is frequently an amplidyne in order to provide faster response and more amplification.

Another advantage of the amplidyne for such a purpose lies in the fact that its control field windings normally do not require much power and thus may be supplied from an electron-tube amplifier. The amplifier itself is not unusual in design, but the output must provide a d-c voltage of reversible polarity in order to control the direction of motion of the gun mount. The input to the amplifier is the so-called "error signal"; that is, it is some signal indicating the displacement of the gun mount from the desired position. The error signal in general indicates two things—the direction of such a displacement and the magnitude of the displacement.

Various devices are available for providing such an error signal. In this discussion, it is assumed that the device used is a pair of selsyns, connected as a synchro generator, and a control transformer. (For a detailed discussion of these devices, see Appendix II.)

To utilize a synchro-generator–control-transformer combination as an error detector for the gun director, one shaft is rotated to indicate the command, i. e., the desired position or velocity, and the other shaft is used to indicate the actual position of the gun mount. The control transformer might be geared to the gun mount so that a specific position of the synchro shaft corresponds to a definite direction for the gun. The synchro generator would then be the command station, and its shaft might be rotated by hand or by some automatic command system. The complete system is shown in the diagram of Fig. 1-5a.

It is readily seen from the diagram of Fig. 1-5a that the system forms a closed loop. It can also be seen that the amplifier design cannot be that of an ordinary audio amplifier since the input is at constant frequency and variable amplitude, while the output of the amplifier must provide an unbalance in the control field which has a polarity depending on the phase of the input signal and a magnitude proportional to the magnitude of the input signal.

The operation of the system of Fig. 1-5a may be described qualitatively as follows:

1. Assume that the gun mount is stationary and the synchros are aligned so that no error signal is applied to the amplifier.

2. It is desired to turn the gun to a new position so that the shaft of the synchro generator is turned through 45°.

3. The synchros are no longer aligned, and so an error signal is applied to the amplifier. This signal is amplified and unbalances the amplidyne field, thus permitting a net generated voltage.

4. The amplidyne then provides power to the motor which drives the gun mount in the proper direction* to reduce the error to zero.

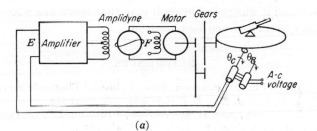

(a)

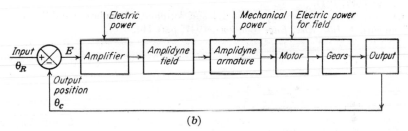

(b)

FIG. 1-5. (a) Gun-director servo. (b) Block diagram for a gun-director servo.

5. If the system has been designed to provide rapid acceleration, the gun mount will probably overshoot the desired position. The error signal is then reversed 180° in phase, and the motor also reverses to bring the mount back to the desired position.

6. This overshooting, or hunting, may occur only a few times before the gun becomes stationary. It is one of the purposes of servomechanism design to control this feature.

The block diagram of the gun-director servo is shown in Fig. 1-5b. The justification of most of the blocks should now be obvious from the examples previously cited. It may be noted that, in this case, the error detector is specifically the combination of two synchros which actually

* The connections required for the proper direction of rotation must be predetermined.

compare the mechanical position of the two shafts and produce an electrical error signal. The synchros are thus both an error-detector combination and an electromechanical transducer. Note that there is a feedback of energy from output to input; this makes the system a closed-loop system.

1-8. Summary. This chapter has presented the basic definitions of an automatic-control system. The need for such systems has been pointed out, and several illustrations of different types of feedback control systems were given. In addition to a physical explanation of the operation of each illustrative system, the block diagram of the system was determined, and it was noted in each case that there was a feedback path making the system a closed-loop system.

REFERENCES

FORSTER, E. W., and L. C. LUDBROOK, Some Industrial Electronic Servo and Regulator Systems, *J. Inst. Elec. Eng. (London)*, 1947, part IIa.

LAUER, H., R. LESNICK, and L. E. MATSON, "Servomechanism Fundamentals," McGraw-Hill Book Company, Inc., New York, 1947.

SMITH, E. S., "Automatic Control Engineering," McGraw-Hill Book Company, Inc., New York, 1944.

WHITELEY, A. L., Fundamental Principles of Automatic Regulators and Servomechanisms, *J. Inst. Elec. Eng. (London)*, 1947, part IIa.

CHAPTER 2

GENERAL ASPECTS OF ANALYSIS AND DESIGN

2-1. Introduction. The purpose of this chapter is to give the reader a broad general view of the problems encountered in working with servo-mechanisms and feedback control systems. A secondary purpose is to indicate the need for several types of mathematical analysis, with the hope that the reader will then be more interested in the mathematical developments and component analyses which necessarily precede the study of complete elementary systems.

The first step is to show what type of performance may be required of a servomechanism, the type of reasoning which leads to the selection of basic components to do a specific job, and the total inadequacy of physical reasoning in determining how well such a combination of components will perform. This leads logically to a discussion of mathematical methods which are capable of determining performance, and these methods are considered in the light of their usefulness in both analysis and design. A brief résumé is given of transient methods and their advantages and disadvantages, and the possibility of using frequency-response methods is explained and illustrated.

2-2. Performance Requirements of Automatic-control Systems. A detailed or quantitative discussion of complex systems containing more than one feedback loop is beyond the scope of this text. The performance requirements of most automatic-control systems, however, are basically the same, and although the quantitative discussions in this text are largely restricted to single-loop systems, the following discussion of performance requirements applies much more generally.

The general function of any automatic-control system is to control a specific load in some predetermined fashion. An automatic-control system is always a dynamic system, and the control problem may therefore be divided into two parts, i. e., system performance in steady state and system performance during transient periods.

Steady-state Performance. Where a load is mechanical, a system may be expected to control one or more of three quantities:

1. Position
2. Velocity
3. Acceleration

If a load is not mechanical, the above terminology does not apply directly, but in almost every case the equations of a specific system indicate that the controlled quantity (output) is equivalent to a position, velocity, or acceleration.

The steady-state performance of a given system is measured in terms of the accuracy with which the load is controlled. If the command signal requires that the load be moved to a given position, the servomechanism has perfect steady-state performance provided the desired position is obtained exactly. A similar statement is equally true for systems controlling velocity or acceleration. If the system is not perfect, and of course few are, the accuracy of the system may be expressed in terms of the deviation of the output from the desired value, i. e., in terms of the error. The performance of a given system is good enough for the intended application if the error is less than some value which has been specified, usually by the user.

It should be reasonably obvious that a good positioning system will not necessarily be a good velocity or acceleration control, and vice versa. However, some applications require that more than one quantity be controlled simultaneously by the same system. For example, the gun-director servo previously discussed must not only rotate the gun mount at some velocity specified by the command signal, but it must point the gun itself in a specified direction, since rotation at the proper speed is useless if the gun is pointing behind the aircraft. In this and similar cases, the steady-state performance of the system is acceptable only if the velocity control is perfect and the position error is kept within acceptable limits. One of the important problems in servomechanism design is that of reducing such errors to very small values.

Transient Performance—General. The transient-performance requirements of an automatic-control system are more varied than the steady-state requirements though, in many ways, equally important. Before considering the transient requirements, two important facts must be emphasized. First, because of the feedback loop, it is possible that improper design or adjustment may make the system hunt continuously (oscillate), so that steady state is never reached. Such a system is said to be unstable and, except in very special applications, this hunting has to be eliminated. Normal transient requirements do not apply to unstable systems. The second important fact is that definite transient specifications exist for each application; a system which is considered to have good transient performance for its application might be very unsatisfactory in another application.

The term "transient" refers, of course, to the time period when the system is changing from one steady-state condition to another. For example, if a positioning system is commanded to move its load from one position to another, the transient period is the time interval between the instant the command is given and the instant the new steady state is achieved.   During this transient period the error has instantaneous values far greater than are acceptable during steady state.   Such a condition is not ideal, but is unavoidable in practical systems.   The important problem is to achieve the new steady state in as short a time as is consistent with the limitations of the equipment and in such a fashion that the condition of the output is within specified limits.

Since the preceding statements are very general, the following qualitative explanations are used to convey a more concrete physical picture. Suppose that a positioning servomechanism is given an instantaneous

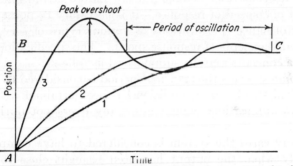

FIG. 2-1. Response curves of a simple positioning servomechanism.

command to move its load from position A to position B.   Then the input, or command signal, would undergo a step variation, as shown by curve ABC in Fig. 2-1.   In general, no physical load can duplicate such an input variation.   The output may eventually reach the new steady state indicated by the line BC, and the variation may be similar to one of the curves 1, 2, or 3.   The time required for this transient period may vary from a fraction of a second to several hours, depending on the nature of the control application.

Curves 1 and 2 approach the new steady state slowly but never exceed it.   Curve 3 approaches and reaches the new steady state rapidly but overshoots and then oscillates about the steady state before coming to rest.   A response such as that of curve 1 is very slow, or sluggish. Technically, it is called an "overdamped" response.   In general, its only desirable characteristic is the fact that it does not overshoot, but since this characteristic is also shown by other curves which reach steady state more rapidly (such as curve 2), an overdamped system is seldom, if ever, used.   Curve 2 approaches steady state more rapidly than curve 1, but does not overshoot.   If no curve can lie to the left of curve 2 without overshooting, then curve 2 is said to be a "critically damped" response. Any curve which overshoots, such as curve 3, represents an "underdamped" response. Damping is that property of the system which opposes existing motion. Most damping devices produce forces opposing the motion which are proportional to the velocity. The most common form of natural damping is viscous friction.

The important features of transient performance, which may be visualized from Fig. 2-1, are:

1. Speed of response and settling time
2. Peak overshoot (if any exists)
3. Frequency of transient oscillation

Each of these is explained in detail in the following paragraphs, and its practical importance is pointed out.

Speed of Response and Settling Time. Before defining and discussing the concept of "speed of response," it is necessary to point out that the general performance specifications of various types of servomechanisms permit several concepts of response speed. The specifications which give rise to these concepts may be summarized as follows:

1. For some systems the transient period is considered to be over only when the final steady-state condition has been attained.

2. Certain applications cannot allow any overshoot during the transient period.

3. In many cases the system is considered to have completed its job satisfactorily when the output has been brought close to the desired condition and kept within specified tolerance limits about that desired condition.

Where the system requirements are as in case 1 or 2, it is often true that the critically damped system is best, unless very complicated and expensive controls are used. That is, for a simple linear single-loop system, the critically damped condition provides the fastest response possible without overshoot, and therefore would probably be used where specifications such as those in case 2 are encountered. It may also be shown mathematically that a given system, when critically damped, approaches steady state faster than the same system when underdamped and therefore would be used with specifications as in case 1.

If the system considered is a simple system, i. e., if its characteristic equation is a quadratic, the curve of its critically damped time response is a simple exponential curve. A "time constant" for such curves may be defined as the reciprocal of the constant factor in the exponent, i. e., if

$$y = ae^{-xt}$$

then the time constant is defined as

$$\tau = \frac{1}{x} \quad \text{sec}$$

For such cases, the speed of response may be defined as the time corresponding to a given number of time constants. A commonly used figure of merit derived from this concept is that the speed of response is four time constants. The number four is selected because evaluation of a simple exponential equation shows that in a time interval corresponding to four time constants 98 per cent of the possible change has been made, and thus, after four time constants, the output of a critically damped system is within 2 per cent of its new steady-state value.

When it is of primary importance to drive the output close to the desired steady-state condition as rapidly as possible, it is frequently true that an underdamped servomechanism accomplishes this purpose better

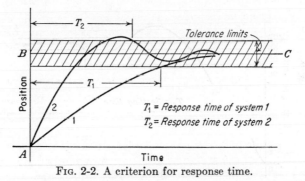

Fig. 2-2. A criterion for response time.

than a critically damped system. This is illustrated in Fig. 2-2, where it is again assumed that the command signal moves the input rapidly from A to B, so that the new steady state is indicated by the line BC. Curve 1 represents the response of a critically damped system and curve 2 that of an underdamped system. It is seen that the critically damped system reaches final steady state more rapidly, but if the important criterion is to get the output within the limits indicated by the crosshatched band, then the underdamped system accomplishes this more rapidly.

When such a criterion is used for system speed of response (and it is a common criterion in control applications), it is not possible to define the speed of response in terms of time constants. In fact, a criterion cannot be readily defined at all, since the speed of response depends not only on the specific system and the amount of underdamping but also on the tolerance limits of the application. Design of an underdamped system to obtain a specified speed of response is largely based on figures of merit that have been set by experience and good performance in the resulting system depends largely on the designer's experience. Some of the figures of merit which are used are discussed in the following sections on peak overshoot and the frequency of the transient oscillation.

The concept of settling time is similar to that of speed of response, but it is defined more specifically. When a system is underdamped, the oscillations in the output gradually die out, and the system "settles down" to steady state. For purposes of definition, the oscillations are considered negligible when 98 per cent of the possible change has been accomplished. The time required to accomplish this is called the "settling time." The meaning is illustrated graphically in Fig. 2-3.

Peak Overshoot. When an automatic-control system is designed as an underdamped system, the output overshoots the desired steady-state condition, and a transient oscillation occurs. The first overshoot is always the greatest, and its maximum value is called the "peak overshoot," or "maximum overshoot." Thus, if any undesirable features

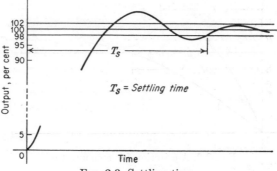

FIG. 2-3. Settling time.

result from overshooting, they are most noticeable on the first overshoot, and subsequent undershoots or overshoots should generally be less important. It is essential to know what objectionable features may result from overshooting and what limitations should be placed on the peak overshoot to minimize or eliminate such conditions.

There are two basic objections to large overshoots: One lies in the possibility of damaging some part of the system; the other lies in the fact that, while slightly underdamped systems may have a faster speed of response than critically damped systems, badly underdamped systems usually approach steady state rather slowly. The possibility of damaging the system arises from the relatively high accelerations which must be used to get a large overshoot and the resulting stresses in the operating and structural parts of the system. If the stresses are not excessive, the only reasons for limiting overshoot lie in the performance requirements of the system.

While it does not require much thought to see that a badly underdamped system would actually take a long time to approach steady state, it is not easy to see what quantitative limits should be set on the peak overshoot. It has been found by experience that satisfactory performance is most frequently obtained if the peak overshoot is limited to 1.5 or less. By this is meant that, for a command signal of unit amplitude, the output should swing from zero to no more than 1.5. There are exceptions to this in both directions, of course, and it is not possible at present to formulate a brief rule which is more specific, although some work has been done in this direction.

Frequency of the Transient Oscillation. An underdamped system hunts, or oscillates, about the final steady-state condition, as may be seen from Fig. 2-1. The frequency of this oscillation is important for several reasons. If the frequency happens to be near a natural frequency of some part of the system or of the structure on which the system is mounted, mechanical coupling can transmit the vibration and cause a mechanical resonance. This may either cause unsatisfactory results in terms of over-all performance, or it may actually result in destruction of the system or component.

On the other hand, a knowledge of the frequency of the transient oscillation is an aid to estimating system performance. In general, if the peak overshoot is limited to some fixed value, say 1.4, then for systems with a peak overshoot of 1.4, that system which has the highest transient oscillating frequency normally responds the fastest. This fact is another qualitative figure of merit which is quite useful in design, but which cannot readily be expressed in numbers. Further reference to this figure of merit will be made later in the text.

2-3. Design Specifications. From the preceding discussion, the nature of the basic design specifications for an automatic-control system is readily seen. Obviously, the designer must know the physical nature of the quantity to be controlled. To make the discussion more concrete and more readily correlated with the preceding sections, it will be assumed that the problem is to control the position and velocity of a mechanical rotational load.

The design specifications for such a load must include:

1. The moment of inertia and the coefficient of friction of the load, or other information which implicitly contains these data

2. The velocity, or range of velocities, for expected operation

3. The time allowed for the drive motor to achieve the desired load velocity, i. e., the desired speed of response

4. The maximum permissible overshoot, if any

5. The permissible steady-state position error

The above are necessary specifications. Many additional detailed requirements are normally specified, but the discussion in this chapter is restricted to these items.

2-4. Selection of System Components from Design Specifications. Knowing the load to be driven and the performance expected of the load, the designer must select a motor capable of driving it. The motor must not only have sufficient power capacity for the steady-state load requirements, but it must be capable of supplying the peak transient power. If a motor is tentatively selected on a power basis, a check must be made to see if it is capable of accelerating the load rapidly enough to satisfy the speed-of-response requirement. This usually involves knowledge of the starting torque and the torque-to-inertia ratio of the motor.

Having selected the drive motor, the designer must then choose other components, such as:

1. A controller for the motor
2. A measuring device to monitor the load position and velocity
3. A data input device to accept the command signal
4. An error detector to compare the command signal with the output measurement
5. A means of operating the controller from the error signal

In each case, the minimum qualifications of the selected component are physical suitability, power capacity, and accuracy, but many other factors are involved. Note that in each case the component is selected primarily on a physical basis. Little mathematics is needed, and system performance specifications act as limits, not as values to be obtained exactly.

Using such methods, the designer obtains a basic system which is physically capable of doing the task required. That is, the system has sufficient power capacity, measurements are sufficiently accurate, and corrective power is applied when there is an error. It does not follow, however, that the system would be satisfactory if assembled and tested. At least one factor, the allowable overshoot, has not been considered at all, and the speed of response and steady-state position error have not been explicitly used in selecting the components. The obvious next step is an investigation of this preliminary design, not just to check performance (because acceptable performance can hardly be expected), but to determine what else must be done to obtain the specified performance.

It is reasonably obvious that the transient and steady-state performances of such a combination of components cannot be checked by physical reasoning. There is no physical way to tell whether the system is overdamped or underdamped, except to build it and test it. Since the engineer normally wants a reasonable assurance that the system can work before building it, the logical procedure is to perform a preliminary mathematical analysis.

2-5. The Choice of Mathematical Tools. To find the performance of a physical system, the obvious mathematical approach is through direct solution of the differential equation of the system. When analysis is the main purpose of a mathematical study of a servomechanism, the differential equation is solved. When the main purpose of the mathematical study is that of determining what must be done to obtain a desired performance, the differential equation is not an optimum tool. The automatic-control problem is seldom one of analysis only; in general, it is a very definite design problem, and because of the design features the solution of the differential equations involved is not necessarily a profitable undertaking.

It has been found that the design of servomechanisms and other feedback control systems is most conveniently accomplished using frequency-response methods, with transfer functions employed as an intermediate tool. The following sections indicate the advantages and disadvantages of differential-equation solutions, and show the possibility of using frequency-response methods.

2-6. The Differential Equation of a Positioning Servomechanism. In order to illustrate the advantages and disadvantages of the differential

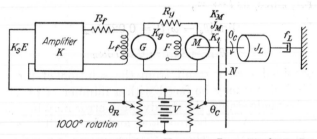

FIG. 2-4. A positioning servomechanism. $K = 100$, $R_f = 50$ ohms, $L_f = 5$ henrys, $R_g = 48.8$ ohms, $J = 1.0$ slug-ft^2, $f_L = 0.00143$ ft-lb/rad/sec, $V = 100$ volts, $N = 50/1$, $J_M = 8 \times 10^{-4}$ slug-ft^2, $K_t = 0.812$ ft-lb/amp, $K_M = 1.25$ volts/rad/sec, $K_g = 200$ volts/amp, and $K_s = 5.73$ volts/rad.

equation as a tool for design purposes, an illustrative positioning servomechanism is considered, as shown in Fig. 2-4. This system is essentially the same as the gun-director servo of Fig. 1-5a, and so no descriptive discussion is needed.

The differential equation of this system may be derived by any convenient method, and is

$$\frac{L_f R_g}{K_g K_t}\left(J_m N + \frac{J_L}{N}\right)\frac{d^3\theta_C}{dt^3}$$

$$+ \left[\frac{R_g R_f}{K_g K_t}\left(J_m N + \frac{J_L}{N}\right) + \frac{L_f R_g f_L}{K_g K_t N} + \frac{K_m L_f N}{K_g}\right]\frac{d^2\theta_C}{dt^2}$$

$$+ \left(\frac{K_m R_f N}{K_g} + \frac{R_g R_f f_L}{K_g K_t N}\right)\frac{d\theta_C}{dt} + KK_s\theta_C = KK_s\theta_R \quad (2\text{-}1)$$

Equation (2-1) is seen to be a third-order equation. An algebraic solution of such an equation is possible* but is quite laborious, and the resultant solution contains combinations of parameter values difficult to interpret.

Using the numerical parameter values given with Fig. 2-4, the numerical differential equation becomes

$$0.09 \frac{d^3\theta_c}{dt^3} + 2.462 \frac{d^2\theta_c}{dt^2} + 15.62 \frac{d\theta_c}{dt} + 573\theta_c = 573\theta_R \qquad (2\text{-}2)$$

Assuming that the input, θ_R, is initially at rest, and then is put into constant-velocity rotation, $\theta_R = \omega_R t$, the solution to Eq. (2-2) is

$$\theta_c = \omega_R[t - 0.0273 + 0.0063e^{-28.95t} + 0.0538e^{+0.794t} \sin (14.79t - 203°) \qquad (2\text{-}3)$$

Equation (2-3) expresses the time performance of the system for the parameter values used. It shows that the system is unstable (exponential term with positive exponent). It shows that the oscillatory frequency is 14.79 rad/sec. If the system were stable there would be a steady-state position error, since, as $t \to \infty$,

$$\lim_{t \to \infty} [\theta_c - \omega_R t] = 0.0273\omega_R$$
$$\theta_{css} = \theta_{Rss} - 0.0273\omega_R \qquad (2\text{-}4)$$

Having obtained such a result from the solution of the differential equation, the designer may be faced with a number of problems. The system must be made stable, the steady-state error may be too large, the response of the system may be too slow, and there will be a problem of controlling the transient overshoot after the system is stabilized. While all these items may not be important in a specific application, certainly several of them will be, and the designer must determine whether the desired conditions can be obtained by adjustment of the selected components or whether a more drastic change must be made.

In any physical system not all the parameters are adjustable. In the system of Fig. 2-4, the only parameters readily adjustable are:

K_s the error-detector sensitivity
K, the amplifier gain

These may be readily increased or decreased. Certain other parameters may be increased, but in general they may not be decreased. These are:

R_f, the generator field resistance
R_g, the armature resistance
J_L, the load inertia
f_L, the load friction

The gear ratio, N, has a small range of variation in an experimental setup, but has none in a finished product. The motor constants, K_t and K_m, can

---

*Lauer, H., R. Lesnick, and L. E. Matson, "Servomechanism Fundamentals," McGraw-Hill Book Company, Inc., New York, 1947.

be altered by changing the field excitation, but the range of adjustment is not great.   No other parameter values (in the system of Fig. 2-4) can be changed except by replacing an existing component with a new one.

The effect of varying a parameter value is not readily determined. Perhaps the easiest way to show this is to consider Eq. (2-1) and study the effect of parameter changes on the coefficients.   Changes in K_s and K affect only one term in the characteristic equation, and the forcing-function term.   Changes in R_f, R_g, J_L, f_L, N, K_t, or K_m affect at least two coefficients in the characteristic equation.   Thus K_s and K are convenient adjustments, not only because a wide variation is possible, but also because the effect of any variation is easily studied, and a trend may be established.   The other possible adjustments are not usually desirable because their effect on system performance is complicated, and trends are not readily established.   In any event, the effect of a parameter change usually can be determined only by computing the new values of the coefficients of the differential equation and solving it again.   This is certainly a laborious process, particularly when a number of trials may be necessary.

It should not be assumed that the performance of a servomechanism can be set to specified values by parameter adjustment alone; in fact, the reverse is more commonly true, i. e., it usually is necessary to insert additional components.   After the basic system is shown to have unsatisfactory performance, the first problem of the designer is really that of determining whether or not adjustment is a possible means of obtaining satisfactory performance.   This may be quite difficult to determine from the differential equation.   Assuming that adjustment is feasible, the parameters to be adjusted and the amount of adjustment normally can be determined only by trial and error.   Such computations are a laborious undertaking—so laborious that construction of the system and experimental adjustment are often the best solution.

If preliminary investigations show that adjustment will not produce satisfactory performance, then the designer must decide what changes must be made in the system.   The differential equation of the system usually does not give any clues to the type of change needed.   These must be obtained from other sources, and the general theory is discussed in Chap. 3.   It may be stated that the most common procedure is to add a filter to the system to compensate for the performance deficiencies.   The addition of such a device normally changes the system differential equation, usually increasing the order.   That is, Eq. (2-1) is a third-order linear differential equation, and the addition of a filter to the system of Fig. 2-4 would produce a linear differential equation of at least fourth order.   When a filter is added, the amplifier gain usually must be increased, and suitable values for the filter parameters must be determined. To do this, using only the differential equation, requires trial-and-error methods and considerable labor, since the order of the equation has been increased.

From the preceding discussion it should be obvious that the differential equation of a servomechanism and its solution are not satisfactory tools for design procedures. In addition to the labor involved, the trial-and-error methods needed usually do not lead to an optimum result, i. e., although the result obtained may meet specifications, it is possible that even better performance may be obtainable.

2-7. The Possibility of Using Frequency-response Techniques for Servomechanism Analysis and Design. A detailed justification for the use of frequency-response methods to analyze and design servomechanisms is clearly not possible at this point; the bulk of this book is devoted to such justification and to the methods and techniques used. However, the basic physical and mathematical facts which make possible the use of frequency-response methods can be stated and explained. This is done in the following paragraphs.

The time domain and the frequency domain are formally related by the Fourier integral. This means that the transient (time) response of a system should be calculable if the frequency response is known for all frequencies from minus to plus infinity. Such calculations are impractical, but certain approximations are available. If the frequency response of a system is known, some of the salient features of the transient response may be estimated with reasonable accuracy. It is well known that the height of the resonance peak in a frequency-response curve is indicative of the amount of damping present, but if such a system is actuated by a sudden disturbance (step function), it will undergo transient oscillations, and the amount of damping present obviously determines the per cent maximum overshoot and the time required to damp out the oscillations. Thus the height of the resonance peak in the frequency-response curve of a servomechanism is indicative of the maximum overshoot and of the settling time, or speed of response. In like manner, the frequency at which resonance occurs is related to the frequency of the transient oscillation, and this is indicative of the speed of response of the system.

Unfortunately, the relationship between frequency-response values and transient-response values is not readily expressed in a simple equation for even the simplest type of servomechanism. The height of the resonance peak and the value of the resonant frequency do not define exactly the maximum transient overshoot, nor the oscillating frequency, nor the speed of response. However, certain general empirical relationships exist which permit fair correlation between frequency-response performance and transient performance. These relationships are:

1. The resonance peak of the frequency response (expressed as a ratio

of output amplitude to input amplitude) is greater than the maximum overshoot of the transient response (expressed as a ratio of maximum output variation to the magnitude of the step input disturbance) for reasonable values of the resonance peak, say from 1.2 to 2.5.

2. The frequency at which resonance occurs is essentially the same as the transient oscillating frequency.

3. Systems having the same height of resonance peak have transient oscillations that damp out in essentially the same number of overshoots and undershoots, so that systems with high resonant frequencies have transient responses that damp out in short time intervals. Thus, a system with a high resonant frequency, but a reasonable resonance peak, has a fast response.

4. A well-damped system—one having perhaps two overshoots and one undershoot—has a minimum response time of about twice the reciprocal of the resonant frequency, if this frequency is expressed in radians per second.

The above criteria are certainly not exact. They are based on a number of observations, starting with a study of the simplest type of servomechanism, coupling the results of this study with experience, and limiting them to apply to the range of performance normally expected of servos. They are, however, the historical basis for modern frequency-response methods of analysis and design. If the frequency response of a given system is computed or measured, the resonance peak and the resonant frequency indicate the transient overshoot and the speed of response fairly accurately. Conversely, if a system is to be designed so that its transient performance lies within certain limits as to overshoot and response speed, the designer may select a resonance peak and resonant frequency which are suitably correlated and may then design the system using frequency-response methods.

As previously stated, the correlations are not exact. Furthermore, no exact correlations of this type can be hoped for, since the differential equation of a servomechanism may be of second order or higher, and it is unreasonable to expect that a correlation between the resonance peak and transient overshoot of a second-order system would hold equally well for a fourth- or fifth-order system. In fact, it is surprising that the correlations are as good as experience has shown them to be. It should also be noted that the correlations stated thus far refer only to performance during the transient period. Computation of steady-state performance is also conveniently accomplished in the frequency domain, but it cannot be presented here because it depends on the mathematical developments in later chapters.

The preceding paragraphs have indicated only the possibility of using frequency-response methods for the analysis and design of servomechanisms, but have made no attempt to justify their use. Perhaps the best justification lies in the fact that frequency-response methods are very widely used today, while the differential-equation approach has been obsolete for years. The reasons for this lie in a few simple facts: Computation is much less laborious and time-consuming with the frequency-response methods; trends may be established, and an optimum solution obtained; the addition of components to a system does not invalidate all previous computations, and does not particularly complicate additional calculations. The bulk of this text verifies these statements by developing the frequency-response techniques and applying them to specific problems.

REFERENCES

BROWN, G. S., Transient Behavior and Design of Servomechanisms, *NDRC paper,* 1943.

CHESTNUT, H., and R. W. MAYER, "Servomechanism and Regulating System Design," vol. I, John Wiley & Sons, Inc., New York, 1951.

LAUER, H., R. LESNICK, and L. E. MATSON, "Servomechanism Fundamentals," McGraw-Hill Book Company, Inc., New York, 1947.

THALER, G. J., and R. G. BROWN, "Servomechanism Analysis," McGraw-Hill Book Company, Inc., New York, 1953.

CHAPTER 3

TRANSIENT ANALYSIS OF SERVOMECHANISMS

3-1. Introduction. As noted in the preceding chapter, the transient response of a given servomechanism, or of any automatic-control system, may be obtained by writing and solving the differential equations of the system for the desired boundary conditions. The solutions may be obtained using any of the standard mathematical methods, although operational methods and, in particular, the Laplace transformation are favored by most workers in the field.

The differential equation of the simplest ideal servomechanism is a second-order differential equation. In general, there are few practical systems with differential equations of such low order. However, the best starting plan for the study of the basic theory is to begin with the simple ideal servo.

The purpose of this chapter is threefold:

1. To point out that there are three basic physical parameters which limit the performance possibilities of the simplest idealized servomechanism, and to study the effect of these parameters on performance.

2. To show that the deficiencies of the simple ideal system may be decreased or eliminated by adding components which compensate for, or counterbalance, the physical parameters responsible for the deficiencies.

3. To show the basic mathematical nature of the compensation devices needed.

To accomplish this threefold purpose it is necessary to write the differential equations of a number of idealized systems, and to solve them for the transient response of the system. In order to have a transient response, however, the system must be subjected to some disturbance, i. e., there must be some change in input conditions or in load conditions. Mathematically speaking, there must be a forcing function which can be inserted in the differential equation. Thus, in order to write the differential equations, suitable forcing functions must be chosen.

In view of the preceding comments, the first part of this chapter deals with the types of disturbances which may be expected in the normal operation of servomechanism and other automatic-control systems. The mathematical functions chosen to represent these disturbances are defined, and the reasons for the choice of these mathematical functions are

27

explained. It then becomes practical to define the simple ideal system, and to write and solve its differential equation for both transient and steady-state performance. Analysis of the solutions shows clearly the limitations of the system and the effects of the physical parameters involved. Further analysis leads logically to methods of compensating for these limitations.

3-2. Disturbances Which Produce Transient Responses in Control Systems, and Mathematical Functions Used to Simulate Them. A simple automatic-control system has only two points at which disturbances are to be expected. These are at the input, or command station, and at the output, or load. The disturbances actually experienced depend on the physical nature of the specific system and the application in which it is used. For a system with mechanical input and output, the input disturbances may take the form of a position change, a velocity, an acceleration, or an oscillation; the output disturbances usually are load changes, which may be expressed as a force or torque. If the input and output members are not mechanical in nature, the disturbances could probably be described by other words, but are analogous to mechanical disturbances. Therefore, the following discussion is worded as if the input and output of the system were mechanical rotating shafts, but the comments apply to any physical system.

Step-displacement Function. One type of input disturbance is a sudden rotation of the input shaft. It is desired to predict the transient and steady-state performance of the servomechanism following such a disturbance. In practice, such a disturbance cannot be instantaneous, but the shaft rotation may be very fast. When analyzing the performance by solving the differential equation of the system, the disturbance must be described mathematically as a "forcing function," and it is desirable to standardize on an expression for it. The accepted standard is to assume that the change in shaft position is instantaneous. This has several advantages: It is conveniently represented mathematically; it is a faster change than can be obtained physically so that pessimistic results are obtained, i. e., the transient performance of the actual system following an actual disturbance will be better than predicted; and, finally, such standardization permits ready comparison of performance between different systems.

The instantaneous change in input position is called a "step-displacement function" because a plot of input-shaft position, θ_R, vs. time, t, looks like the profile of a step, owing to the instantaneous displacement of the input shaft. This is shown in Fig. 3-1. The mathematical expression for this is

$$\theta_R = 0 \qquad t < t_1$$
$$\theta_R = K \qquad t \geqq t_1$$

Step-velocity or Ramp Functions. In many applications the input member may be initially at rest, but is put into motion and ultimately operated at constant velocity or nearly constant velocity. The transient and steady-state performances of a system due to such a disturbance are not adequately described by the results obtained using a step-displacement function, and a different type of forcing function must be defined. Again it is desired to standardize on a forcing function which is readily expressed mathematically and which is reasonably representative of actual disturbances.

FIG. 3-1. Step displacement of θ_R at time $t = t_1$.

The function selected assumes that the input is initially at rest and is suddenly put in rotation at constant velocity. Such a function accurately represents the steady-state condition if the velocity chosen is the same as the steady-state velocity of the actual system. The instantaneous change from zero velocity to a finite velocity is more rapid than can be obtained physically, and the comments made for the step-displacement function apply here also.

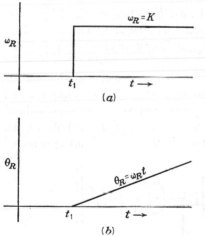

FIG. 3-2. The step-velocity function.
(a) Step change in velocity at $t = t_1$
(b) A *ramp* of position starting at $t = t_1$

If input velocity is plotted vs. time, as in Fig. 3-2a, the sudden change in velocity appears as a step, and the function is therefore called a "step-velocity function." On the other hand, if the input position is plotted vs. time, as in Fig. 3-2b, the curve appears as a rising straight line, or ramp, and is therefore called a "ramp function." In either case, the basic equation for the disturbance is $\theta_R = \omega_R t$, where ω_R is the velocity in radians per second.

Acceleration and Oscillatory Input Disturbances. A pure acceleration input disturbance is rarely encountered. A step-acceleration function could be defined if needed. Most normal disturbances include finite accelerations, but if the basic disturbance is a positional change, the intermediate accelerations and velocities are ignored and the step displacement function is used, while if the basic disturbance is a change in velocity, the step-velocity function is suitable.

Oscillatory, or periodic, input disturbances are best handled by studying the frequency response of the system, and solution of the differential equation is not required, as is shown later in the text. If the periodic input occurs simultaneously with some other disturbance, then the principle of superposition may be applied. In fact, for any number of different combinations of disturbances, superposition is applicable as long as the system is linear.

Load Disturbances. For a system with mechanical rotational output, load disturbances may be considered as torques. The torque may act in either direction of rotation as a constant quantity, or it may vary in magnitude and direction. For most analysis and design purposes, it is represented either as a constant quantity or as a sinusoidally varying quantity. In either case, the mathematical expression representing the load disturbance is readily incorporated in the differential equation, and normal methods of solution apply.

3-3. A Basic Servomechanism. The purpose of a servomechanism is to control the position of its output. The output member may be capable of linear or angular motion, and the driving device may be a linear actuator or a rotational motor. It is assumed for this discussion that

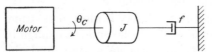

both the motor and the load rotate, and that the combination of motor and load are characterized by a net rotational inertia J and a viscous friction f. They may be represented schematically, as in Fig. 3-3.

Fig. 3-3. Schematic representation of a motor-load combination.

In order to control the output position, a command signal must be supplied and the output position must be measured. The command and output must be compared and the motor energized by the signal obtained from this comparison. If these requirements are added symbolically to the system of Fig. 3-3, the result is the simple closed-loop system of Fig. 3-4.

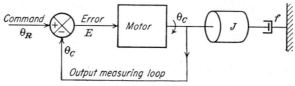

Fig. 3-4. A simple closed-loop system.

The system shown in Fig. 3-4 is idealized in the following ways:

1. The output position is assumed to be measured instantaneously and exactly.

2. The error detector is assumed to compare the command and output signals, producing an error signal E which is the instantaneous difference between them.

3. It is assumed that the error signal is at a power level sufficiently high to drive the motor directly.

Further idealization is provided by assuming that the motor is a torque motor producing an output torque T directly proportional to the instantaneous error signal.

The differential equation of the system is readily obtained by noting that

$$T = J\frac{d^2\theta_c}{dt^2} + f\frac{d\theta_c}{dt} \tag{3-1}$$

$$T = KE \tag{3-2}$$

$$E = \theta_R - \theta_c \tag{3-3}$$

From these equations,

$$J\frac{d^2\theta_c}{dt^2} + f\frac{d\theta_c}{dt} + K\theta_c = K\theta_R \tag{3-4}$$

It should be noted that the possibility of an external torque applied to the load is neglected in the above equation.   Load torque is considered later in the discussion.

3-4. Servomechanism with Viscous Damping Subjected to Step Input Displacement.   If the initial conditions are applied to the system described by Eq. (3-4), the procedure is as follows:

1. It is convenient to rearrange the equation by defining new parameters for use as coefficients.   These do not simplify the equation or its solution, but they do simplify the interpretation of the results.   Therefore, let

$$\omega_n = \sqrt{\frac{K}{J}}$$

f_c = friction coefficient required for critical damping = $2\sqrt{JK}$

$\zeta = \dfrac{f}{f_c} = \dfrac{f}{2\sqrt{JK}}$ = damping ratio

Substituting in Eq. (3-4),

$$\frac{d^2\theta_c}{dt^2} + 2\zeta\omega_n\frac{d\theta_c}{dt} + \omega_n{}^2\theta_c = \omega_n{}^2\theta_R \tag{3-5}$$

2. Using classical methods, the characteristic equation is

$$\frac{d^2\theta_c}{dt^2} + 2\zeta\omega_n\frac{d\theta_c}{dt} + \omega_n{}^2\theta_c = 0 \tag{3-6}$$

If the system is underdamped, the roots are

$$r_1; r_2 = -\zeta\omega_n \mp j\omega_n\sqrt{1-\zeta^2} \tag{3-7}$$

and the transient solution is

$$\theta_c = Ae^{(-\zeta\omega_n - j\omega_n\sqrt{1-\zeta^2})t} + Be^{(-\zeta\omega_n + j\omega_n\sqrt{1-\zeta^2})t} \tag{3-8}$$

3. For an initial step-displacement input of $\theta_R = 1$, the steady-state output position will be $\theta_C = 1$. Since the complete solution of the differential equation is the sum of the transient and steady-state solutions,

$$\theta_C = 1 + Ae^{(-\zeta\omega_n - j\omega_n\sqrt{1-\zeta^2})t} + Be^{(-\zeta\omega_n + j\omega_n\sqrt{1-\zeta^2})t} \qquad (3\text{-}9)$$

This may be manipulated into the form

$$\theta_C = 1 + e^{-\zeta\omega_n t}[C \sin (\sqrt{1 - \zeta^2}\, \omega_n t + \phi)] \qquad (3\text{-}10)$$

where $\phi = \tan^{-1} (\sqrt{1 - \zeta^2}/\zeta)$

4. To evaluate the coefficient C note that, at $t = 0$, $\theta_C = 0$. Also, owing to the inertia of the load, the output cannot attain a finite velocity at $t = 0$, even though accelerated. Thus, at $t = 0$,

$$\frac{d\theta_C}{dt} = 0$$

Applying these conditions to Eq. (3-10),

$$0 = 1 + C \sin \phi \qquad (3\text{-}11)$$
$$0 = -\zeta\omega_n(C \sin \phi) + C\omega_n \sqrt{1 - \zeta^2} \cos \phi \qquad (3\text{-}12)$$

from which

$$C = -\frac{1}{\sqrt{1 - \zeta^2}} \qquad (3\text{-}13)$$

Thus the solution of the differential equation is

$$\theta_C = 1 - \frac{e^{-\zeta\omega_n t}}{\sqrt{1 - \zeta^2}} \sin \left(\sqrt{1 - \zeta^2}\, \omega_n t + \tan^{-1} \frac{\sqrt{1 - \zeta^2}}{\zeta} \right) \qquad (3\text{-}14)$$

3-5. Discussion of Transient Response to Step-displacement Input. The curves of Fig. 3-5a show the variation of the output quantity θ_C as a function of the dimensionless product $\omega_n t$ when the positioning system is subjected to a step-displacement input, $\theta_R = 1.0$. These curves, in conjunction with Eqs. (3-14) and (3-5), permit some basic conclusions with regard to the performance limitations of the servomechanism and the adjustment of that performance.

It is readily seen from the curves that the system becomes more oscillatory as ζ decreases in magnitude. Since the value of ζ is indicative of the viscous friction, it is apparent that the oscillatory tendencies may be suppressed by increasing the friction.

The speed of response is indicated on the curves by the dimensionless abscissa $\omega_n t$. If it is desired that the system reach steady state in a short time, then, in general, ω_n should be large. For example, if the curves of Fig. 3-5a are consulted, and it is decided that a value for ζ of $\zeta = 0.6$ is desirable, and if it is further decided that the system is sufficiently close

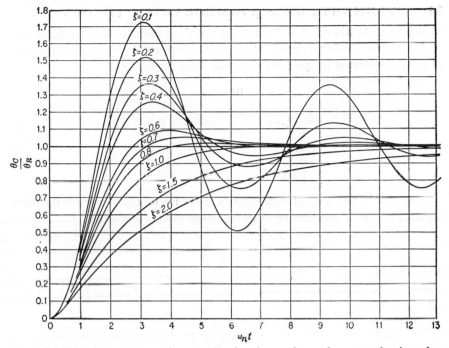

FIG. 3-5a. Transient response of a second-order viscous-damped servomechanism when disturbed with a step-displacement input.

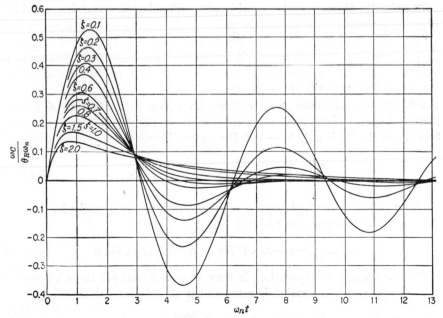

FIG. 3-5b. Velocity response of a second-order viscous-damped servomechanism when disturbed with a step-displacement input.

to steady state when $\omega_n t = 5$, then the required value of ω_n may be determined from the desired speed of response.   Table 3-1 shows the variation in ω_n as a function of specified response time for $\omega_n t = 5$.

TABLE 3-1

Specified response time T, sec	$\omega_n = \omega_n t/T = 5/T$
1	5
0.5	10
0.1	50
0.01	500

There is no theoretical difficulty in meeting almost any specification for such a simple positioning system.   One merely notes that

$$\omega_n = \sqrt{\frac{K}{J}}$$

and selects a motor with a sufficiently large torque-to-inertia ratio.   Then one notes that

$$\zeta = \frac{f}{2\sqrt{KJ}}$$

and selects a viscous damper with the proper value of f.

Practically, there may be considerable difficulty in obtaining a drive with the desired torque-to-inertia ratio which also meets specifications of weight, size, and cost.   Similar difficulties arise in selecting a viscous-damping device.   Furthermore, if the system may be used with inputs other than a step displacement, its performance may be entirely unsatisfactory, as indicated in the next section.

3-6. Servomechanism with Viscous Damping Subjected to a Step-velocity Input.   If the basic servomechanism of Fig. 3-4 is to be subjected to a step-velocity input, $\theta_R - \omega_R t$, the same differential equation applies;

$$\frac{d^2\theta_c}{dt^2} + 2\zeta\omega_n \frac{d\theta_c}{dt} + \omega_n^2\theta_c = \omega_n^2\theta_R \qquad (3\text{-}5)$$

Using classical methods to solve this equation, the transient solution (for the underdamped case) is still

$$\theta_c = Ae^{(-\zeta\omega_n - j\omega_n\sqrt{1-\zeta^2})t} + Be^{(-\zeta\omega_n + j\omega_n\sqrt{1-\zeta^2})t} \qquad (3\text{-}8)$$

For the steady-state solution, it may be noted that for large values of time the output acceleration is zero, and it then follows that

$$\theta_{css} = \omega_R t - \frac{2\zeta\omega_R}{\omega_n} \qquad (3\text{-}15)$$

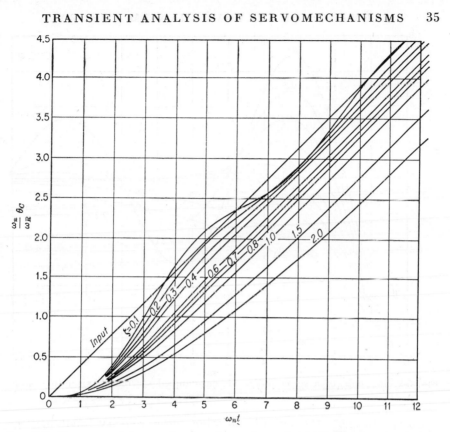

FIG. 3-6. Response of a second-order viscous-damped servomechanism to a step-velocity input.

The complete solution is then

$$\theta_C = \omega_R t - \frac{2\zeta\omega_R}{\omega_n} + Ae^{(-\zeta\omega_n - j\omega_n\sqrt{1-\zeta^2})t} + Be^{(-\zeta\omega_n + j\omega_n\sqrt{1-\zeta^2})t}$$

$$= \omega_R t - \frac{2\zeta\omega_R}{\omega_n} + (C\cos\omega_n\sqrt{1-\zeta^2}t + D\sin\omega_n\sqrt{1-\zeta^2}t)e^{-\zeta\omega_n t} \quad (3\text{-}16)$$

The boundary conditions are: at $t = 0$, $\theta_C = 0$, and $d\theta_C/dt = 0$, from which

$$C = \frac{2\zeta\omega_R}{\omega_n}$$

$$D = \frac{\omega_R}{\omega_n}\frac{2\zeta^2 - 1}{\sqrt{1 - \zeta^2}}$$

Substituting in Eq. (3-16) and manipulating, the variation of θ_C as a function of time may be expressed as

$$\theta_C = \omega_R\left[t - \frac{2\zeta}{\omega_n} + \frac{e^{-\zeta\omega_n t}}{\omega_n\sqrt{1 - \zeta^2}}\sin\left(\omega_n\sqrt{1 - \zeta^2}t + \tan^{-1}\frac{2\zeta\sqrt{1 - \zeta^2}}{2\zeta^2 - 1}\right)\right]$$

$$(3\text{-}17)$$

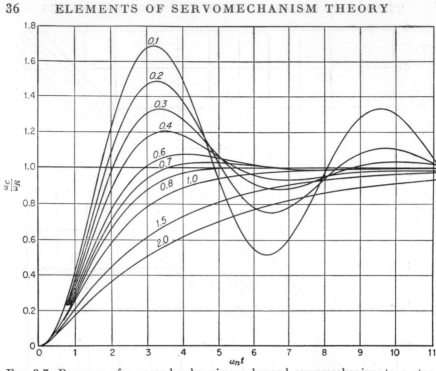

Fig. 3-7. Response of a second-order viscous-damped servomechanism to a step-velocity input.

Curves to show the output variation for a velocity input may be plotted in two ways: $(\omega_n/\omega_R)\theta_c$ vs. $\omega_n t$, as in Fig. 3-6, or $(d\theta_c/dt)/\omega_R$ vs. $\omega_n t$, as in Fig. 3-7.

3-7. Discussion of Performance with Velocity Input. It is readily seen from both the curves and the equations that a servomechanism subjected to an input-velocity signal reproduces the input velocity, i. e., the steady-state output velocity is identical with the input velocity. The output position, however, does not provide correspondence with the input position. This is discussed in a later paragraph.

During transient conditions a servomechanism hunts if it is under-damped. Specifically, the output velocity oscillates above and below the input velocity until the transient is damped out. The amplitude, frequency, and duration of this oscillation depend on the ζ and ω_n of the system. The output position hunts correspondingly, but about its steady-state condition, not about the commanded position. If the system is well damped, the output and input may not attain even instantaneous position correspondence.

The lack of steady-state position correspondence under velocity operation can be a serious defect in a servomechanism. The physical reason for the steady-state error is quite simple; the viscous friction provides a retarding torque during velocity operation, and the motor must provide a counterbalancing drive torque to produce torque equilibrium, but it can only produce a torque proportional to the position error, and so a position error must exist.

It is obvious that the friction drag can be reduced by reducing ζ, but this also reduces the damping, and overshooting may be excessive in the transient period. It is also possible to increase the gain so that a large driving torque is provided for a small error, but this also decreases ζ and gives poor transient performance. Some improvement may be obtained by increasing both the friction and the gain, but this is not practical if appreciable velocities are to be used, because the energy dissipated by the friction becomes excessive.

There are several ways to reduce the steady-state velocity lag error, only one of which uses viscous friction. This is a special device, developed by A. C. Hall, which utilizes a fluid chamber connected to the load (or motor) shaft. The chamber contains an inertia disk which is spring-coupled to the shaft so that it provides damping action only during oscillatory periods and causes no drag during constant velocity. So far, it has been applied only to very small servos. Other methods of reducing steady-state velocity lag errors are discussed in later sections.

3-8. Effect of External Load Torque. If the output (or load) of a servomechanism is subjected to some external torque, the basic differential equation of the system is affected, since the equilibrium condition becomes one for which the drive torque must counterbalance the algebraic sum of the normal load torque and the external load torque. The solution of the differential equation is not appreciably more involved than for a normal case, and it is not presented here.

If such external torque is applied to a static-positioning servomechanism, the steady-state output is not in correspondence with the input. This follows logically from the fact that a torque equilibrium must be maintained and the drive can only supply a torque if there is an error. Therefore, there must be an error to provide the necessary torque.

The same reasoning applies to a servo with velocity input and external load torque. The drive must supply sufficient torque to counterbalance the algebraic sum of the friction torque and the external load torque. If both are in the same direction, the error is greater than would be encountered without the external torque.

3-9. Methods for Improving the Performance of a Servomechanism— General Discussion. The preceding paragraphs indicate that there are two important inherent defects in a servomechanism driven by a signal proportional to the position error and having only viscous friction for damping. These defects are:

1. The inability to combine low steady-state position error with good transient performance when operated under velocity conditions (constant or near-constant input velocities).

2. The inability to compensate for externally applied load torques.

It is apparent that improvement in the performance of the system can be obtained either by reducing the magnitude of the errors or by completely eliminating them. From a theoretical point of view, complete elimination seems to be the proper step, but, from a practical point of view, some error can often be tolerated, and the choice between small error and no error is frequently an economic problem. It is therefore necessary to investigate both possibilities.

The reduction of steady-state error due to viscous drag during velocity operation (the reduction of *velocity-lag error*) may be accomplished in several ways. The first requirement is that the viscous friction must be reduced, since this is the basic cause of the velocity-lag error. When the viscous friction is reduced, the damping coefficient, ζ, is also reduced, and something must be done to provide damping during the transient period. The possible sources of additional damping may be found from an analysis of the basic equations of the system and from physical reasoning.

First, consider the equations for the basic servomechanism.

$$\frac{d^2\theta_C}{dt^2} + 2\zeta\omega_n \frac{d\theta_C}{dt} + \omega_n{}^2\theta_C = \omega_n{}^2\theta_R$$

$$E = \theta_R - \theta_C$$

$$\zeta = \frac{f}{2\sqrt{KJ}}$$

$$\omega_n = \sqrt{\frac{K}{J}}$$

Note that the damping, ζ, is part of the coefficient of the first derivative of the output. If ζ is reduced, but the over-all coefficient is kept at the same value by introducing another term, then the damping remains unchanged. This suggests the possibility of introducing an additional first-derivative signal to compensate for the reduction in ζ. Furthermore, since the error, output, and input signals are interrelated, it seems possible that a derivative of any one of these quantities should have some effect on the damping. These possibilities are discussed later.

Next, consider the expression for the damping coefficient, and note that the inertia, J, appears in the denominator of this expression. It is then apparent that if f is reduced but J is also reduced, acceptable damping may possibly be obtained. This is logical from a physical viewpoint also. Overshooting during the transient period is caused by kinetic energy stored in the system inertia, so that reducing the inertia should decrease the overshoot.

In practical servomechanisms, however, it is usually not possible to reduce the physical inertia appreciably, because this is set by the load to be driven, the motor required to drive that load, and the necessary interconnections, such as gears. Thus any reduction in inertia must be an apparent or effective change rather than a physical reduction.

If the differential equation of the servomechanism is written in its basic form

$$J \frac{d^2\theta_c}{dt^2} + f \frac{d\theta_c}{dt} = KE$$

it is seen that J is the coefficient of the second-derivative term. Then, if a signal proportional to a second derivative is introduced, it may be possible to reduce the value of the net coefficient of the second-derivative term, which is equivalent to reducing the system inertia. Again, there are three possible signals available, owing to the interrelation between input, output, and error. These will be investigated in a later section.

The preceding paragraphs suggest the use of derivative signals to reduce velocity-lag error, but they do not indicate their effect when a load torque is encountered; a little thought shows that they can have no effect whatsoever. This is especially obvious for the case of a load torque on a static-positioning servomechanism, because in this case the input and output are both stationary and all derivatives are zero, so that no reduction in error is possible with a signal proportional to a derivative.

Since derivative signals merely reduce velocity-lag error and do not affect load-torque error, attention is turned to the possibility of eliminating such errors. Consider the steady-state condition of a servomechanism with velocity input or a stationary positioning system with load torque. In either case, there is a constant positional displacement between input and output which is called the error. The only way to reduce this error is to increase the drive torque. Thus the introduction of an additional signal related to the error seems in order. Such a signal cannot be a derivative signal, because the error is not changing, nor can it be proportional to the error itself, because it would then decrease as the error decreased and a new equilibrium condition would be reached without eliminating the error. The remaining possibility is to introduce a signal proportional to the integral of the error. If a drive torque proportional to the time integral of the error is added to the normal drive torque which is proportional to the error, it is readily seen that the error must ultimately be reduced to zero. This is apparent from simple logic, since the integral term eventually becomes infinite if the error does not disappear and would then apply infinite torque.

3-10. Mathematical Relationships for First-derivative Compensation Signals. Figure 3-8 shows three block diagrams indicating the addition of first-derivative signals to a basic servomechanism. These diagrams are idealized, and it is not necessary that the input and output signals be fed through separate amplifiers to take their derivatives, nor need they be fed into the main loop at the points indicated. It should be noted that each of the derivative signals is symbolized as "plus or minus," owing to the fact that either condition may be obtained physically. Only one sign is

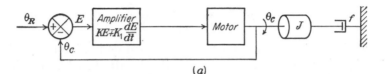

(a)

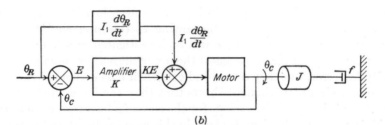

(b)

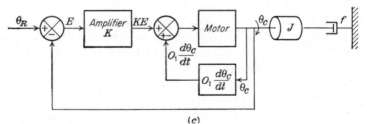

(c)

FIG. 3-8. Block diagrams for the addition of first-derivative compensation to a basic servomechanism.
(a) First-derivative error added to system
(b) First-derivative input added to system
(c) First-derivative output added to system

used in the following treatment, and analysis of the remaining cases is left to the student.

The differential equations are set up for each case, using K, J, and f as coefficients, rather than the dimensionless coefficient, since most of the effects are more readily seen with the equation in this form. Furthermore, a detailed solution of each equation is not attempted. As far as is possible, conclusions are drawn from the differential equation itself, and a solution of the equation is left to the discretion of the student.

First-derivative Error.   The torque-equilibrium equation is

$$J\frac{d^2\theta_c}{dt^2} + f\frac{d\theta_c}{dt} = KE + K_1\frac{dE}{dt} \tag{3-18}$$

Substituting $E = \theta_R - \theta_c$,

$$\frac{dE}{dt} = \frac{d\theta_R}{dt} - \frac{d\theta_c}{dt}$$

$$J\frac{d^2\theta_c}{dt^2} + f\frac{d\theta_c}{dt} = K(\theta_R - \theta_c) + K_1\left(\frac{d\theta_R}{dt} - \frac{d\theta_c}{dt}\right) \tag{3-19}$$

Rearranging,

$$J\frac{d^2\theta_c}{dt^2} + (f + K_1)\frac{d\theta_c}{dt} + K\theta_c = K\theta_R + K_1\frac{d\theta_R}{dt} \tag{3-20}$$

Equation (3-20) shows that the coefficient of the first-derivative output term is now $f + K_1$. Therefore, the transient solution of the equation can be made the same as for the basic servomechanism previously discussed, if f is reduced by the numerical value of K_1 so that the sum $f + K_1$ remains the same as the value of f used for the basic system. Thus effective damping can be obtained by use of a derivative error signal. It follows logically that the steady-state velocity-lag error is reduced, because f has been reduced. (Note that the introduction of a derivative error signal, of itself, has no effect on steady-state error.)

First-derivative Input.   The torque-equilibrium equation is

$$J\frac{d^2\theta_c}{dt^2} + f\frac{d\theta_c}{dt} = KE + I_1\frac{d\theta_R}{dt} \tag{3-21}$$

Substituting $E = \theta_R - \theta_c$ and rearranging,

$$J\frac{d^2\theta_c}{dt^2} + f\frac{d\theta_c}{dt} + K\theta_c = K\theta_R + I_1\frac{d\theta_R}{dt} \tag{3-22}$$

Equation (3-22) shows that the characteristic equation is not affected by the input derivative signal. Therefore, the roots are unchanged, and the transient performance is not altered. Any reduction in friction, therefore, causes underdamping and poor transient response (except insofar as the input derivative signal affects the coefficients of the oscillatory terms and thus the amplitude of the transient overshoot).

The right-hand side of Eq. (3-22) shows that the input derivative signal affects the steady-state solution for an input-velocity signal (for a displacement input, $d\theta_R/dt = 0$ for $t > 0$). The *steady-state* solution to Eq. (3-22) is

$$\theta_c = \theta_R - \frac{f}{K}\left(1 - \frac{I_1}{f}\right)\omega_R \tag{3-23}$$

From Eq. (3-23) it may be seen that an input-velocity signal can control the steady-state error even though it cannot control the transient performance. For example, if $I_1 = f$, then $\theta_C = \theta_R$ and there is *no* position error. If $I_1 > f$, then the output actually *leads* the input instead of lagging.

First-derivative Output. The torque-equilibrium equation, as determined from Fig. 3-8c, is

$$J \frac{d^2\theta_C}{dt^2} + f \frac{d\theta_C}{dt} = KE \mp O_1 \frac{d\theta_C}{dt} \tag{3-24}$$

Substituting $E = \theta_R - \theta_C$ and rearranging give

$$J \frac{d^2\theta_C}{dt^2} + (f \mp O_1) \frac{d\theta_C}{dt} + K\theta_C = K\theta_R \tag{3-25}$$

Equation (3-25) shows that the use of a feedback signal proportional to the first derivative of the output has exactly the same effect on the differential equation as changing the viscous friction. The transient performance is therefore damped when the feedback signal adds to the frictional effect. Under conditions of velocity operation, the velocity-lag error is also increased by increasing the damping effect. However, components used to accomplish such feedback (a tachometer, for example) do not dissipate energy as would additional viscous friction, and thus are sometimes advantageous.

3-11. Mathematical Relationships for Second-derivative Compensation Signals. Figure 3-9 shows three block diagrams indicating the methods for adding second-derivative compensation signals to a basic servomechanism. In the following paragraphs the equations are handled in the same fashion as for the first-derivative signals.

Second-derivative Error. From the block diagram of Fig. 3-9a, the torque-equilibrium equation is

$$J \frac{d^2\theta_C}{dt^2} + f \frac{d\theta_C}{dt} = KE \mp K_2 \frac{d^2E}{dt^2} \tag{3-26}$$

Substituting $E = \theta_R - \theta_C$ and rearranging,

$$(J \mp K_2) \frac{d^2\theta_C}{dt^2} + f \frac{d\theta_C}{dt} + K\theta_C = K\theta_R \mp K_2 \frac{d^2\theta_R}{dt^2} \tag{3-27}$$

The second-derivative error signal thus changes a coefficient of the characteristic equation, and so the transient performance is affected. However, if the input is a step displacement or step velocity, no second derivatives exist when the system reaches steady state; thus, a second-derivative error signal does not directly affect steady-state errors.

The damping coefficient of the system and the natural frequency are

$$\zeta' = \frac{f}{2\sqrt{K(J \mp K_2)}}$$

$$\omega'_n = \sqrt{\frac{K}{J \mp K_2}}$$

(3-28)

If the polarity of the second-derivative error signal is such that the minus sign is used, then both the damping and the natural frequency are

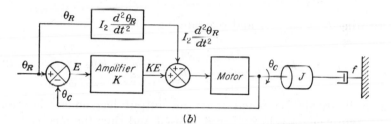

(a)

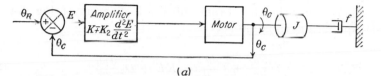

(b)

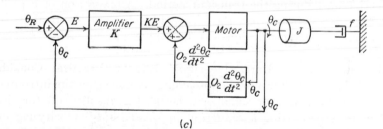

(c)

FIG. 3-9. Block diagrams for the addition of second-derivative compensation to a basic servomechanism.

(a) Second-derivative error added to system
(b) Second-derivative input added to system
(c) Second-derivative output added to system

increased.   This means that the speed of response is increased and the peak overshoot is reduced, both of which are improvements in transient response.   If K_2 is made large enough, f may be reduced while still obtaining suitable damping.   Since the natural frequency is still increased by such a procedure, the system will respond more quickly, yet the reduction in f decreases the steady-state velocity-lag error.

While the above analysis indicates certain advantages obtained from a second-derivative error signal, practical difficulties exist.   A true second-derivative signal is very difficult to obtain with existing components, and consequently is seldom used.

Second-derivative Input. For a step-displacement input or a step-velocity input, the input signal has a second derivative of zero for $t > 0$. Thus the use of a second-derivative input signal cannot affect either the transient or steady-state response to a velocity input and is mentioned here only for the sake of completeness. There may be possible uses with systems subjected to acceleration inputs, but discussion of these is beyond the scope of this text.

Second-derivative Output. From the block diagram of Fig. 3-9c, the torque-equilibrium equation is

$$J \frac{d^2\theta_c}{dt^2} + f \frac{d\theta_c}{dt} = KE + O_2 \frac{d^2\theta_c}{dt^2} \tag{3-29}$$

Substituting $E = \theta_R - \theta_c$ and rearranging,

$$(J \mp O_2) \frac{d^2\theta_c}{dt^2} + f \frac{d\theta_c}{dt} + K\theta_c = K\theta_R \tag{3-30}$$

Again it should be noted that the output has no acceleration in steady state when a velocity input is used and thus the feedback signal is effective only during the transient period. Comparison of Eq. (3-30) with Eq. (3-27) shows that the left-hand sides are identical in form. Therefore, the same conclusions can be drawn, and no further discussion is needed.

3-12. Summary of Derivative-signal Effects—Practical Considerations. It has been shown in the preceding sections that the introduction of a first-derivative error signal can be used as a substitute for viscous friction, thus permitting a reduction in steady-state velocity-lag error. A first-derivative input signal does not affect the roots of the differential equation and thus cannot be used as a substitute for friction damping. It can control the steady-state error, however. A first-derivative output signal, when fed back, acts exactly as viscous friction in that it provides damping, but also it increases the velocity-lag error. It does so, however, without absorbing the large amounts of energy required by a viscous damper.

Second-derivative signals affect the apparent inertia of the system. Therefore, if they are properly used, the friction may be reduced, and good transient performance is still available while the steady-state velocity-lag error is reduced.

No mention was made of the effect of an external load torque. It is readily seen that derivative signals are incapable of compensating for errors due to a load torque, and other methods are required when load torques are anticipated.

From a practical point of view, second-derivative signals are seldom used because it is extremely difficult to obtain a good second-derivative signal. They probably will be used more frequently as better equipment and simpler methods are developed. First-derivative input signals are seldom, if ever, used, for two reasons. First, it is usually necessary to reduce the viscous friction below values which provide adequate damping, and some damping means must be provided. An input derivative signal in addition to such damping is hard to justify economically. Secondly, if the input signal is a mechanical motion, it often is at too low a power level to drive the measuring device needed for the input derivative signal.

First-derivative error signals are very commonly used since very many systems have an electronic amplifier to amplify the error signal, and a differentiating circuit is easily inserted. However, true differentiation is seldom used, for reasons which will be presented later in the text.

First-derivative output signals are frequently used and have proved very satisfactory. The obvious method for obtaining such a signal is to gear a tachometer to the output. This is commonly done, but certain difficulties should be mentioned:

1. If a d-c tachometer is used, commutator ripple causes difficulties. Also, if the drive is a two-phase motor, the power channel will be a-c, and difficulties are encountered in introducing the output derivative signal.

2. If an ordinary a-c tachometer is used, such as a permanent-magnet-field type, both the magnitude and the frequency of the output voltage vary with the output velocity, and rather complex circuits must be used with it.

3. A two-phase induction tachometer, if available, provides a constant-frequency variable-amplitude signal. Rectification and filtering for use with d-c systems are not too difficult. With a-c systems some phase shifting may be required. The most important drawback is economic; induction tachometers are fairly expensive.

In general, while the advantages of derivative signals are clear, the components available usually provide an approximate rather than a true derivative. Thus the effects obtained, while qualitatively close to those of the true derivative, cannot be computed with the simple equation presented. It is necessary to write and solve the equations for the specific components used, and these equations are usually higher-order differential equations.

3-13. Integral-error Compensation. Since derivative compensators do not eliminate steady-state velocity-lag error and are ineffective where external load torques are encountered, attention is turned to the analysis of integral-error compensation. It has already been shown qualitatively that an integral-of-error signal, added to the proportional signal, should be capable of eliminating steady-state errors; the following treatment concerns itself with the mathematical verification of this conclusion. A complete solution is not attempted.

Figure 3-10 shows a block diagram of a simple servomechanism with integral-error compensation. The torque-equilibrium equation is

$$\mp T_L + J\frac{d^2\theta_C}{dt^2} + f\frac{d\theta_C}{dt} = KE + K_3 \int_0^t E\, dt \qquad (3\text{-}31)$$

To verify the conclusion that the steady-state error is zero, it is con-

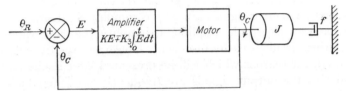

FIG. 3-10. Servomechanism with integral-error compensation.

venient to substitute $\theta_C = \theta_R - E$; then

$$\mp T_L + J\frac{d^2\theta_R}{dt^2} + f\frac{d\theta_R}{dt} = J\frac{d^2E}{dt^2} + f\frac{dE}{dt} + KE + K_3 \int_0^t E\, dt \quad (3\text{-}32)$$

Considering only the steady-state condition for $t \gg 0$ and a step-velocity input,

$$\frac{d^2\theta_R}{dt^2} = 0 \qquad \frac{d\theta_R}{dt} = \omega_R$$

$$\frac{d^2E}{dt^2} = 0 \qquad \frac{dE}{dt} = 0$$

and the equation reduces to

$$\mp T_L + f\omega_R = KE_{ss} + K_3 \int_0^\infty E\, dt \qquad (3\text{-}33)$$

The left-hand side of this equation is finite, and the term KE_{ss} is either finite or zero.   Then, by inspection, $E_{ss} = 0$, for if $E_{ss} \neq 0$, $\int_0^\infty E\, dt \to \infty$. It is obvious that the same conclusion may be drawn for a step-displacement input and a load torque.

Equation (3-32) is a third-order linear differential equation.   Its solution is straightforward, though some labor is involved.   Since there must be three roots, the general form of the solution is

$$E = Ae^{\alpha t} + Be^{\beta t} + Ce^{\gamma t} \qquad (3\text{-}34)$$

In the symbolic form of Eq. (3-34), all the physical possibilities are not immediately obvious. There are at least three cases to be considered:

1. α, β, and γ are all real and negative. Then the terms all become zero for the large values of t, and the steady-state error is zero. This corresponds to a critically damped or an overdamped condition.

2. α may be real and negative while β and γ are complex conjugates. If the real parts of the complex roots are negative, then there is a transient oscillation which is eventually damped out and the steady-state error is still zero. This corresponds to an underdamped condition.

3. One of the roots, α, β, or γ, may be real and positive, or the real part of the complex roots may be positive. In this case, the terms of Eq. (3-34) do not all approach zero as $t \to \infty$. The system is said to be unstable.

It should be reasonably obvious that the roots of the cubic equation depend on the values of K_3, the integrating coefficient. If K_3 is a small number, additional torque is produced very slowly and, though the steady-state error is ultimately eliminated, the transient performance is essentially the same as if the integrator had not been added. On the other hand, if K_3 is a very large number, then a very large torque is introduced in a short time. This increases the effective torque-to-inertia ratio and thus decreases the damping. The transient oscillations become violent with large overshoots. If K_3 is large enough, it may even produce roots with positive real parts, in which case the system will oscillate continuously and never reach steady state.

For intermediate values of K_3, the system ultimately reaches steady state with no steady-state error. The transient performance is adversely affected, however; i. e., the overshoot increases and the response time increases.

Thus, several practical points must be considered. When adding an integrating device, a reasonably large value for K_3 must be used in order to eliminate the steady-state error in a suitable time period. Because the transient performance is adversely affected, it is usually desirable to increase the damping; this is normally done with some derivative device.

It should also be noted that integration may not always eliminate steady-state error in a practical system. There are two reasons for this. First of all, a true integrator is not always convenient or practical, and approximate integrators which are not capable of doing a perfect job in eliminating the error are used. Second, it is necessary to put an upper limit on the integration, i. e., the torque produced by the integral term $K_3 \int_0^t E \, dt$ cannot approach infinity as a practical limit and therefore, if the limit selected in design is less than the external-load torque or the friction-drag torque, the error is reduced by the integrator but may not become identically zero.

PROBLEMS

3-1. In the system of Fig. 3P-1, the motor has an inertia of 10^{-6} slug-ft^2 and the load has an inertia of 0.009 slug-ft^2.   The viscous friction at the motor is 10^{-5} ft-lb/rad/sec,

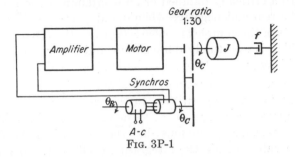

Fig. 3P-1

and at the load it is $4{,}500 \times 10^{-6}$ ft-lb/rad/sec.   The gear ratio from motor to load is 1:30.

   a. Compute the effective inertia and friction at the load shaft.

   b. Compute the effective inertia and friction at the motor shaft.

3-2. The motor of Fig. 3P-1 may be considered an ideal torque motor, which means that it produces a torque at its shaft which is directly proportional to the voltage supplied by the amplifier.   Assume that the motor torque constant is 30×10^{-6} ft-lb/volt.   If a voltage of 100 volts is applied to the motor,

   a. What will be the steady-state motor speed in radians per second?   In rpm?

   b. What will be the steady-state load speed?

3-3. The amplifier of Fig. 3P-1 may be considered ideal, and has a gain of 20. The synchro error-detector system produces a voltage which is proportional to the angular misalignment (for small angles, up to perhaps 15°) between the shafts of the generator and motor.   For the units of Fig. 3P-1, the signal produced is 1.0 volt/deg. Write the differential equation of the system, and

   a. Compute the transient response if the input shaft (θ_R) is suddenly rotated 10°.

   b. Compute the transient response if the input shaft is suddenly given a rotational velocity of 10 deg/sec.

3-4. It is decided that the system of Fig. 3P-1 should be critically damped, and that the viscous friction should be reduced.   To increase the damping, the amplifier is redesigned to differentiate the error signal, the resulting amplifier equation being

$$e_o = 20e_i + A \frac{de_i}{dt}$$

Viscous friction is reduced by redesigning the bearings in the load, so that the load friction becomes negligible.

   a. Determine the value of the coefficient A for critical damping.

   b. Compute the steady-state velocity-lag error for an input velocity of 10 deg/sec.

   c. If the system operates at a constant velocity of 10.0 rad/sec, how much *power* is saved by using error-rate damping instead of viscous damping?   (Consider a case where critical damping is to be obtained with viscous friction only.)

3-5. It is decided to damp the system of Fig. 3P-1 by tachometer feedback rather than by redesigning the amplifier.   The resulting circuit is shown in Fig. 3P-2, where

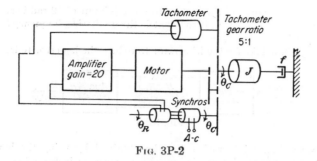

FIG. 3P-2

the voltage at the input to the amplifier is $K_sE - N_tK_t(d\theta_c/dt)$. The tachometer voltage constant is $K_t = 0.02$ volt/rpm. The gear ratio from load shaft to tachometer is a stepup of 5:1 to provide reasonable tachometer speeds. The inertia and friction of the tachometer are negligible.

a. With the constants given, determine the system response to a step-displacement input of 10°, and to a step-velocity input of 10 deg/sec.

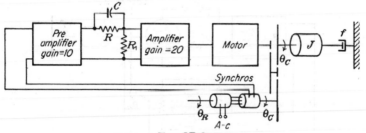

FIG. 3P-3

b. In what ways can the system be adjusted to obtain critical damping?

c. Under critically damped conditions, how does tachometer feedback compare with error-rate damping in regard to velocity-lag error and power consumption for a system velocity of 10 rad/sec?

3-6. Approximate derivative damping may be obtained with passive filter networks. One practical type is shown in Fig. 3P-3. The filter illustrated may be used only with d-c signals. The preamplifier must therefore demodulate the synchro error signal, and some changes would be required in the main amplifier. Normally the input impedance of the main amplifier would be made much greater than R_1 to prevent loading of the filter.

Compute the response of the system to a sudden input displacement of 10° if $R = 9.0$ megohms, $C = 0.3$ μf, and $R_1 = 1.0$ megohm. Use a preamplifier gain of 10, and all other parameters as in Prob. 3-3 except that the load component of friction is zero.

3-7. The system of Fig. 3P-1 is to be operated at an output velocity of 10 rad/sec. With the specified friction in motor and load, the resultant velocity-lag error will be 7.5°, which is considered excessive. It is decided to eliminate the error by replacing the amplifier with an integrating amplifier, for which the voltage equation is

$$e_o = 20e_i + 5\int_0^t e_i \, dt$$

Since an added integrator normally makes a system more oscillatory, the damping is increased by doubling the load component of viscous friction.

  a. Compute the response of the system to a ramp input of 10 rad/sec.

  b. Is the system oscillatory?   If so, what is the oscillating frequency?   How long will hunting persist?

  c. How long will it take for the integrator to reduce the lag error to less than 0.5°?

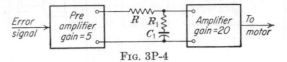

FIG. 3P-4

3-8. An approximate integration may be obtained by using the low-pass filter of Fig. 3P-4 instead of the integrating amplifier suggested in Prob. 3-7.   If the load component of viscous friction is doubled (over that of Prob. 3-1), and if R is 4 megohms, R_1 is 1 megohm, and C_1 is 10 μf,

  a. Compute the transient response of the system to a ramp input of 10 rad/sec.

  b. What is the steady-state error?

  c. What is the oscillating frequency?

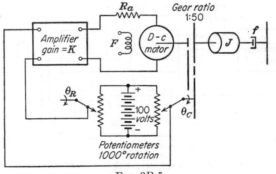

FIG. 3P-5

3-9. The parameters of the positioning system shown in Fig. 3P-5 are:

  J = load inertia = 1.0 slug-ft^2
  f = load viscous friction = 0.00143 ft-lb/rad/sec
  J_m = motor inertia = 8.0 × 10^{-4} slug-ft^2
  f_m = motor viscous friction = 0
  K_t = motor torque constant = 0.812 ft-lb/amp
  K_e = motor back-emf constant = 1.25 volts/rad/sec
  R_a = motor armature resistance = 24.4 ohms
  K = amplifier gain = 250

It is assumed that the armature-leakage inductance is negligible and that the equivalent output impedance of the amplifier is also negligible.

  a. Write the differential equation of the system and evaluate its coefficients.   What is the effect of the motor back-emf on damping?

  b. Compute the transient response to a 10° step input.   What is the oscillating frequency?   What is the maximum overshoot?

  c. Compute the transient response to a ramp input of 1.0 rad/sec.   What is the velocity-lag error?

  3-10. Compute the parameter values for a preamplifier and differentiating filter which will critically damp the system of Fig. 3P-5.

3-11. Compute the parameter values for a preamplifier and integrating filter which will reduce the velocity-lag error of the system of Fig. 3P-5 to 0.5°.

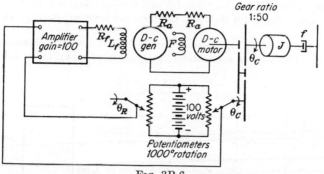

FIG. 3P-6

3-12. In the system of Fig. 3P-6, the motor is driven by a rotating amplifier (generator) rather than by a static amplifier. The motor, load, and error-detector system are the same as in Prob. 3-9. The generator parameters are:

R_a = armature resistance = 24.4 ohms
K_g = 200 volts/amp
R_f = 50 ohms
L_f = 5 henrys

a. Compute the transient response to a 10° step input. What is the oscillating frequency? What is the settling time?

b. Compute the response to a 1-rad/sec ramp input. What is the velocity-lag error?

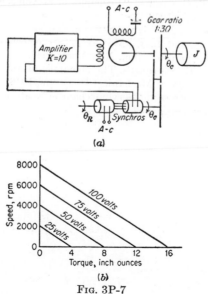

(a)

(b)

FIG. 3P-7

3-13. Figure 3P-7 shows a servomechanism in which the drive motor is a two-phase induction motor. Such systems are called carrier-frequency servos, since the motor is driven by a constant-frequency voltage, and the command is transmitted to the motor by modulating the amplitude of the voltage applied to the control phase. If the inertia of the motor is 10^{-6} slug-ft^2, and the load inertia is 10^{-4} slug-ft^2, while the synchro sensitivity is 1.0 volt/deg, compute the transient response to a 10° step input.

3-14. The system of Fig. 3P-7 is modified to include error-rate damping as shown in Fig. 3P-8. The filter is a parallel-T, and is one of many filters called "notch

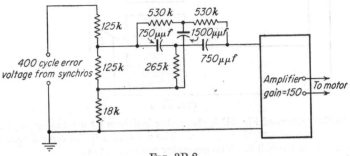

Fig. 3P-8

filters" because the frequency-response curve has a V, or notch, shape with the notch centered at the carrier frequency. The amplifier gain is increased to counteract the filter attenuation. Compute the transient response of the modified system to a 10° step input.

REFERENCES

Brown, G. S., and D. P. Campbell, "Principles of Servomechanisms," John Wiley & Sons, Inc., New York, 1948.

Harris, H., The Analysis and Design of Servomechanisms, *OSRD Rept.* 454.

Lauer, H., R. Lesnick, and L. C. Matson, "Servomechanism Fundamentals," McGraw-Hill Book Company, Inc., New York, 1947.

Oldenbourg, R. C., and H. Sartorius, The Dynamics of Automatic Control (translation), American Society of Mechanical Engineers, 1948.

Thaler, G. J., and R. G. Brown, "Servomechanism Analysis," McGraw-Hill Book Company, Inc., New York, 1953.

CHAPTER 4

TRANSFER FUNCTIONS

4-1. Definitions and Interpretations. When a signal is applied to the input of a physical device, the signal is transmitted to the output where it appears in modified form, the modifications being due to the physical nature of the device through which the signal travels. When the input signal is a sine wave, and the system is allowed to reach steady state, then (for linear systems) the output signal is also a sinusoidal wave differing from the input only in amplitude and phase. Thus it may be said that a linear physical device has the ability to transfer information from its input to its output. Any mathematical function which correctly describes the effect of the physical device on the information transferred through it may be called a "transfer function." When sinusoidal signals are transferred, the effect of a linear physical component is to alter the magnitude and phase of the signal. The transfer function must therefore express the amplitude relationship and the phase relationship between output and input, for all frequencies. Such a transfer function can conveniently be expressed as a ratio.

For the purposes of this text, the frequency transfer function* of any linear component is defined as the ratio of the steady-state sinusoidal output of that device to the steady-state sinusoidal input which is causing that output expressed in complex numbers. Such transfer functions may be derived by the application of basic a-c circuit theory.

4-2. Transfer Functions of Specific Devices. In this seciton, the definition of a transfer function is applied, and a number of specific transfer functions are derived. Simple filter networks are considered first, since the circuit analysis is elementary; then a few mechanical and electromechanical devices are introduced. In each case, the resulting transfer function is manipulated to permit the definition of time constants (constants having the dimensions of time). It will be seen in later chapters

---

* The transfer function of a physical device is formally defined as the Laplace transform of the response of that device to a unit impulse input. The algebraic form in s of the transfer function obtained by using Laplace-transform methods is identical with that obtained in $j\omega$ by using the methods of circuit theory. In practice, either method may be used to derive a transfer function, the engineer usually selecting that method which is most easily applied to the specific problem.

that the arrangement used is most convenient for the graphical manipulations needed in system analysis and design.

In applying the laws of circuit theory, one may use either the instantaneous-value notation or the complex-number notation. The instantaneous notation (i. e., the differential equation) is always applicable, though somewhat more laborious. The complex-number notation is readily applied to electric circuits, but does not always have an obvious interpretation when dealing with electromechanical devices or purely mechanical or hydraulic systems. In such cases it is perhaps better to use the instantaneous notation. In the following paragraphs, the first two filters considered are treated by both methods, but for the remainder of the derivations the author has selected the method which seems most readily applicable.

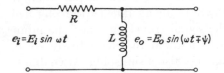

FIG. 4-1. *RL* high-pass filter.

RL High-pass Filter. Figure 4-1 shows a simple high-pass *RL* filter. If a sinusoidal voltage is applied to the input terminals, the circuit equations are

$$e_i = E_i \sin \omega t; \text{ thus } \bar{e}_i = E_i\underline{/0^\circ} \tag{4-1}$$

$$e_i = iR + L\frac{di}{dt}; \text{ thus } \bar{e}_i = \bar{i}R + L\overline{\frac{di}{dt}} \tag{4-2}$$

$$e_o = E_o \sin (\omega t \mp \psi); \text{ thus } \bar{e}_0 = E_o\underline{/\mp\psi} \tag{4-3}$$

$$e_o = L\frac{di}{dt}; \text{ thus } \bar{e}_o = L\overline{\frac{di}{dt}} \tag{4-4}$$

but

$$i = I \sin (\omega t - \theta); \text{ thus } \bar{\imath} = I\underline{/-\theta} \tag{4-5}$$

$$\frac{di}{dt} = \omega I \cos (\omega t - \theta); \text{ thus } \overline{\frac{di}{dt}} = j\omega I\underline{/-\theta} \tag{4-6}$$

Using only the vector form of Eqs. (4-1) through (4-6), and substituting in Eqs. (4-2) and (4-3),

$$\bar{e}_i = RI\underline{/-\theta} + j\omega LI\underline{/-\theta} \tag{4-7}$$

$$\bar{e}_o = j\omega LI\underline{/-\theta} \tag{4-8}$$

from which

$$\frac{\bar{e}_o}{\bar{e}_i} = \frac{j\omega LI\underline{/-\theta}}{RI\underline{/-\theta} + j\omega LI\underline{/-\theta}} \tag{4-9}$$

and

$$\frac{\bar{e}_o}{\bar{e}_i} = \frac{j\omega(L/R)}{j\omega(L/R) - 1} = \frac{j\omega\tau}{j\omega\tau + 1} \tag{4-10}$$

Equation (4-10) is the transfer function* of the filter.

* In this text the term "transfer function" normally means "frequency transfer function."

Repeating the derivation with the complex-number notation,

$$\bar{E}_i = \bar{I}R + j\omega L \bar{I} \qquad (4\text{-}11)$$

$$\bar{E}_o = j\omega L \bar{I} \qquad (4\text{-}12)$$

$$\frac{\bar{E}_o}{\bar{E}_i} = \frac{j\omega L \bar{I}}{j\omega L \bar{I} + R\bar{I}} = \frac{j\omega L}{j\omega L + R} = \frac{j\omega(L/R)}{j\omega(L/R) + 1} = \frac{j\omega\tau}{j\omega\tau + 1} \qquad (4\text{-}13)$$

RC High-pass Filter. Figure 4-2 shows a simple high-pass *RC* filter.

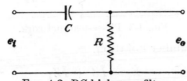

Fig. 4-2. *RC* high-pass filter.

For a sinusoidal applied voltage, the circuit equations are:

$$e_i = E_i \sin \omega t; \text{ thus } \bar{e}_i = E_i/\underline{0} \qquad (4\text{-}14)$$

$$e_i = \int \frac{i\,dt}{C} + iR; \text{ thus } \bar{e}_i = \frac{1}{C}\int i\,dt + R\bar{\imath} \qquad (4\text{-}15)$$

$$e_o = E_o \sin (\omega t \mp \psi); \text{ thus } \bar{e}_o = E_o/\mp\psi \qquad (4\text{-}16)$$

$$e_o = iR; \text{ thus } \bar{e}_o = R\bar{\imath} \qquad (4\text{-}17)$$

but

$$i = I \sin (\omega t + 0); \text{ thus } \bar{\imath} = I/\underline{+\theta} \qquad (4\text{-}18)$$

$$\int i\,dt = -\frac{I}{\omega}\cos (\omega t + \theta); \text{ thus } \int i\,dt = \frac{I/\underline{+\theta}}{j\omega} \qquad (4\text{-}19)$$

Again using only the vector form of Eqs. (4-14) through (4-19),

$$\bar{e}_i = E_i/\underline{0} = \frac{I/\underline{+\theta}}{j\omega C} \qquad (4\text{-}20)$$

$$\bar{e}_o = E_o/\underline{+\psi} = RI/\underline{+\theta} \qquad (4\text{-}21)$$

$$\bar{e}_o = \frac{RI/\underline{+\theta}}{\dfrac{I/\underline{+\theta}}{j\omega C} + RI/\underline{+\theta}} = \frac{R}{\dfrac{1}{j\omega C} + R} \qquad (4\text{-}22)$$

$$= \frac{j\omega CR}{j\omega CR + 1} = \frac{j\omega\tau}{j\omega\tau + 1}$$

where $\tau = RC$. Equation (4-22) is the transfer function of the filter.

Repeating the derivation with the complex-number notation,

$$\bar{E}_i = \bar{I}R + \frac{\bar{I}}{j\omega C} \qquad (4\text{-}23)$$

$$\bar{E}_o = \bar{I}R \qquad (4\text{-}24)$$

$$\frac{\bar{E}_o}{\bar{E}_i} = \frac{\bar{I}R}{\bar{I}R + \bar{I}/j\omega C} = \frac{j\omega CR}{j\omega CR + 1} = \frac{j\omega\tau}{j\omega\tau + 1} \qquad (4\text{-}25)$$

Phase-lead Network.   Figure 4-3 shows a phase-lead network of a type commonly used for the series compensation of d-c servomechanisms.

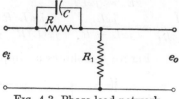

FIG. 4-3. Phase-lead network.

Using the complex-number notation,

$$\bar{E}_i = \bar{I}Z + \bar{I}Z_1 \tag{4-26}$$

where $Z = \dfrac{R/j\omega C}{R + 1/j\omega C}$ and $Z_1 = R_1$.

$$\bar{E}_o = \bar{I}R_1 \tag{4-27}$$

$$\frac{\bar{E}_o}{\bar{E}_i} = \frac{\bar{I}R_1}{\bar{I}[R/(j\omega CR + 1)] + \bar{I}R_1} = \frac{R_1(j\omega CR + 1)}{R + (j\omega CR + 1)R_1}$$

$$= \frac{j\omega CRR_1 + R_1}{j\omega CRR_1 + R_1 + R} = \frac{R_1}{R + R_1}\frac{j\omega CR + 1}{j\omega CR[R_1/(R + R_1)] + 1}$$

$$= \alpha\,\frac{j\omega\tau + 1}{j\omega\alpha\tau + 1} \tag{4-28}$$

where $\alpha = R_1/(R + R_1)$ and $\tau = RC$.   Equation (4-28) is the transfer function of the network.

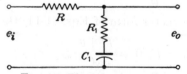

FIG. 4-4. Phase-lag network.

Phase-lag Network.   Figure 4-4 shows a simple phase-lag network frequently used in the compensation of d-c servomechanisms.   Using the complex-number notation,

$$\bar{E}_i = \bar{I}R + \bar{I}R_1 + \frac{\bar{I}}{j\omega C_1} \tag{4-29}$$

$$\bar{E}_o = \bar{I}R_1 + \frac{\bar{I}}{j\omega C_1} \tag{4-30}$$

$$\frac{\bar{E}_o}{\bar{E}_i} = \frac{\bar{I}(R_1 + 1/j\omega C_1)}{\bar{I}(R + R_1 + 1/j\omega C_1)} = \frac{j\omega C_1 R_1 + 1}{j\omega C_1(R + R_1) + 1}$$

$$= \frac{j\omega\tau_1 + 1}{j\omega\tau_2 + 1} \tag{4-31}$$

where $\tau_1 = R_1 C_1$ and $\tau_2 = (R + R_1)C_1$.   Equation (4-31) is the transfer function of the network.

Gear Train. Figure 4-5 shows a schematic diagram of a gear train. N_1 and N_2 are the ratios of the respective pitch diameters taken as the ratio of the larger diameter to the smaller. Assuming no backlash and no binding, when the input shaft is moved with sinusoidal motion and

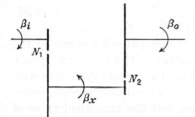

an amplitude β_i, the intermediate shaft moves in time phase but with an amplitude

$$\beta_x = \frac{\beta_i}{N_1} \qquad (4\text{-}32)$$

In like manner, the output shaft has an amplitude

FIG. 4-5. Schematic diagram of a gear train.

$$\beta_o = \frac{\beta_x}{N_2} \qquad (4\text{-}33)$$

Combining these equations,

$$\frac{\beta_o}{\beta_i} = \frac{1}{N_1 N_2} \qquad (4\text{-}34)$$

Equation (4-34) is the transfer function of the gear train. If binding or backlash is present, the gear train is nonlinear, and the transfer function of Eq. (4-34) is not valid.

Electronic Amplifiers. The electronic amplifiers normally used for servo applications may be classified in two general groups, d-c amplifiers and carrier-frequency amplifiers, and are most commonly used to drive d-c motors or two-phase motors (60-cycle or 400-cycle), respectively. The d-c amplifier may have to pass signals containing harmonic frequencies up to 50 or 60 cycles; the carrier-frequency amplifiers must pass amplitude-modulated signals, and the amplifier pass band must extend above and below the carrier frequency for about 15 per cent of the carrier frequency. Thus the band of frequencies to be passed has a maximum width of about 120 cycles (for a 400-cycle carrier). In general, phase shift presents no problem in such an ampli-

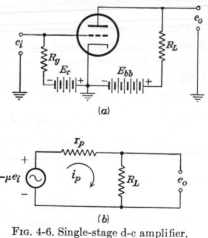

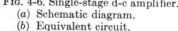

FIG. 4-6. Single-stage d-c amplifier.
(a) Schematic diagram.
(b) Equivalent circuit.

fier, since the frequencies are so low that the interelectrode capacities of the tubes have negligible effect, and the coupling circuits can readily be designed to give negligible phase shift for the desired frequency range.

Figure 4-6a shows the schematic diagram of a single-stage d-c amplifier, and Fig. 4-6b shows its equivalent circuit. From the equivalent circuit,

$$-\mu\bar{e}_i = \bar{\imath}_p(r_p + R_L) \qquad (4\text{-}35)$$

$$\bar{e}_o = \bar{\imath}_p R_L \qquad (4\text{-}36)$$

$$\frac{\bar{e}_o}{\bar{e}_i} = \frac{-\mu R_L}{r_p + R_L} \qquad (4\text{:}37)$$

Equation (4-37) is the transfer function of the amplifier stage in the low-frequency range and is seen to be a constant. The usual 180° phase shift is present, but this is readily handled in the over-all system design.

In the case of carrier-frequency amplifiers, the coupling circuits introduce time constants in the transfer function, but the numerical value of these time constants is such that they may be neglected at the frequencies actually passed through the amplifier. Thus, in general, the transfer function of a servo amplifier is simply its gain constant.

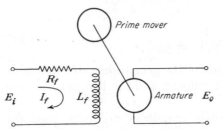

FIG. 4-7. Schematic diagram of a d-c generator.

Many servo amplifiers are used as modulators or demodulators in addition to utilizing their amplification properties. This does not affect their phase-shift characteristics unless transformers having appreciable phase shift are used.

A D-C Generator. A d-c generator is normally operated with its shaft driven at constant speed by some prime mover. Electric output is obtained from the armature by applying a voltage to the field circuit. Figure 4-7 shows a schematic diagram of a d-c generator. Its transfer function may be derived as follows:

$$\bar{E}_i = \bar{I}_f(\tilde{R}_f + j\omega L_f) \qquad (4\text{-}38)$$

where $\bar{E}_i$ and $\bar{I}_f$ are complex numbers. In the time domain

$$\phi(t) = K_1 i_f(t); \; e_o(t) = K_2 \phi(t) \qquad (4\text{-}39)$$

thus

$$e_o(t) = K_1 K_2 i_f(t); \; \bar{E}_o = K_1 K_2 \bar{I}_f \qquad (4\text{-}40)$$

where K_1 and K_2 are proportionality constants, and E_o is the effective output voltage. Solving simultaneously,

$$\frac{\bar{E}_o}{\bar{E}_i} = \frac{K_1 K_2}{j\omega L_f + R_f} = \frac{K_g/R_f}{j\omega\tau_f + 1} \qquad (4\text{-}41)$$

where $K_g = K_1 K_2$ and $\tau_f = L_f/R_f$.

This derivation assumes linear operation, i. e., the field circuit is unsaturated and hysteresis is negligible, and the load is moderate so that armature reaction effects are negligible. It should also be noted that the output voltage is defined to be the voltage developed with the load terminals open-circuited, which is equivalent to the generated voltage.

D-C Motors. When d-c motors are used to drive a load in a servomechanism, they are usually connected with the field separately excited and the armature supplied from relays or from a generator. (Constant-speed motors connected to the load by clutches or fluid transmissions are not considered in this text.) Figure 4-8a shows a schematic diagram of a d-c motor without load. It should be noted that, in this case, the

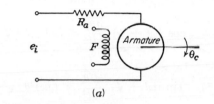

(a)

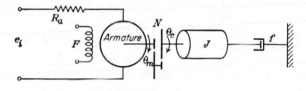

(b)

FIG. 4-8. D-C-motor schematic diagrams. (a) A d-c motor without load. (b) A d-c motor with inertia and friction load.

input is a voltage and the output is a mechanical rotation, and so the transfer function is not dimensionless.

Applying Kirchhoff's law to the electric circuit and using instantaneous values,

$$E_m \sin \omega t = iR_a + K_e \frac{d\theta_c}{dt}; \; E_m/\underline{0} = \bar{i}R_a + K_e \frac{\overline{d\theta_c}}{dt} \tag{4-42}$$

where E_m = maximum applied voltage
i = instantaneous current
R_a = armature resistance
K_e = motor back-emf constant, volts/rad/sec
θ_c = instantaneous angular position of output shaft, radians

Applying Newton's law to the mechanical system,

$$J_m \frac{d^2\theta_c}{dt^2} = K_t i; \; J_m \frac{\overline{d^2\theta_c}}{dt^2} = K_t \bar{i} \tag{4-43}$$

where J_m = the motor inertia, slug-ft²
K_t = motor torque constant, ft-lb/amp

To determine the transfer function from these equations, note that in steady state the motor shaft must have simple harmonic motion, because the input voltage is sinusoidal and the system is linear. Therefore assume that

$$\theta_c = \theta_{max} \sin(\omega t + \psi); \quad \bar{\theta}_c = \theta_{max}\underline{/+\psi} \qquad (4\text{-}44)$$

The transfer function is then the ratio

$$\frac{\theta_c}{E_i} = \frac{\theta_{max} \sin(\omega t + \psi)}{E_m \sin \omega t}; \quad \frac{\bar{\theta}_c}{\bar{E}_i} = \frac{\theta_{max}\underline{/+\psi}}{E_m\underline{/0}} \qquad (4\text{-}45)$$

Note that

$$\frac{d\theta_c}{dt} = \omega\theta_{max} \cos(\omega t + \psi); \quad \frac{\overline{d\theta_c}}{dt} = j\omega\theta_{max}\underline{/+\psi} \qquad (4\text{-}46)$$

and

$$\frac{d^2\theta_c}{dt^2} = -\omega^2\theta_{max} \sin(\omega t + \psi); \quad \frac{\overline{d^2\theta_c}}{dt^2} = (j\omega)^2\theta_{max}\underline{/+\psi} \qquad (4\text{-}47)$$

Using only the vector equations, and combining Eqs. (4-42) and (4-43),

$$E_m\underline{/0} = \frac{J_m R_a}{K_t}(j\omega)^2\theta_{max}\underline{/+\psi} + K_e j\omega\theta_{max}\underline{/+\psi} \qquad (4\text{-}48)$$

Substituting Eqs. (4-46) and (4-47) gives:

$$E_m\underline{/0} = (j\omega)^2 \frac{J_m R_a}{K_t}\theta_{max}\underline{/+\psi} + j\omega K_e\theta_{max}\underline{/+\psi}$$

$$= \left[(j\omega)^2 \frac{J_m R_a}{K_t} + j\omega K_e\right]\theta_{max}\underline{/+\psi} \qquad (4\text{-}49)$$

From Eq. (4-49),

$$\frac{\bar{\theta}_c}{\bar{E}_i} = \frac{\theta_{max}\underline{/+\psi}}{E_m\underline{/0}} = \frac{1}{j\omega[j\omega(J_m R_a/K_t) + K_e]}$$

$$= \frac{1/K_e}{j\omega(j\omega\tau_m + 1)} \qquad (4\text{-}50)$$

where $\tau_m = J_m R_a/K_t K_e$ = motor time constant. Equation (4-50) is the transfer function of the motor.

In most applications the motor is geared to a load. Since the normal running speed of most electric motors is much higher than the speed desired of the load, it is necessary to use reduction gearing to obtain the desired output. For example, if a motor is rated at 1,800 rpm and the load is to rotate normally at 9 rpm, a reduction of perhaps 100:1 might be used. Note that the gear reduction is not the same as the nominal speed reduction. This is to provide for necessary accelerations and for the possibility that higher load speeds may be required at times. When gear reductions are used, the error detector is usually connected to the load, not to the motor, shaft and the transfer function is desired in terms of θ_C measured at the load shaft.

Many loads consist of inertia and viscous friction. Figure 4-8b shows such an arrangement in schematic form. The electric circuit is still described by Eq. (4-42), but the mechanical-system equation becomes

$$K_t i = J_{eq} \frac{d^2 \theta_m}{dt^2} + f_{eq} \frac{d\theta_m}{dt} \tag{4-51}$$

where $J_{eq} = J_m + J_L/N^2$ = equivalent inertia of motor and load lumped at motor shaft

$f_{eq} = f_m + f_L/N^2$ = equivalent viscous-friction coefficient of motor and load referred to motor shaft, ft-lb/rad/sec

N = over-all motor-to-load gear ratio taken as ratio of motor-shaft revolutions to load shaft revolutions

Using the relationships of Eqs. (4-44) through (4-47),

$$E_m/0 = (j\omega)^2 \frac{J_{eq}R_a}{K_e} \theta_{max}/+\psi + j\omega \frac{f_{eq}R_a}{K_t} \theta_{max}/+\psi + j\omega K_e \theta_{max}/+\psi \tag{4-52}$$

$$E_m/0 = \left[(j\omega)^2 \frac{J_{eq}R_a}{K_t} + j\omega \left(\frac{f_{eq}R_a}{K_t} + K_e \right) \right] \theta_{max}/+\psi \tag{4-53}$$

$$\frac{\bar{\theta}_c}{\bar{E}_t} = \frac{\theta_{max}/+\psi}{E_m/0} = \frac{1}{j\omega \left(j\omega \frac{J_{eq}R_a}{K_t} + \frac{f_{eq}R_a}{K_t} + K_e \right)}$$

$$= \frac{K_t/(f_{eq}R_a + K_t K_e)}{j\omega(j\omega\tau_m + 1)} \tag{4-54}$$

where $\tau_m = J_{eq}R_a/(f_{eq}R_a + K_t K_e)$.

The preceding equations neglect the leakage inductance of the motor armature and are therefore only approximations. However, many small

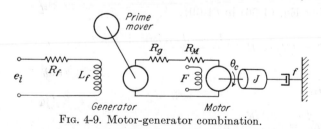

Generator   Motor

FIG. 4-9. Motor-generator combination.

d-c servomotors have such a high armature resistance that the effect of the leakage inductance is completely negligible, and in larger motors (up to about 1/4 hp) the leakage-inductance effect is small.

Motor-generator Combination. Figure 4-9 shows the schematic diagram of a motor-generator combination commonly used in servo systems.

The transfer function is readily derived from the following equations:

$$K_t i_a = (J_m + J_L)\frac{d^2\theta_c}{dt^2} + f\frac{d\theta_c}{dt}; K_t \bar{i}_a = (J_m + J_L)\overline{\frac{d^2\theta_c}{dt^2}} + f\overline{\frac{d\theta_c}{dt}} \quad (4\text{-}55)$$

$$e_g = i_a(R_g + R_m) + K_v\frac{d\theta_c}{dt}; \bar{e}_g = \bar{i}_a(R_g + R_m) + K_v\overline{\frac{d\theta_c}{dt}} \quad (4\text{-}56)$$

$$e_g = K_g i_1; \bar{e}_g = K_g \bar{i}_1 \quad (4\text{-}57)$$

$$e_i = i_1 R_1 + L_1\frac{di_1}{dt}; \bar{e}_i = \bar{i}_1 R_1 + L_1\overline{\frac{di_1}{dt}} \quad (4\text{-}58)$$

Assuming

$$e_i = E_i \sin \omega t; \bar{e}_i = E_i/\underline{0} \quad (4\text{-}59)$$

then

$$i_1 = I_1 \sin (\omega t - \theta); \bar{i}_1 = I_1/\underline{-\theta} \quad (4\text{-}60)$$

$$\frac{di_1}{dt} = \omega I_1 \cos (\omega t - \theta); \overline{\frac{di_1}{dt}} = j\omega I_1/\underline{-\theta} \quad (4\text{-}61)$$

$$i_a = I_a \sin (\omega t - \beta); \bar{i}_a = I_a/\underline{-\beta} \quad (4\text{-}62)$$

$$\theta_c = \Theta_c \sin (\omega t - \psi); \bar{\theta}_c = \Theta_c/\underline{-\psi} \quad (4\text{-}63)$$

$$\frac{d\theta_c}{dt} = \omega\Theta_c \cos (\omega t - \psi); \overline{\frac{d\theta_c}{dt}} = j\omega\Theta_c/\underline{-\psi} \quad (4\text{-}64)$$

$$\frac{d^2\theta_c}{dt^2} = -\omega^2\Theta_c \sin (\omega t - \psi); \frac{d^2\theta_c}{dt^2} = (j\omega)^2\Theta_c/\underline{-\psi} \quad (4\text{-}65)$$

Substituting Eqs. (4-59) through (4-65) in the preceding relationships,

$$K_t I_a/\underline{+\beta} = (J_m + J_L)(j\omega)^2 + f(j\omega)\Theta_c/\underline{-\psi} \quad (4\text{-}66)$$

$$K_g I_1/\underline{-\theta} = I_a/\underline{-\beta}(R_g + R_m) + K_v(j\omega)\Theta_c/\underline{-\psi} \quad (4\text{-}67)$$

$$E_i/\underline{0} = I_1/\underline{-\theta}(R_1 + j\omega L_1) \quad (4\text{-}68)$$

$$\frac{K_g E_i/\underline{0}}{R_1 + j\omega L_1} = I_a/\underline{-\beta}(R_g + R_m) + K_v(j\omega)\Theta_c/\underline{-\psi} \quad (4\text{-}69)$$

Substituting Eq. (4-66) in (4-69),

$$\frac{K_g E_i/\underline{0}}{R_1 + j\omega L_1} = (R_g + R_m)\frac{(J_m + J_L)(j\omega)^2 + f(j\omega)}{K_t}\Theta_c/\underline{-\psi}$$
$$+ K_v(j\omega)\Theta_c/\underline{-\psi} \quad (4\text{-}70)$$

from which

$$\frac{\bar{\theta}_c}{\bar{e}_i} = \frac{\Theta_c/\underline{-\psi}}{E_i/\underline{0}} = \frac{K_g}{(j\omega L_1 + R_1)}$$

$$\left\{\frac{1}{[(J_m + J_L)K_t](R_g + R_m)(j\omega)^2 + [j\omega f(R_g + R_m)/K_t] + j\omega K_v}\right\}$$

$$= \frac{K}{j\omega(j\omega\tau_m + 1)(j\omega\tau_f + 1)} \quad (4\text{-}71)$$

where
$$K = \frac{K_t K_g}{R_1[f(R_g + R_m) + K_t K_v]}$$
$$\tau_m = \frac{(J_m + J_L)(R_g + R_m)}{f(R_g + R_m) + K_t K_v}$$
$$\tau_f = \frac{L_1}{R_1}$$

Synchro Generator and Control Transformer. Figure 4-10 shows the synchro system commonly used as an error-detector system in servomechanisms. The synchro generator supplies the command signal by a rotation of its shaft, θ_R, and the shaft of the control transformer (not

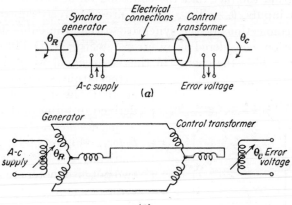

FIG. 4-10. Diagrams of synchro error-detector system. (*a*) Block schematic. (*b*) Wiring schematic.

shown) is connected or geared to the load, measuring the output position, θ_C, by the position of its shaft. Any angular difference between these shaft positions results in an electrical signal, e_o, which is a measure of the difference, i. e., an error signal.

If the input shaft is rotated through a complete revolution, with the control-transformer shaft held stationary, the amplitude of the error voltage, e_o, goes through one cycle of a sinusoidal variation. The variation of the output-voltage amplitude is

$$e_o = K_s \sin (\theta_R - \theta_C) = K_s \sin E \qquad (4\text{-}72)$$

where $E = \theta_R - \theta_C$.

The transfer function is

$$\frac{e_o}{E} = \frac{K_s \sin E}{E} \qquad (4\text{-}73)$$

In most servomechanism designs, however, it is not desirable to permit great angular difference between the input and output, so that the maximum difference between the input and output is normally restricted to small angles.   Under these conditions, the variation of e_o is linear, i. e.,

$$e_o = K_s(\theta_R - \theta_c) = K_s E; \text{ thus } \bar{e}_o = K_s \bar{E} \qquad (4\text{-}74)$$

$$\frac{\bar{e}_o}{\bar{E}} = K_s \qquad (4\text{-}75)$$

It should be noted that the transfer function for the synchro combination is expressed as the ratio of the output voltage to the error signal. This arises from the fact that the combination of two synchros has two independent inputs, θ_R and θ_c.   These are effectively subtracted by the design and connections of the synchros so that the equivalent input to the combination, considered as an error detector, is the difference signal, $E = \theta_R - \theta_c$.   It is the energy in this error signal which is transferred to the output, so that it is quite proper that the transfer function be derived in terms of the error signal.

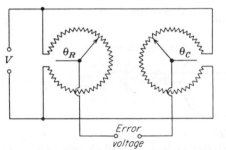

Potentiometers Used as Error Detectors.   Figure 4-11 shows schematically the basic arrangement of two potentiometers to be used as an error-detector system.   One potentiometer is connected to the command shaft to measure θ_R and the other is connected to the output shaft to measure θ_c.   If the two

Fig. 4-11. Potentiometer arrangement for error detection.

contacts on the potentiometers are preset so that they are both at the same potential when θ_R and θ_c are in correspondence, no error signal appears at the terminals e_o.   If one of the shafts is displaced, the contacts are misaligned by the error angle $E = \theta_R - \theta_c$.   Assuming that the potentiometers are wound linearly, then the voltage per unit angle is the total supply voltage, V, divided by the permissible rotation over which this voltage is distributed.   This voltage per unit angle may be called the potentiometer sensitivity, K_s, and

$$K_s = \frac{V}{B} \qquad (4\text{-}76)$$

where V = supply voltage
B = permissible angular rotation of potentiometer

If the potentiometer contacts are displaced by an error angle, E, the output voltage, e_o, is

$$e_o = K_s E \qquad (4\text{-}77)$$

The transfer function is then

$$\frac{e_o}{E} = K_s \qquad (4\text{-}78)$$

It should be noted that, if ordinary potentiometers are used, the servo-mechanism may be controlled only through somewhat less than one revolution of the potentiometer shaft. The rotation of the load itself may be much greater if gearing is used properly. Potentiometers with helical windings are available so that rotation of the potentiometer through a number of revolutions is possible.

Two-phase Induction Motor. In many servomechanism applications, particularly where the systems are of the instrument type and require powers less than 100 watts, two-phase induction motors are convenient power devices to drive the load. There are various reasons why the two-phase motor is desirable. It is small, rugged, and comparatively cheap; it requires no servicing; it may be energized from a single-phase source with the help of a phase-splitting device; and it may be controlled from a simple a-c amplifier rather than troublesome d-c amplifiers.

Figure 4-12a shows the schematic diagram of a two-phase motor, and Fig. 4-12b shows speed-torque curves typical of the small two-phase motors used in servo applications. The transfer function of this type of motor may be derived from the general equation for the torque of a two-phase motor, idealized as in Figure 4-12b, is:

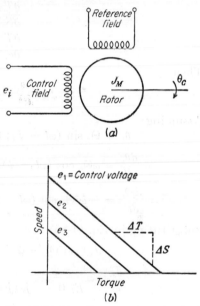

Fig. 4-12. Two-phase servo motor.
(a) Schematic diagram.
(b) Speed-torque curves.

$$T = \frac{\partial T}{\partial S} S + \frac{\partial T}{\partial I_m} I_m \qquad (4\text{-}79)$$

where $S = d\theta_c/dt$. Physically, this equation means that the torque produced by an induction motor has a component due to the speed and a component due to the current in the control or driving winding.

In the usual two-phase servo motor, ball bearings are used, so that there is very little friction. Assuming no external load, the reaction torque is

$$T = J_m \frac{d^2\theta_c}{dt^2} \qquad (4\text{-}80)$$

The equilibrium equation is

$$J_m \frac{d^2\theta_c}{dt^2} = \frac{\partial T}{\partial S} S + \frac{\partial T}{\partial I_m} I_m = \frac{\partial T}{\partial S} \frac{d\theta_c}{dt} + \frac{\partial T}{\partial I_m} \frac{\partial I_m}{\partial e_i} e_i \qquad (4\text{-}81)$$

This reduces to

$$J_m \frac{d^2\theta_c}{dt^2} = \frac{\partial T}{\partial S} \frac{d\theta_c}{dt} + \frac{\partial T}{\partial e_i} e_i \qquad (4\text{-}82)$$

The partial derivatives $\partial T/\partial S$ and $\partial T/\partial e_i$ may be evaluated numerically from the torque-speed characteristics of the motor; for operation on those portions of the characteristics which are straight and parallel, they may be considered constants.   Let

$$\frac{\partial T}{\partial S} = -A \qquad (4\text{-}83)$$

$$\frac{\partial T}{\partial e_i} = B \qquad (4\text{-}84)$$

Then

$$J_m \frac{d^2\theta_c}{dt^2} + A \frac{d\theta_c}{dt} = Be_i \qquad (4\text{-}85)$$

Assuming

$$\theta_c = \Theta_c \sin (\omega t - \psi); \text{ thus } \theta_c = \Theta_c \underline{/-\psi} \qquad (4\text{-}86)$$

$$\frac{d\theta_c}{dt} = \omega\Theta_c \cos (\omega t - \psi); \text{ thus } \overline{\frac{d\theta_c}{dt}} = j\omega\Theta_c \underline{/-\psi} \qquad (4\text{-}87)$$

$$\frac{d^2\theta_c}{dt^2} = -\omega^2\Theta_c \sin (\omega t - \psi); \text{ thus } \overline{\frac{d^2\theta_c}{dt^2}} = (j\omega)^2\Theta_c \underline{/-\psi} \qquad (4\text{-}88)$$

Substituting in Eq. (4-85),

$$J_m(j\omega)^2\Theta_c \underline{/-\psi} + Aj\omega\Theta_c \underline{/-\psi} = BE_i \underline{/0} \qquad (4\text{-}89)$$

$$\frac{\bar{\theta}_c}{\bar{e}_i} = \frac{\Theta_c \underline{/-\psi}}{E_i \underline{/0}} = \frac{B}{j\omega(j\omega J_m + A)} = \frac{B/A}{j\omega(j\omega\tau_m + 1)} \qquad (4\text{-}90)$$

This transfer function must be modified if there is a load connected to the shaft.   It should also be noted that the effect of any time constant in the control field winding has been neglected.   This would normally be considered in the output circuit of the device controlling the motor.

4-3. Precautions in Deriving and Using Transfer Functions.   It should be noted that all the transfer functions derived are subject to certain limitations.   The primary limitation is that of linearity.   If any of the devices operate nonlinearly, then the transfer functions are invalid, though, if the nonlinearity is slight, the linear transfer function may be a useful approximation.

A second limitation is that of loading.   Note that all electric-circuit transfer functions were derived assuming that the output terminals were open-circuited. In practical systems, the output is not open, but if it is fed into a sufficiently high impedance, such as the grid of an electron tube, the transfer function is not appreciably affected. However, if the output is fed into a low-impedance load, the transfer function is not correct, and must be rederived so as to include the effect of the load. For example, if two identical filters are connected in series, a transfer function must be derived for the two-loop network. Note also that the transfer function of a d-c generator was derived neglecting the armature resistance. This is correct only if the armature resistance is included with the load resistance when a load is added. This was done in deriving the transfer function of the motor-generator combination.

4-4. Types of Transfer Functions and Their Use in Servomechanism Analysis and Design. In dealing with servomechanisms, it is most convenient to use the type of transfer function which is derived for an assumed sinusoidal input. It is desirable to point out, however, that a variety of expressions derived on the sinusoidal basis may be termed "transfer functions." Most of these have uses in servomechanism work and are explained briefly here, although this text is concerned mainly with the simple, or "direct," transfer function already defined.

Four general types of transfer functions are used in servomechanisms. They are:

1. *Direct transfer function* $= \dfrac{\text{output signal}}{\text{input signal}}$, where the device considered is a simple series component

2. *Loop transfer function* $= \dfrac{\text{feedback signal}}{\text{input signal} - \text{feedback signal}}$, where the function desired is the ratio of the feedback signal fed into the comparison device to the signal derived from the comparison device

3. *System function* $=$ *frequency-response function* $= \dfrac{\text{output signal}}{\text{command signal}}$, where the device considered has a closed loop, and both signals are external to the loop itself

4. *Inverse functions*, which are the reciprocals of the three transfer functions defined above.

The direct transfer function is the function most commonly used in servomechanism work. It is used to set up the system equation, since a system normally consists of many components, each of which has a transfer function. The resulting system equation is then used to compute the steady-state performance, the resonance peak of the frequency response, and the resonant frequency of the closed-loop system. It is also used in obtaining the loop transfer function, the system function, and the inverse functions.

The loop transfer function is needed in analyzing and designing systems in which the feedback path that closes the loop affects the signal relationships. Consider the block diagrams of Fig. 4-13. Figure 4-13a shows a simple servomechanism in which the output quantity, θ_C, is measured and fed directly back to the error detector in such a way that the feedback signal is a faithful reproduction of the actual output signal, θ_C. The loop transfer function for such a system is the ratio of the feedback signal at the error detector to the actual system input signal, E, because this ratio indicates the transfer of energy around the loop. It is obvious that, for the conditions of Fig. 4-13a, the loop transfer function is the same as the direct transfer function.

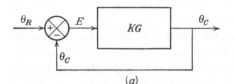

(a)

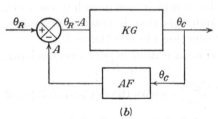

(b)

FIG. 4-13. Block diagrams of single-loop systems.
(a) Simple closed-loop system.
(b) System with component in feedback path.

For the system of Fig. 4-13b, the loop transfer function is also the ratio of the feedback signal at the error detector to the actual system input, E. This is obviously different from the direct transfer function, which is the ratio of the system output, θ_C, to the actual input signal, E. This difference is due to the component in the feedback path, which has its own transfer function, of course, and therefore produces a signal different from the output θ_C. The component in the feedback path may be an actual unit inserted for a specific purpose, or it may represent imperfections in the device used for measuring the output. In either case, the signal fed back into the error detector is different from the actual output signal, and the loop transfer function must be used in computing the system performance. The manipulations used with the loop transfer function are slightly different from those used with the direct transfer function, as will be shown later in the text.

The system function is the ratio of the output signal to the command signal. From either diagram in Fig. 4-13, it may be seen that this is the ratio of θ_C to θ_R. This response is related to the direct transfer function and the loop transfer function as follows: For the system of Fig. 4-13a, where there is no component in the feedback path, the transfer function is

$$\frac{\theta_C}{\theta_R - \theta_C} = KG \qquad (4\text{-}91)*$$

* The symbols for a transfer function are often followed by a parenthetical notation which is not a multiplier but an indication of the variable in terms of which the transfer

where the symbols KG represent the specific function which is characteristic of the components in the box marked "System."   Solving Eq. (4-91)
for the frequency-response function gives

$$\frac{\theta_c}{\theta_R} = \frac{KG}{1 + KG} \tag{4-92}$$

For the system of Fig. 4-13b, where there is a component in the feedback
path, the loop transfer function is

$$\frac{A}{\theta_R - A} = KGAF \tag{4-93}$$

Here the symbols AF represent the direct transfer function of the component in the feedback path.   Equation (4-93) may be derived by remem-
bering that the output of a device is computed by multiplying its input
by its transfer function; accordingly,

$$\theta_c = (\theta_R - A)KG \tag{4-94}$$
$$A = \theta_c AF \tag{4-95}$$

Thus

$$\frac{A}{AF} = (\theta_R - A)KG \tag{4-96}$$

and

$$\frac{A}{\theta_R - A} = KGAF \tag{4-97}$$

The frequency-response equation may be obtained by substituting Eq.
(4-95) in Eq. (4-93) and solving.   Thus,

$$\frac{\theta_c AF}{\theta_R - \theta_c AF} = KGAF \tag{4-98}$$

from which

$$\frac{\theta_c}{\theta_R} = \frac{KG}{1 + KGAF} \tag{4-99}$$

If the system under consideration is just a single-loop servomechanism,
the direct transfer function or the loop transfer function is derived and
used to obtain the specific frequency data (resonance peak and resonant
frequency) needed for design purposes.   The frequency-response equation would probably not be derived or used.   In other applications, however, the servomechanism system may be more complex and may contain
within itself one or more closed-loop systems, such as those of Fig. 4-13.

---

function is to be expressed.   Examples are $KG(j\omega)$ or $KG(s)$, where the notation $(j\omega)$
or (s) indicates the variable.   In this text only one variable, $(j\omega)$, is used.   Therefore
the parenthetical notation is omitted, since there is no need to distinguish between
variables.

In such a case, the closed-loop system within the over-all servomechanism is just a component as far as the servomechanism is concerned, and its transfer function must be determined.   It is readily seen, then, that the frequency-response function of the simple closed-loop system is its direct transfer function as far as the rest of the servomechanism is concerned. In such cases, the frequency-response function may be derived and used as a direct-transfer-function expression.

Inverse transfer functions may be obtained by taking the reciprocal of the normal transfer functions.   They are not as commonly used as

TABLE 4-1
TRANSFER FUNCTIONS OF COMPONENTS

Equation No.	Component	Transfer function	K	G
(4-10)	RL filter	$\dfrac{j\omega\tau}{j\omega\tau + 1}$	1	$\dfrac{j\omega\tau}{j\omega\tau + 1}$
(4-22)	RC filter	$\dfrac{j\omega\tau}{j\omega\tau + 1}$	1	$\dfrac{j\omega\tau}{j\omega\tau + 1}$
(4-28)	Phase-lead network	$\alpha\,\dfrac{j\omega\tau + 1}{j\omega\alpha\tau + 1}$	α	$\dfrac{j\omega\tau + 1}{j\omega\alpha\tau + 1}$
(4-31)	Phase-lag network	$\dfrac{j\omega\tau_1 + 1}{j\omega\tau_2 + 1}$	1	$\dfrac{j\omega\tau_1 + 1}{j\omega\tau_2 + 1}$
(4-34)	Gear train	$\dfrac{1}{N_1 N_2}$	$\dfrac{1}{N_1 N_2}$	$\cdots$
(4-37)	Electronic amplifier	$-\dfrac{\mu R_L}{r_p + R_L}$	$-\dfrac{\mu R_L}{r_p + R_L}$	$\cdots$
(4-41)	D-C generator	$\dfrac{K_g/R_f}{j\omega\tau_f + 1}$	$\dfrac{K_g}{R_f}$	$\dfrac{1}{j\omega\tau_f + 1}$
(4-50)	D-C motor; inertia load	$\dfrac{1/K_e}{j\omega(j\omega\tau_m + 1)}$	$\dfrac{1}{K_e}$	$\dfrac{1}{j\omega(j\omega\tau_m + 1)}$
(4-54)	D-C motor, geared; inertia and friction load	$\dfrac{K_t/(f_{eq}R_a + K_eK_t)}{j\omega(j\omega\tau_m + 1)}$	$\dfrac{K_t}{f_{eq}R_a + K_tK_e}$	$\dfrac{1}{j\omega(j\omega\tau_m + 1)}$
(4-71)	Generator-motor	$\dfrac{K}{j\omega(j\omega\tau_m + 1)(j\omega\tau_f + 1)}$	K	$\dfrac{1}{j\omega(j\omega\tau_m + 1)(j\omega\tau_f + 1)}$
(4-75)	Synchro error detector	K_s	K_s	$\cdots$
(4-90)	Two-phase motor	$\dfrac{B/A}{j\omega(j\omega\tau_m + 1)}$	$\dfrac{B}{A}$	$\dfrac{1}{j\omega(j\omega\tau_m + 1)}$

the normal transfer functions, but they are more convenient in various specific applications.   Some of their advantages are seen in a later chapter.   It should be noted that the inverse transfer function does not indicate a transfer of energy in the reverse direction.   Most of the components used in servomechanism systems have unidirectional properties as far as energy transfer is concerned, and thus their inverse transfer functions still refer to energy transfer in the same direction as is specified by the direct transfer functions.

The symbols KG and AF are merely shorthand notations for direct transfer functions.   The KG notation is used for the direct transfer functions of components which are in the main transmission path, while the AF notation is used for the direct transfer functions of components which are in feedback paths. The use of subscripts instead of a change in letters is common practice, the choice in notation being a matter of personal preference. Two letters are used instead of a single letter because most transfer functions are readily factored into a constant factor, which is represented by the K, and a frequency-variable factor, which is represented by the G. Table 4-1 lists the transfer functions previously derived in this chapter, and indicates the value of K and G for each. Note that in some cases the value of K is unity, and thus the K need not be used in symbolizing such a component. This indicates another advantage of the double-letter representation; when only the frequency-variant factor is of interest, the specific transfer function may be symbolized by the G only, thus indicating that K has an assumed value of unity for the manipulation under consideration.

4-5. Block Diagrams. In Chap. 1, functional block diagrams were used as an aid in explaining qualitatively the performance of servo-mechanism systems. In the analysis and design of servomechanisms, block diagrams have a twofold use: first, to clarify the operation of the system and the purpose of various components; and secondly, to aid in setting up the equations of the system. This second use of block diagrams is considered here.

In previous sections, the transfer functions of various components have been derived. These components, when used in servomechanisms, are interconnected. If the over-all schematic diagram of the system is inspected, it is usually possible to subdivide the system into these simple components. A convenient method for indicating this subdivision is to enclose the individual components in blocks. The transfer function for each component is then obtained, and, since the actual circuit is no longer of value, once the equations are known, the individual blocks are redrawn with the equations inserted in them. In this manner a block diagram is obtained which consists of a number of interconnected blocks, each identified mathematically. It is also convenient to mark the lines interconnecting the blocks with symbols representing the signal which is fed from one block to the next.

Once the block diagram has been set up in this fashion, it is only necessary to combine the transfer functions properly to obtain the equations needed in analyzing or designing the system. Certain rules must be established for manipulating the transfer-function equations, but the rules are simple and will be derived as needed. It should also be noted that the subdivision of a system diagram into blocks is not necessarily an automatic procedure. Care must be taken to enclose all interacting components in the same block; otherwise the transfer functions are incorrect. To illustrate the methods used in setting up block diagrams and in order to derive the simple rules needed to manipulate the transfer functions, an example is worked out in the following paragraphs.

Figure 4-14 shows the schematic diagram of a positioning servomechanism. The diagram has been subdivided into four blocks. The reasoning behind this subdivision is as follows:

Block 1. This contains the error-detector system, which consists of a synchro generator and control transformer. The two units are electrically and functionally interconnected so that both must be included in the same block, and the only other factor to be considered is the possibility that some other component interacts with the synchros and should also be included in the block. That no such interaction exists is readily determined. The input signal θ_R is an independent variable; the output

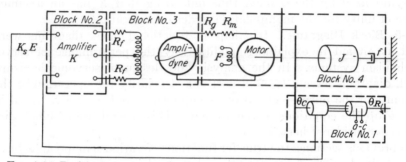

Fig. 4-14. Positioning servomechanism—to illustrate block-diagram methods.

signal is fed in mechanically from the load and may be considered as another independent variable; the output of the control transformer is fed into the amplifier input, which normally would be a very high impedance and effectively an open circuit. Thus the inclusion of the error-detector system in a block by itself is justified.

Block 2. This contains the amplifier which is assumed to be an electronic device, but it does not include the amplidyne field. It is assumed that the amplifier is capable of converting the a-c synchro signal to a d-c signal suitable for the control fields, and it is also assumed that the amplifier has been designed so that it has no phase shift over the range of frequencies important to system operation. The design of such an amplifier is not difficult, though in some designs the amplidyne field could not be external to block 2. To avoid divergent discussion at this point, no specific amplifier circuit is given.

Block 3. This contains the amplidyne generator but not the resistance of the generator armature. This arrangement is used because the terminal voltage of a generator is affected by the drop across the armature resistance, but the generated voltage is not, as long as the generator is operated as a linear device, i. e., as long as armature reaction is too small appreciably to distort the magnetic field. By the simple expedient of placing the generator armature resistance external to block 3, the output of the block is the generated voltage, and there is no interaction with the motor.

Block 4. This lumps together the generator armature resistance, the motor, the gearing, and the load, because all these units interact in the sense that the performance of the motor cannot be calculated unless all are considered.

Once the blocks have been set up on the schematic diagram, the transfer function of each block is obtained, and a new block diagram is drawn, as in Fig. 4-15. In this case the transfer functions of blocks 1, 2, and 4 are determined as in previous sections.

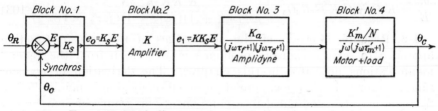

Fig. 4-15. Block diagram of a positioning servomechanism.

The complete derivation of a transfer function for an amplidyne generator is beyond the scope of this text. However, if the mutual inductances between fields are neglected, the amplidyne is approximately equivalent to two d-c generators connected in tandem, and an approximate transfer function for the amplidyne is

$$K_3G_3 = \frac{K_g}{(j\omega\tau_f + 1)(j\omega\tau_q + 1)} \qquad (4\text{-}100)$$

where K_g = over-all gain, volts/volt
 τ_f = control-field time constant
 τ_q = quadrature-field time constant

The next step is to determine the direct transfer function of the system by combining the transfer functions of the components. By definition, the direct transfer function of the system is the ratio of the output to the activating input. The output obviously is θ_C. The activating input is the error signal $E = \theta_R - \theta_C$. Thus the system transfer function is

$$K_sG_s = \frac{\theta_C}{E} \qquad (4\text{-}101)$$

Since all the blocks are connected in cascade, K_sG_s may be obtained simply by multiplying together all the transfer functions. This may be proved from the basic definition of transfer functions, as follows: by definition,

$$K_1 G_1 = K_s = \frac{e_o}{E}$$

$$K_2 G_2 = K = \frac{e_1}{e_o}$$

$$K_3 G_3 = \frac{K_g}{(j\omega\tau_f + 1)(j\omega\tau_q + 1)} = \frac{e_g}{e_1}$$

$$K_4 G_4 = \frac{K'_m/N}{j\omega(j\omega\tau'_m + 1)} = \frac{\theta_C}{e_g}$$

but

$$\frac{e_o}{E}\frac{e_1}{e_o}\frac{e_g}{e_1}\frac{\theta_C}{e_g} = \frac{\theta_C}{E} \tag{4-102}$$

Thus

$$\frac{\theta_C}{E} = K_1 G_1 K_2 G_2 K_3 G_3 K_4 G_4 = \frac{K_s K K_g K'_m/N}{j\omega(j\omega\tau'_m + 1)(j\omega\tau_f + 1)(j\omega\tau_q + 1)} \tag{4-103}$$

4-6. Résumé. Certain of the advantages of the transfer-function approach to servomechanism problems may be seen from the general manipulations presented in this chapter. The derivation of transfer functions for individual components is a relatively simple manipulation. Systems may be subdivided into components or groups of components by using the block-diagram technique. Over-all transfer functions for simple series circuits are obtained from the block diagram by simple multiplication (when components are not all in series, the manipulation is only slightly more complicated).

Several other advantages which are particularly convenient in design work may be seen from Eq. (4-103). In this equation all expressions are multiplied together, and the terms representing the characteristics of individual components appear as factors. Thus, if it is decided to replace some component with a different device, a simple substitution of transfer functions is all that is necessary; the entire equation need not be rederived. For example, if a different error detector is to be used, the term K_s is removed from Eq. (4-103) and the transfer function of the new error detector replaces it; or if a different motor is to be used, the K'_m and τ'_m (and possibly the N) are removed and replaced by the corresponding constants for the new motor-load combination. Also, if it is decided that an additional series component is required to obtain desired performance, the equation for the new system is obtained by simply multiplying the original transfer-function equation by the transfer function of the additional component.

PROBLEMS

4-1. Derive the algebraic transfer functions for the electric networks of Fig. 4P-1.

4-2. Derive the algebraic transfer function for the filter of Fig. 4P-2.

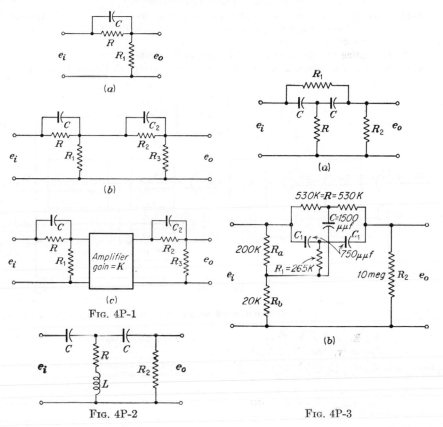

FIG. 4P-1

FIG. 4P-2

FIG. 4P-3

4-3. The filters of Fig. 4P-3 are normally used in carrier-frequency servos, and the voltage applied is a suppressed carrier amplitude-modulated wave. Derive appropriate transfer functions.

4-4. For the system of Prob. 3-3, derive the numerical direct transfer function and the frequency-response function (system function).

4-5. Derive the algebraic transfer function for the differentiating amplifier of Prob. 3-4.

4-6. Obtain the numerical transfer function and the system function for the servo of Prob. 3-4.

4-7. For the system of Prob. 3-5,
  a. What is the loop transfer function for the tachometer loop?
  b. What is the direct transfer function for the system?
  c. What is the frequency-response function?

4-8. What is the direct transfer function for the system of Prob. 3-6?

4-9. What is the transfer function of the integrating amplifier of Prob. 3-7? What are the system function and the direct transfer function for the servo?

4-10. Determine the transfer function for the system of Prob. 3-8.

4-11. Draw the block diagram for the system of Fig. 3P-5. Using the numerical values given in Prob. 3-9, compute the transfer function for each block, and the direct transfer function of the system.

4-12. Draw the block diagram for the system of Fig. 3P-6.   Compute the transfer function of each block, using the numerical data of Prob. 3-12.   Compute the direct transfer function of the system.

4-13. Determine the direct transfer function of the system of Prob. 3-13.

4-14. What is the direct transfer function of the system described by the block diagram of Fig. 4P-4?

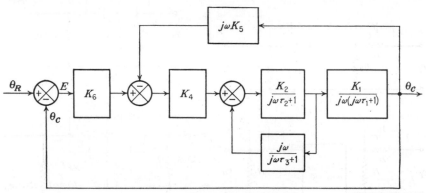

FIG. 4P-4

REFERENCES

AHRENDT, W. R., and J. F. TAPLIN, "Automatic Feedback Control," McGraw-Hill Book Company, Inc., New York, 1951.

BROWN, G. S., and D. P. CAMPBELL, "Principles of Servomechanisms," John Wiley & Sons, Inc., New York, 1948.

THALER, G. J., and R. G. BROWN, "Servomechanism Analysis," McGraw-Hill Book Company, Inc., New York, 1953.

CHAPTER 5

TRANSFER-FUNCTION PLOTS

5-1. Introduction. As previously indicated, the analysis and design of servomechanisms are concerned primarily with the transient, or time, response of a closed-loop system, where the term "transient" includes the final steady-state response. The use of frequency-response methods instead of differential-equation methods is justified partly because it saves time and labor, but mostly because it permits an optimum, or nearly optimum, design for systems which are not readily handled with the differential equation. The transfer-function equations may be considered as an intermediate step in determining the important parts of the frequency response.

The use of frequency-response methods arises from the mathematical correlations between frequency response and transient response. It would therefore seem logical to manipulate the transfer-function equations so as to obtain the frequency-response equation for a closed-loop system. This can be done readily, as shown by Eq. (4-92).

$$\frac{\theta_c}{\theta_R} = \frac{KG}{1 + KG} \qquad (4\text{-}92)$$

The frequency response of the system can then be calculated, plotted, and interpreted in terms of the transient response, but in general this is not necessary, since the only features of the frequency response needed for transient interpretation are the height of the resonance peak and the resonant frequency. Furthermore, frequency-response equations are not readily adaptable to design work, i. e., if the height of the resonance peak and the resonant frequency are not as desired, something in the system must be changed and the response recalculated; because of the vector relationships in the frequency-response equation, such repeated calculations are very laborious. Finally, the steady-state performance of the system is not readily determined from the frequency-response equation or from the frequency-response curves.

The direct transfer function (KG) of a closed-loop system does not directly give the frequency response of a servomechanism, but is related to it, as shown by Eq. (4-92). By working with this transfer function, it is possible to determine the height of the resonance peak of the *closed-*

loop system, that is, the peak of the frequency-response curve, and it is also possible to determine the resonant frequency. The methods involved are graphical, i. e., plotting curves for the transfer-function equation and interpreting these curves. It is also possible to determine the steady-state performance of the *closed-loop system from the transfer-function equation*, and for certain types of plots it is possible to determine the steady-state performance from the plot.

This chapter is concerned primarily with methods of plotting the transfer-function curves, and with methods of determining the relationships between these curves and the frequency response or the transient response. The treatment assumes that the systems are known to be stable (i. e., do not oscillate continuously). The important question of stability, which can also be determined from the plots, is reserved for the next chapter, as is the question of steady-state performance.

5-2. Types of Transfer-function Plots. It must be remembered that the transient response of a component or system cannot be determined from its response to a single frequency, but only from its response to all frequencies from zero to infinity. The necessary procedure is, therefore, to substitute in the transfer-function equation a number of numerical values for the frequency, ω, and plot the results. The transfer function is, in general, a complex expression, and the numbers obtained by substitution for ω are vectors having a magnitude and a phase angle. Thus there are three parameters to be considered in plotting: the frequency, the magnitude, and the phase.

There are a number of ways to plot curves representing the transfer-function equations. These are:

1. Plot magnitude vs. frequency and phase vs. frequency on rectangular coordinates.

2. Plot as vectors on polar coordinates, obtaining a vector for each value of ω, and connect the tips of the vectors to form a polar curve.

3. Use logarithmic coordinates, i. e., plot log magnitude vs. log ω, and phase angle vs. log ω.

4. Plot log magnitude vs. phase angle, with frequency as a parameter.

Of these, method 1 is not used because the resulting curves are not readily interpreted. Method 2 is particularly convenient for explaining the concepts involved; it permits ready determination of stability, resonance peak, and resonant frequency; and it gives a qualitative indication of steady-state performance. It may also be used to compute the frequency-response and phase-shift curves of the closed-loop system. It is usable for design work, though not necessarily optimum.

Method 3 is particularly useful for preliminary design work. It permits ready determination of the steady-state performance, and conveniently shows the effects of important system adjustments and the effect of adding components. The height of the resonance peak may be estimated, but not accurately, and the system natural frequency may be estimated, but not the resonant frequency. The over-all frequency-response curves cannot be calculated from the plots of method 3. Recently, methods have been devised for computing the transient-response curve from the curves used in method 3, but a discussion of this is beyond the scope of this text.

Method 4 is roughly equivalent to method 2 in that it is the logarithmic counterpart of the polar plot. It has certain definite advantages in design work and would normally be used. Its major disadvantage is that the steady-state performance is not available from the plot.

In practical design, the logarithmic methods are most commonly used because they are faster and give results that are as good as, if not better than, the results of polar-plot design. The polar plot, however, has advantages in certain specific problems, and should be considered as a valuable tool.

5-3. Polar Plot of the Transfer Function—Relationships with the Frequency Response. To illustrate the plotting of the transfer-function curve on polar coordinates, consider Eq. (4-103), which is the transfer-function equation of a positioning servomechanism:

$$KG = \frac{\theta_C}{E} = \frac{K_s K K_g K'_m / N}{j\omega(j\omega\tau'_m + 1)(j\omega\tau_f + 1)(j\omega\tau_q + 1)} \qquad (4\text{-}103)$$

No numbers are used at this point because the general shape of the curve may be determined by inspection of the equation, and a sketched curve is sufficient for purposes of explanation.

To determine the general shape of the curve, consider that ω is zero. Two things may be noted from Eq. (4-103): First, the magnitude of KG is infinite, since there is a zero factor in the denominator; second, the phase of KG is $-90°$ since the phase of $j\omega$ is $+90°$, while all other terms have a phase angle of zero, and the $j\omega$ term is in the denominator. Thus, one end of the polar curve is a point, $\omega = 0$, located at infinity on the negative imaginary axis. As ω increases, the phase of the other terms in the denominator becomes appreciable, but the magnitude of the denominator increases and the magnitude of KG decreases. Thus, for increasing values of ω, points on the polar locus move into the third quadrant and come closer to the origin. At some value of ω, the total phase angle of the denominator is $180°$, and so the locus crosses the negative real axis into the second quadrant, with the magnitude of KG continually decreasing. At some other value of ω the phase of the denominator is $270°$, and the locus enters the first quadrant. Finally, as ω approaches infinity, the phase approaches $360°$, and the locus approaches the origin along the positive real axis.

Figure 5-1 is a sketch illustrating the general shape of the locus of Eq. (4-103). The actual curvature of the various portions of the curve depends on the numerical values assigned to the time constants τ'_m, τ_f, and τ_q, and an actual plot for assigned numerical values might have an appreciably different shape. It should also be noted that the length of each vector depends primarily on the numerator of Eq. (4-103), i. e., on the system gain. Thus the points a and b at which the plot crosses the axes are not unique, but depend on the system gain and may be moved along the axes simply by adjusting the system gain.

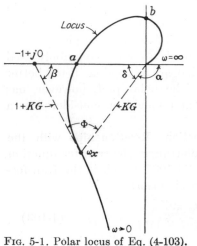

FIG. 5-1. Polar locus of Eq. (4-103).

The relationships between the transfer-function curve and the frequency-response curve may also be established from Fig. 5-1. The vector KG is illustrated in the figure. If the distance from the $-1 + j0$ point to the origin is considered as a vector $(+1)$, then the vector $1 + KG$ is a line from the $-1 + j0$ point to the point ω_x on the curve. Equation (4-92) shows that the frequency response is

$$\frac{\theta_C}{\theta_R} = \frac{KG}{1 + KG} \qquad (4\text{-}92)$$

Thus, by constructing the vector $1 + KG$, the magnitude of the ratio θ_C/θ_R may be determined at any ω by measuring the lengths KG and $1 + KG$ and performing the indicated division. If this is done at a number of frequencies, a plot of the magnitude of the output/input ratio vs. frequency may be obtained, and the height of the resonance peak, as well as the resonant frequency, may be determined.

The phase relationships for the frequency response may also be obtained from the polar plot. From Fig. 5-1 it is seen that the angle of KG at frequency ω_x is α, and the angle of $1 + KG$ is β. Then the angle of the frequency response is

$$\bigg/\frac{\theta_C}{\theta_R} = \alpha - \beta \qquad (5\text{-}1)$$

Thus the phase may be determined at any and all frequencies by computing or measuring the angles indicated. However, it is readily shown that the angle Φ between the KG and $1 + KG$ vectors is also the angle of the frequency response, so that only one measurement is needed. Defining counterclockwise rotation to be positive:

$$\alpha - \delta = 180° \qquad (5\text{-}2)$$
$$\beta + \Phi - \delta = 180° \qquad (5\text{-}3)$$

Then

$$\Phi = 180° - \beta + \delta \tag{5-4}$$

Substituting Eq. (5-2) in (5-4),

$$\Phi = \alpha - \delta - \beta + \delta = \alpha - \beta \tag{5-5}$$

In general, the over-all frequency-response curve is not needed and would not be calculated. The height of the resonance peak and the resonant frequency are needed and must be determined. They may be computed by the method indicated, but easier methods are available. Discussion of these methods is reserved till later in this chapter.

5-4. Logarithmic Plots   Magnitude in Decibels vs. Log ω and Phase Angle vs. Log ω. The transfer-function equation may be plotted on logarithmic coordinates. One preliminary advantage of this method lies in the fact that the numerical computation of points on the curves is considerably simplified, and usually the plots of log magnitude vs. log ω may be approximated to engineering accuracy with straight-line asymptotes, thus further simplifying the plots.

The transfer function of a servomechanism may be generalized and expressed as

$$KG = K \frac{(j\omega\tau_a + 1) \;\cdots\; [(j\omega)^2\tau_b + j\omega A + 1] \;\cdots}{(j\omega)^N(j\omega\tau_1 + 1) \;\cdots\; [(j\omega)^2\tau_2 + j\omega B + 1]} \tag{5-6}$$

There may be any number of terms in either the numerator or the denominator; the denominator is usually of higher order than the numerator. The exponent N takes only positive integral values such as 0, 1, 2, 3, etc., and is seldom greater than 2. Single time-constant terms, such as $j\omega\tau_a + 1$, are most common, quadratic terms are occasionally encountered, and cubic or quartic terms can occur but are rare.

The terms in Eq. (5-6) are complex numbers, and therefore their magnitudes and phase angles are handled separately. Taking logarithms of both sides and using the base 10,

$$\log_{10}|KG| = \log_{10}|K| + \log_{10}|j\omega\tau_a + 1| \;\cdots$$
$$+ \log_{10}|(j\omega)^2\tau_b + j\omega A + 1| \;\cdots\; - N\log_{10}|j\omega|$$
$$- \log_{10}|j\omega\tau_1 + 1| \;\cdots\; - \log_{10}|(j\omega)^2\tau_2 + j\omega B + 1| \tag{5-7}$$

To express the magnitudes in decibels, which is a more convenient form, the terms are multiplied by 20; thus,

$$20\log_{10}|KG| = 20\log_{10}|K| + 20\log_{10}|j\omega\tau_a + 1| \;\cdots$$
$$- 20N\log_{10}|j\omega| \;\cdots \tag{5-8}$$

The phase angle is given by

$$\underline{/KG} = \underline{/K} + \tan^{-1}\omega\tau_a \;\cdots\; + \tan^{-1}\frac{\omega A}{1 - \omega^2\tau_b} \;\cdots\; - (90N)°$$
$$- \tan^{-1}\omega\tau_1 \;\cdots \tag{5-9}$$

The computational advantage of the logarithmic form is immediately apparent from Eq. (5-8) (there is no advantage in the angle calculation). From Eq. (5-8) it is seen that each term may be considered as a separate unit, its magnitude found, and the log determined and converted into decibels. The individual terms are then added or subtracted as required. Thus addition and subtraction are substituted for multiplication and division.

When the results are plotted, semilog paper is usually used, with the magnitude, in decibels, and the phase angle plotted as ordinates on the

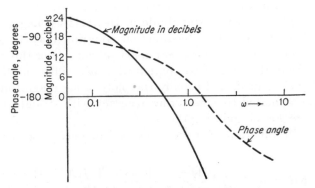

Fig. 5-2. Plot of magnitude and phase angle vs. frequency.

rectangular scale, and the frequency plotted as abscissa on the logarithmic scale. In setting up the ordinate scales, it is normal practice to make the 0-db and $-180°$-phase-angle divisions coincide. This results in a combined plot of magnitude and phase-angle curves which is readily interpreted in terms of system performance, for reasons which will be explained later. Figure 5-2 shows a sketched log plot for the system of Eq. (4-103).

As further simplification, it may be shown that various portions of the magnitude plot are essentially the same as their straight-line asymptotes, so that the asymptotes may usually be used instead of the actual curve. This, of course, reduces the number of points that must be calculated. Furthermore, the deviation of the true curve from the asymptote is readily estimated (except for quadratic factors); in any case, if much discrepancy is expected, additional points may be calculated at exactly the frequencies at which they are needed. The following paragraphs indicate the asymptotic approximations of the typical factors encountered in servomechanism equations.

For a term such as $(j\omega)^N$ which normally occurs in the denominator, the decibel expression is $-20N \log_{10} |j\omega|$. This plots exactly as a straight

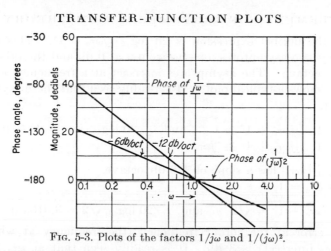

FIG. 5-3. Plots of the factors $1/j\omega$ and $1/(j\omega)^2$.

line. If $N = 1$, the slope of the line is -6 db/octave*; if $N = 2$, the slope is -12 db/octave, etc. These slopes are indicated in Fig. 5-3. That these are correct may be seen from:

$$-20 \log_{10} 1 = 0 \text{ db}$$
$$-20 \log_{10} 2 = -6.02 \text{ db}$$
$$-20 \log_{10} 4 = -12.04 \text{ db}$$
$$-20 \log_{10} 8 = -18.06 \text{ db}$$

which shows a slope of almost exactly -6 db/octave for $N = 1$. Also,

$$-20(2) \log_{10} 1 = 0 \text{ db}$$
$$-20(2) \log_{10} 2 = -12.04 \text{ db}$$
$$-20(2) \log_{10} 4 = -24.08 \text{ db}$$
$$-20(2) \log_{10} 8 = -36.12 \text{ db}$$

which is a slope of -12 db/octave for $N = 2$. The phase-angle curves are, of course, constant at $-90°$ for $N = 1$ and $-180°$ for $N = 2$.

For a term such as $(j\omega\tau_a + 1)$, when in the numerator of the transfer

---

* An octave is a measure of the difference between two frequencies, f_1 and f_2, and may be defined by

$$\text{Number of octaves} = n = \frac{\log_{10}(f_2/f_1)}{\log_{10} 2}$$

One octave separates any two frequencies which are in the ratio of 2 or ½. Thus $f_1 = 40$ is separated by one octave from $f_2 = 80$. Likewise $f_1 = 40$ is separated by one octave from $f_2 = 20$. If it is desired to compute the frequency which is n octaves above a given frequency f_0, then

$$f_x = f_0 2^n$$

and to compute the frequency which is n octaves below f_0

$$f_x = f_0 2^{-n}$$

function, the decibel expression is $20 \log_{10} (j\omega\tau_a + 1)$. This may be replaced by two asymptotes, one horizontal at 0 db and the other rising at $+6$ db/octave. The asymptotes intersect at a frequency $\omega = 1/\tau_a$. Figure 5-4 shows a typical plot. It is readily seen that these asymptotes are correct.

For $\omega\tau_a \ll 1$, $|j\omega\tau_a + 1| \cong 1$ and $20 \log_{10} |j\omega\tau_a + 1| \cong 0$ db
  $\omega\tau_a \gg 1$, $|j\omega\tau_a + 1| \cong |j\omega\tau_a|$

and $20 \log_{10} |j\omega\tau_a|$ has a slope of $+6$ db/octave.

Also, at $\omega\tau_a = 1$,

$$|j\omega\tau_a + 1| = \sqrt{2}   \text{and}   20 \log_{10} \sqrt{2} = 3.0103 \text{ db}$$

Thus the error at the corner frequency (the frequency at which the asymptotes intersect) is 3 db. It is readily seen that at $\omega\tau_a \ll 1$ the

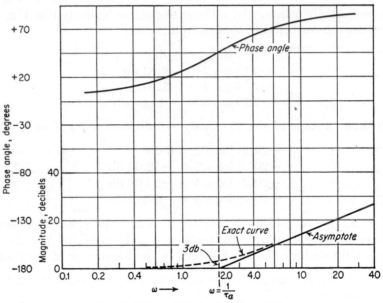

FIG. 5-4. Plot of the factor $(j\omega\tau_a + 1)$.

phase angle is essentially zero, while for $\omega\tau_a \gg 1$ it is $+90°$. When $\omega\tau_a = 1$, then $\tan^{-1} |\omega\tau_a|$ is $45°$. These are also shown in Fig. 5-4.

If a similar term $(j\omega\tau_1 + 1)$ appears in the denominator, then by similar reasoning it is seen that the asymptotes are a horizontal line at 0 db and a line sloping at -6 db/octave, with the corner frequency at $\omega = 1/\tau_1$. The phase relationships are $0°$ at low frequencies, $-45°$ at the corner frequency, and $-90°$ at high frequencies. The magnitude error at the corner frequency is -3 db. Terms such as these may at times be repeated in a transfer function, for example $(j\omega\tau_a + 1)^2$. The exponent does not affect the low-frequency horizontal asymptote, but it changes the slope of the high-frequency asymptote to ∓ 12 db/octave. The corner frequency is also unaffected, but the error at the corner frequency is multiplied by the exponent and is ∓ 6 db. The phase-angle relationship is also modified, since the phase at high frequencies is $\mp 180°$ when the exponent is 2, and at the corner frequency the phase angle is $\mp 90°$.

Quadratic factors such as $(j\omega)^2\tau_b + j\omega B + 1$ are less conveniently handled in asymptotic form. Figure 5-5 is a sketch of the log magnitude of such a term as a function of frequency. It is readily shown that the

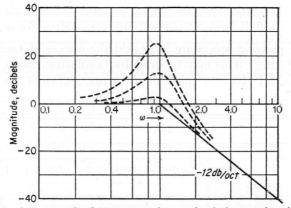

FIG. 5-5. Sketch of the magnitude response of a quadratic factor when in the denominator.

low-frequency asymptote is a horizontal line at 0 db and the high-frequency asymptote slopes at -12 db/octave (if the term is in the denominator). The low-frequency phase angle is 0°, and the high-frequency phase angle is 180°. The corner frequency is $\omega = 1/\sqrt{\tau_b}$. However, the behavior of both the magnitude and the phase angle in the frequency range around the corner frequency depends on the coefficient B. There is no convenient way to estimate the magnitude error, and while the phase angle at the corner frequency is $-90°$, the slope of the phase-angle curve varies considerably with the value of B. In general, when quadratic terms are encountered, the asymptotes are a good starting point, but several exact points should be calculated near the corner frequency.

To illustrate the method of plotting the asymptotic curves, consider Eq. (4-103), which was used to obtain the polar plot of Fig. 5-1. Assume that the numerator of the equation has a numerical value of 4, and that $\tau'_m = 1$, $\tau_f = 0.5$, and $\tau_q = 0.1$. Then the equation becomes

$$KG = \frac{K_s K K_g K'_m / N}{(j\omega)(j\omega\tau'_m + 1)(j\omega\tau_f + 1)(j\omega\tau_q + 1)}$$

$$= \frac{4}{j\omega(j\omega + 1)(0.5j\omega + 1)(0.1j\omega + 1)} \tag{5-10}$$

Most of this equation can be plotted by direct inspection.   The numerical value of the numerator must be converted into decibels; the other terms may be evaluated as follows:

$K = 4$ horizontal line at $+12$ db

$j\omega$ -6 db/octave slope, and is 0 db at $\omega = 1$

$j\omega + 1$ corner frequency at $\omega = 1$; horizontal line at 0 db for $\omega < 1$ and -6 db/octave slope for $\omega > 1$

$0.5j\omega + 1$ corner frequency at $\omega = 1/0.5 = 2$; horizontal line at 0 db for $\omega < 2$; -6 db/octave slope for $\omega > 2$

$0.1j\omega + 1$ corner frequency at $\omega = 1/0.1 = 10$; horizontal line at 0 db for $\omega < 10$; -6 db/octave slope for $\omega > 10$

The basic plotting procedure is to add the curves at each value of ω and plot the sum.   This may be done by tabulating values, as in Table 5-1.   The values given in this table are not sufficient for a complete

TABLE 5-1

ω	Magnitudes in decibels of					
	K	$\left\lvert\dfrac{1}{j\omega}\right\rvert$	$\left\lvert\dfrac{1}{j\omega + 1}\right\rvert$	$\left\lvert\dfrac{1}{0.5j\omega + 1}\right\rvert$	$\left\lvert\dfrac{1}{0.1j\omega + 1}\right\rvert$	Sum
0.5	12	6	0	0	0	+18
1.0	12	0	0	0	0	+12
2.0	12	-6	-6	0	0	0
4.0	12	-12	-12	-6	0	-18
8.0	12	-18	-18	-12	0	-36

curve; many more points would be needed.   But if the asymptotes have been drawn for the individual factors, the desired values are readily obtained from the curves so that no calculation other than addition is required.

A much simpler procedure is to add the slopes of the asymptotes after determining a convenient starting place.   To combine the curves, one first applies the basic procedure of adding the ordinates at one selected value of ω; the convenient starting place is any value of ω where such addition is simplest.   The simplest addition for Eq. (5-10) is at an ω of 1.0, since all curves are zero at this frequency, except the gain constant of 12 db.   Thus, at $\omega = 1$, the net asymptotic curve must have an ordinate of 12 db.   For $\omega < 1$, all curves are horizontal except the term which has a slope of -6 db/octave and rises as ω decreases.   Thus, for values of ω less than 1.0, the net ordinate rises at 6 db/octave from the starting value of 12 db, and a straight line with a -6 db/octave slope may be drawn.   Between the values $\omega = 1$ and $\omega = 2$, two of the asymptotes have a slope of -6 db/octave, and all others have a slope of zero.   Thus the net asymptote between these frequencies must have a slope of -12 db/octave, and at $\omega = 1$ this asymptote must have a value of $+12$ db. Similar reasoning may be applied to the higher frequency ranges.

In general, the addition of asymptotes is done by inspection; sometimes the individual asymptotes are drawn first, but more often the resultant plot may be made directly from the equation. To illustrate this, consider Eq. (5-10). With experience, one simply looks at the equation and draws the following curve:

1. -6 db/octave slope for low frequencies, terminating at 0 db and $\omega = 1$
2. -12 db/octave slope from $\omega = 1$ to $\omega - 2$
3. -18 db/octave slope from $\omega = 2$ to $\omega = 10$
4. -24 db/octave slope from $\omega = 10$ to $\omega = \infty$
5. The entire curve is then raised $+12$ db

The reasoning behind this simple result may be explained by outlining the thought process which is actually being followed.

1. Temporarily assume $K = 1$ so that its log is 0 db, and insert the true value as a last step.

2. There is a $j\omega$ term in the denominator, and so the lowest-frequency slope is -6 db/octave.

3. There are three frequency-varying factors in the denominator. Each such term contributes nothing below its corner frequency, but above the corner frequency each factor produces a slope of -6 db/octave. Thus the net asymptote changes slope by -6 db/octave at each corner frequency.

4. Since the initial slope is -6 db/octave and there are three corner points, the slope of the resultant curve has a sequence -6 db/octave, -12 db/octave, -18 db/octave, and -24 db/octave, with the changes in slope occurring at the corner frequencies.

5. The actual corner frequencies are at $\omega = 1$, 2, and 10. Therefore the slopes are:

-6 db/octave below $\omega = 1$
-12 db/octave from $\omega = 1$ to $\omega = 2$
-18 db/octave from $\omega = 2$ to $\omega = 10$
-24 db/octave above $\omega = 10$

6. At frequencies below $\omega = 1$, all terms have a value of 0 db except the term $-20 \log_{10} |j\omega|$. Therefore, if this term is plotted for $\omega < 1$, it is also the net asymptote (still assuming $K = 1$). But the curve for $-20 \log_{10} |j\omega|$ is a straight line with the -6 db/octave slope passing through 0 db at $\omega = 1$.

7. The net asymptotic curve is therefore located exactly and may be drawn in.

8. Since $K = 4$, and $20 \log_{10} 4 = 12$ db, the entire curve must be raised 12 db to represent correctly the transfer function.

The phase-angle curves would normally be calculated if accuracy is desired. As a short cut, the phase angles may be determined at very low and very high frequencies, and at each corner point. A curve sketched through these points is frequently sufficient for preliminary analysis. Thus, for the system of Eq. (5-10),

For $\omega \ll 1$, $\Phi = -90°$
   $\omega = 1$, $\Phi = -167°$
   $\omega = 2$, $\Phi = -210°$
   $\omega = 10$, $\Phi = -298°$
   $\omega = \infty$, $\Phi = -360°$

The phase-angle curve may then be sketched, as shown in Fig. 5-6.

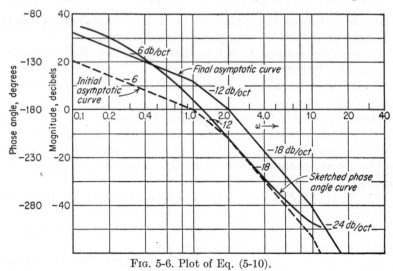

FIG. 5-6. Plot of Eq. (5-10).

The labor of computing phase-angle curves may be reduced by standardizing on a specific phase-angle plotting scale and a specific log ω scale, and constructing a template. Most of the factors in servo transfer-function equations are single time-constant factors of the form $(j\omega\tau + 1)$. The phase angle of such a term is $\Phi = \tan^{-1} \omega\tau$; this is a simple tangent curve. To use a template, note that the phase angle has a value of 45° at $\omega = 1/\tau$ which is the corner frequency; thus, by marking the 45° point on the template and aligning this point at 45° on the plotting scale and at the corner frequency, the phase-angle curve may be drawn for any single time-constant term. The net phase angle is obtained by adding the curves thus determined, plus any phase-angle curves due to other factors.

5-5. Interpretation of Decibel vs. Log ω and Phase-angle vs. Log ω Plots. It has been stated previously that the frequency-response data are not conveniently available from the decibel vs. log ω plots, but that the steady-state performance may be obtained from them, and an estimate of the transient performance may be made. While a detailed explanation of these features is reserved for Chap. 6, a brief statement of the procedures involved is made here so that the reader will not underestimate the value of the logarithmic plot.

1. The existence or absence of a steady-state error for a given application may be noted in most cases by mere inspection of the magnitude plot to determine the slope of the asymptote at lowest frequencies.

2. If a steady-state error is seen to exist in step 1, a number may be read from the plot and used in a simple arithmetic calculation to determine the magnitude of the steady-state error. The commonest manipulation of this type is for systems which operate at essentially constant velocity and have a steady-state error known as a "velocity-lag" error. For such an error, the lowest-frequency asymptote (having a -6 db/octave slope) is extrapolated to intersect the 0-db axis. The frequency at this intercept is read and divided into the known velocity input to determine the steady-state error.

3. In general, both the magnitude plot and the phase-angle plot cross the 0-db axis (this must coincide with the $-180°$ phase axis). For the system to be stable, the phase-angle curve must cross at a higher frequency than the magnitude curve.

4. While there are methods for determining the system transient response from the decibel vs. log ω plots, most of these are beyond the scope of this text. The transient response may be estimated, however, from certain figures of merit called "phase margin" and "gain margin." These quantities may be read directly from the plot. They are defined and explained in Chap. 6.

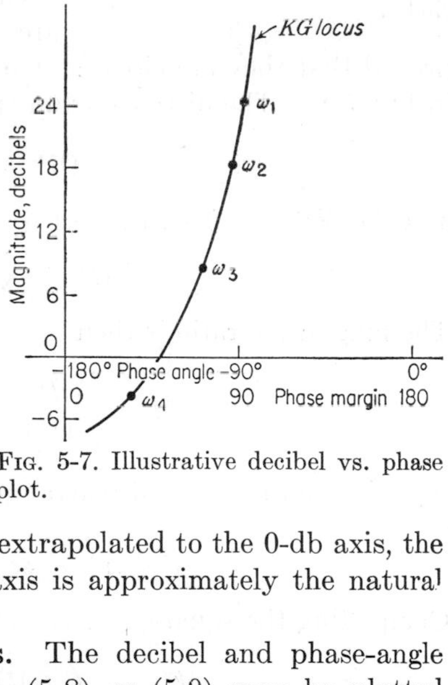

Fig. 5-7. Illustrative decibel vs. phase plot.

5. If the lowest-frequency asymptote having a -12 db/octave slope is extrapolated to the 0-db axis, the frequency at which it intersects the axis is approximately the natural frequency of the system.

5-6. Decibel vs. Phase-angle Plots. The decibel and phase-angle computed from equations such as Eq. (5-8) or (5-9) may be plotted against each other with the magnitude, in decibels, as ordinate and phase angle as abscissa. An illustrative plot is shown in Fig. 5-7. This method of plotting is of particular importance in design work. It is essentially a logarithmic counterpart of the polar plot. From it, the frequency-response characteristics can be determined, and certain changes and adjustments in the servomechanism are readily represented. The methods for determining system frequency response from polar plots and decibel vs. phase-angle plots are derived in the following paragraphs.

5-7. Magnitude Circles on the Polar Plot. It has been shown in Sec. 5-3 that the magnitude of the frequency-response ratio of a closed-loop system at any frequency ω_x may be obtained by drawing the KG vector

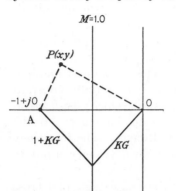

from the origin to the point ω_x on the locus, then drawing a line from the $-1 + j0$ point to ω_x, and computing the ratio of these two lengths. It should then be apparent that every point on the plane corresponds to some magnitude ratio, and loci of constant-magnitude ratios must exist. For example, it is obvious that a straight line parallel to the y axis (see Fig. 5-8) and intersecting the x axis at $-\frac{1}{2}$ is everywhere equidistant from the origin and the $-1 + j0$ point, and is therefore a locus of constant magnitude, $M = 1.0$.

Fig. 5-8. Sketch for deriving the equation of the magnitude circles.

Of course, the constant-magnitude loci are not all straight lines; it will now be proved that they are circles. Consider a general point $P\,(x,y)$ as shown in Fig. 5-8. The distance from the origin to P is

$$OP = \sqrt{x^2 + y^2} \tag{5-11}$$

and the distance from the $-1 + j0$ point to P is

$$|AP| = \sqrt{(1 + x)^2 + y^2} \tag{5-12}$$

The magnitude ratio is then

$$M = \left| \frac{OP}{AP} \right| = \frac{\sqrt{x^2 + y^2}}{\sqrt{(1 + x)^2 + y^2}} \tag{5-13}$$

Squaring both sides and rearranging

$$y^2 + x^2 + 2x\,\frac{M^2}{M^2 - 1} = \frac{-M^2}{M^2 - 1} \tag{5-14}$$

Completing the square,

$$y^2 + x^2 + 2x\,\frac{M^2}{M^2 - 1} + \left(\frac{M^2}{M^2 - 1}\right)^2 = \left(\frac{M^2}{M^2 - 1}\right)^2 - \frac{M^2}{M^2 - 1} \tag{5-15}$$

$$y^2 + \left(x + \frac{M^2}{M^2 - 1}\right)^2 = \frac{M^2}{(M^2 - 1)^2} \tag{5-16}$$

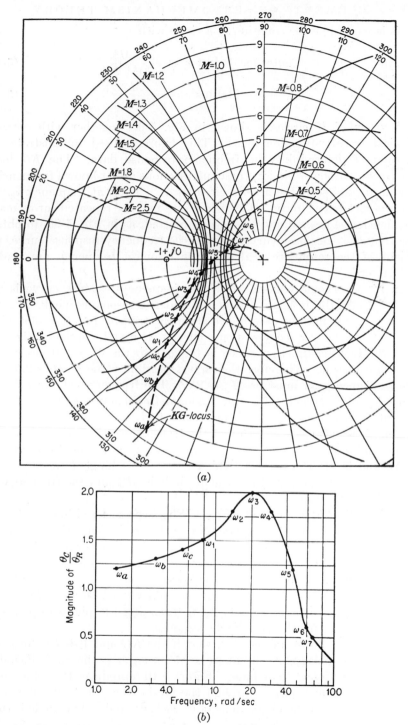

Fig. 5-9. (a) M-circles on the polar plane. (b) Frequency response curve obtained from Fig. 5-9a.

This is seen to be the equation of a circle with

$$\text{Center located at } x = -\frac{M^2}{M^2 - 1} \tag{5-17}$$

$$\text{Radius } r = \left| \frac{M}{M^2 - 1} \right| \tag{5-18}$$

A group of M circles is shown in Fig. 5-9a, together with a hypothetical transfer-function locus. This figure is used to illustrate the method of determining the frequency-response data. The KG locus intersects various M circles; these intersections are at known frequencies. The locus intersects the $M = 1$ circle at ω_5. Thus, at frequency ω_5, the ratio of θ_C to θ_R is unity. This procedure may be repeated for as many frequencies as desired and the results plotted, as in Fig. 5-9b, to obtain the frequency-response curve. From the frequency-response curve, the height of the resonance peak and the resonant frequency are readily determined.

In most servomechanism work, the frequency-response curve is not needed; only the resonant frequency and the resonance peak, M_p, are useful. These may be determined from the transfer-function plot without plotting the frequency-response curve. It may be noted in Fig. 5-9a that the transfer-function curve is tangent to the $M = 2.0$ circle, but does not cross it. Therefore the largest possible value of M is 2.0, and the resonance peak must be $M_p = 2.0$. The frequency at the point of tangency is ω_3, and therefore the resonant frequency is $\omega_r = \omega_3$. Thus, to find the resonance peak and the resonant frequency of any closed-loop system, it is only necessary to plot the transfer function on polar coordinates, add a few M circles (the proper ones are easily chosen by inspection), and locate the point at which the locus is tangent to one of the circles. The M value of the tangent circle is M_p, and the frequency at the point of tangency is ω_r.

Loci for the Phase Angle of θ_C/θ_R. Whenever a closed-loop system is used as a component in a complex servomechanism, the frequency response of the closed-loop system is also its transfer function with respect to the rest of the servomechanism, and both the magnitude and the phase angle of its frequency response are desired. It is therefore convenient to derive and use loci of the constant phase angle for θ_C/θ_R. They perform the same function in determining the phase response as do the M circles for the magnitude response.

It has been shown, in Sec. 5-3, that if the KG and $1 + KG$ lines are drawn on the polar plot, the phase angle of θ_C/θ_R is the angle included at the intersection of these lines. Figure 5-10 reproduces these lines and adds a circle which passes through the origin, the $-1 + j0$ point, and the point at which the phase angle of θ_C/θ_R is desired. The angle is thus inscribed in a circle, and its value is measured by the arc which it subtends. Furthermore, any other point lying on the circumference of this circle but below the x axis (if considered as the junction of the KG and $1 + KG$ lines) subtends the same arc and therefore represents the same value of $/\theta_C/\theta_R$. It is thus seen that any circle passing through both the origin and the $-1 + j0$ point is a locus of the constant phase angle for the frequency response.

The equation of these N circles may be derived from the following considerations: By inspection, the center of all the N circles must lie on the line $x = -\frac{1}{2}$. It is also seen from Fig. 5-10 that the angle of θ_C/θ_R is exactly half the angle at the center of the circle. Therefore,

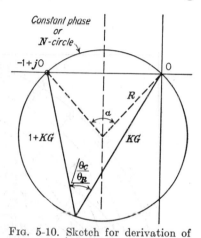

FIG. 5-10. Sketch for derivation of the N-circle equation.

$$\left| /\frac{\theta_C}{\theta_R} \right| = \left| \frac{\alpha}{2} \right| = \tan^{-1} \frac{\frac{1}{2}}{y} \quad (5\text{-}19)$$

where y is one coordinate of the center of the circle. Rearranging Eq. (5-19),

$$y = \frac{1}{2 \tan /\theta_C/\theta_R} \quad (5\text{-}20)$$

and the coordinates of the center of the N circle are thus determined for any chosen value of the angle of θ_C/θ_R. The radius of the circle is, of course,

$$R = \sqrt{(\tfrac{1}{2})^2 + y^2} \quad (5\text{-}21)$$

since the circle must pass through the origin.

N contours are also needed on the decibel vs. phase-angle plot. They may be computed point by point, or equations may be derived. This derivation is left to the student as an exercise.

5-8. Magnitude and Phase Loci on the Inverse Polar Plot. An inverse polar locus is a polar plot of the inverse transfer function or of the inverse system function. When the inverse transfer function is plotted, the magnitude and phase of the frequency response may be determined by means of magnitude and phase loci. Since the inverse transfer function is simply the reciprocal of the direct transfer function, a vector from the origin of the inverse plane is simply $1/KG$, as shown in Fig. 5-11a. The vector from the $-1 + j0$ point to the origin is still $+1$, and so the vector AB from the $-1 + j0$ point to the tip of the $1/KG$ vector is

$$AB = 1 + \frac{1}{KG} \quad (5\text{-}22)$$

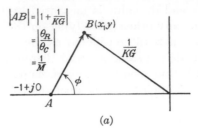

$$(a)$$

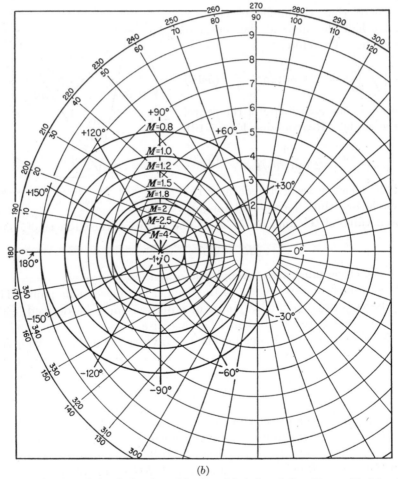

$$(b)$$

Fig. 5-11. (a) Sketch for derivation of inverse M-circle relationships.   (b) M and N loci on the inverse polar plane.

Thus the length of a vector from the $-1 + j0$ point to a point on the KG^{-1} curve is the reciprocal of the magnitude of the frequency response. It therefore follows that circles which are concentric with the $-1 + j0$ point on the inverse polar plane are loci of constant magnitude for the inverse frequency-response function. The value of $M = |\theta_C/\theta_R|$ associated with each circle is numerically equal to the reciprocal of the radius of the circle. The circles are used with the KG^{-1} locus just as the M circles on the polar plane are used with the direct-transfer-function locus. Figure 5-11b shows a family of inverse M circles.

Returning to Fig. 5-11a, the vector AB is also $1/M$ which, by definition, is $|\theta_R/\theta_C|$. The angle $-\Phi$ associated with this vector is then

$$-\Phi = \underline{/\dfrac{\theta_R}{\theta_C}} \qquad (5\text{-}23)$$

The angle desired for the frequency-response function is

$$\underline{/\dfrac{\theta_C}{\theta_R}} = -\underline{/\dfrac{\theta_R}{\theta_C}} = -(-\Phi) = +\Phi \qquad (5\text{-}24)$$

Thus the angle associated with the vector from the $-1 + j0$ point to a point on the KG^{-1} locus is the negative of the angle of the frequency-response function.

5-9. Magnitude Loci on the Decibel vs. Phase-angle Plot. As has been indicated, the decibel vs. phase-angle plot is a logarithmic counterpart of the polar plot, and therefore it should be possible to obtain a series of constant-magnitude loci, or M contours, on this logarithmic plot. There are several ways to accomplish this. The M circle may be transferred point by point by the simple expedient of selecting a point on an M circle, drawing a line from the origin to that point, expressing the length of the line in decibels, measuring the angle between the line and the positive x axis, and plotting on the decibel vs. phase-angle coordinates. This method is not very accurate, however, because of the inherent difficulty in measuring the lengths of the lines and the angles, and it is not used.

The most convenient way to determine the M contours is to derive equations expressing the magnitude in decibels and the phase angle in terms of the value of M. This may be done by manipulating Eq. (5-16). Expanding and rearranging,

$$y^2 + x^2 = \dfrac{M^2}{(M^2-1)^2} - 2x\,\dfrac{M^2}{M^2-1} - \left(\dfrac{M^2}{M^2-1}\right)^2 \qquad (5\text{-}25)$$

from which

$$20\log_{10}\sqrt{y^2 + x^2} = 20\log_{10}\sqrt{\dfrac{M^2}{(M^2-1)^2} - 2x\,\dfrac{M^2}{M^2-1} - \left(\dfrac{M^2}{M^2-1}\right)^2}$$
$$(5\text{-}26)$$

This is the desired result, since $\sqrt{x^2 + y^2}$ is the length of the line from the origin to the point on the M circle. Of course, only the right-hand side of Eq. (5-26) is evaluated. A desired value of M is used, and various values of x are substituted. Note that the proper algebraic sign must be used with the value of x. It should also be noted that this equation is indeterminate for $M = 1$, and further manipulation is required.

To find the phase angle needed with each decibel value, the values of M and x used in Eq. (5-26) are substituted in Eq. (5-16) and the corresponding value of y computed. The phase angle is then

$$\text{Phase angle} = \tan^{-1}\frac{y}{x} \tag{5-27}$$

It is important to use the proper algebraic signs with y and x in Eq. (5-27).

PROBLEMS

5-1. Plot polar loci for each of the following transfer functions:

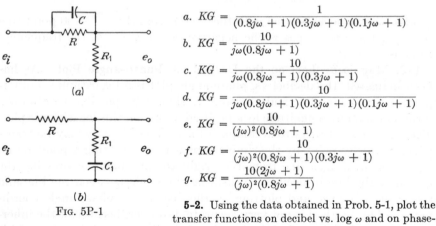

(a)

(b)

FIG. 5P-1

a. $KG = \dfrac{1}{(0.8j\omega + 1)(0.3j\omega + 1)(0.1j\omega + 1)}$

b. $KG = \dfrac{10}{j\omega(0.8j\omega + 1)}$

c. $KG = \dfrac{10}{j\omega(0.8j\omega + 1)(0.3j\omega + 1)}$

d. $KG = \dfrac{10}{j\omega(0.8j\omega + 1)(0.3j\omega + 1)(0.1j\omega + 1)}$

e. $KG = \dfrac{10}{(j\omega)^2(0.8j\omega + 1)}$

f. $KG = \dfrac{10}{(j\omega)^2(0.8j\omega + 1)(0.3j\omega + 1)}$

g. $KG = \dfrac{10(2j\omega + 1)}{(j\omega)^2(0.8j\omega + 1)}$

5-2. Using the data obtained in Prob. 5-1, plot the transfer functions on decibel vs. log ω and on phase-angle vs. log ω coordinates. Draw the asymptotes to the magnitude curves.

5-3. The filters of Prob. 4-1 have the following parameter values:

$$R = 9 \text{ megohms} \qquad C = 0.13\ \mu f$$
$$R_1 = 1.0 \text{ megohm} \qquad C_2 = 0.3\ \mu f$$
$$R_2 = 9.0 \text{ megohms} \qquad K = 1.0$$
$$R_3 = 1.0 \text{ megohm}$$

a. Plot polar loci for the transfer functions of all three filters on the same plot.

b. Plot decibel vs. log ω and phase-angle vs. log ω curves for the transfer functions of all three filters.

5-4. a. For the filter of Fig. 5P-1a, plot polar transfer-function loci (all on the same plot) for the following sets of parameter values:

$$R = 9 \text{ megohms} \qquad C = 0.3\ \mu f \qquad R_1 = 1 \text{ megohm}$$
$$R = 9 \text{ megohms} \qquad C = 0.3\ \mu f \qquad R_1 = 3 \text{ megohms}$$

b. What is the effect on these loci of changing the value of C from 0.3 μf to 0.6 μf?

c. Plot the results of parts *a* and *b* on decibel vs. log ω and phase-angle vs. log ω coordinates.

5-5. *a.* For the filter of Fig. 5P-1*b*, plot polar transfer-function loci (on the same plot) for the following sets of parameter values:

$$R = 4 \text{ megohms} \qquad R_1 = 1 \text{ megohm} \qquad C_1 = 10 \ \mu\text{f}$$
$$R = 9 \text{ megohms} \qquad R_1 = 1 \text{ megohm} \qquad C_1 = 10 \ \mu\text{f}$$

b. What is the effect on these loci of changing C_1 from 10 μf to 5 μf?

c. Plot the results of parts *a* and *b* on decibel vs. log ω and phase-angle vs. log ω coordinates.

5-6. For the system of Prob. 3-3, plot the polar transfer-function locus. (See Prob. 4-4.) Add M circles and determine M_p. Add N circles, and plot the frequency-response and phase-shift curves for the closed-loop system.

5-7. For the system of Prob. 3-3, plot the asymptotic decibel vs. log ω curve and the phase angle vs. log ω curve. (See Prob. 4-4 for the transfer function.)

5-8. For the system of Prob. 3-3, plot the decibel vs. phase angle curve (on an M-N contour chart if available). Determine M_p.

5-9. Plot the polar transfer-function locus for the servo of Prob. 3-4 (see Prob. 4-6). Add M circles and determine M_p and ω_r.

5-10. *a.* Plot the asymptotic decibel vs. log ω and phase-angle vs. log ω curves for the transfer function of the system of Prob. 3-6 (see Prob. 4-8).

b. Plot the decibel vs. phase-angle curve for the system. Add M contours, and determine M_p and ω_r.

5-11. Plot the polar transfer-function locus for the integrating amplifier of Prob. 3-7 (see Prob. 4-9).

5-12. Plot the polar transfer-function locus for the system of Prob. 3-7 (see Prob. 4-9). Add M circles. Determine M_p and ω_r.

5-13. *a.* Plot the polar transfer-function locus for the system of Prob. 3-8 (see Prob. 4-10).

b. Plot the decibel vs. log ω and phase-angle vs. log ω curves for the transfer function.

c. Plot the decibel vs. phase-angle curves.

5-14. *a.* Plot the polar transfer-function locus for the system of Prob. 3-9 (see Prob. 4-11).

b. Plot the decibel vs. log ω and phase-angle vs. log ω curves.

5-15. *a.* Plot the polar transfer-function locus for the system of Prob. 3-12 (see Prob. 4-12).

b. Plot the decibel vs. log ω and phase-angle vs. log ω curves.

5-16. *a.* Plot the polar transfer-function locus for the system of Prob. 3-13 (see Prob. 4-13).

b. Plot the decibel vs. log ω and phase-angle vs. log ω curves.

REFERENCES

Brown, G. S., and D. P. Campbell, "Principles of Servomechanisms," John Wiley & Sons, Inc., New York, 1948.

Thaler, G. J., and R. G. Brown, "Servomechanism Analysis," McGraw-Hill Book Company, Inc., New York, 1953.

CHAPTER 6

ANALYSIS OF SINGLE-LOOP SYSTEMS

6-1. Introduction. The purpose of this chapter is to present in compact form the methods of analyzing system performance from the transfer-function equation and its various plots, and to justify these methods theoretically as far as is convenient and possible. All the analysis methods have uses in the design, adjustment, and compensation of systems, and these uses are investigated in subsequent chapters. The discussion in this chapter is limited to single-loop systems, since the discussion of multiple-loop systems is restricted to a few general comments in Chap. 10.

The three major points of interest in any servomechanism analysis and design are:

1. Is the system stable?
2. Is its steady-state performance satisfactory?
3. Does it meet transient specifications?

These points are listed in the order of importance. If a system is unstable, it is usually of no value whatsoever as a servomechanism, and therefore the question of stability is very important. The purpose of the vast majority of servomechanisms is to maintain some steady-state condition. If the steady-state performance is not satisfactory, then adjustments or changes must be made, and there is no need to check transient performance until after such adjustments or changes have made the steady-state performance acceptable. Finally, if the system is stable and has satisfactory steady-state performance, transient information is required to see if the system responds quickly enough without objectionably large overshoots and with a resonant frequency that is not likely to introduce troubles.

6-2. Stability—Nyquist's Criterion. A system is said to be stable if any existing transient oscillations eventually die out and the system ultimately reaches steady state. Conversely, a system is said to be unstable if transient oscillations never die out, but rather increase in amplitude until they destroy the system or are limited by nonlinearities.

When systems are analyzed by the transient, or differential-equation, method, stability is readily determined from the roots of the equation. If the equation has any positive real roots or any complex roots with positive real parts, the system is unstable. Any stability test using the transfer-function equation or plot must indicate the same facts, i. e., the presence or absence of positive real roots or of complex roots with positive real parts. Stability tests need not determine the numerical values of the roots; it is sufficient to show their existence or nonexistence.

The stability test most commonly used in servomechanism work is the result of a theorem developed by Nyquist in his study of regeneration theory. A complete derivation of this theorem requires complex variable theory and conformal mapping, and is beyond the scope* of this text. A restricted statement of this theorem, which applies rigorously only to single-loop servomechanisms, is:

Nyquist's Stability Criterion for Single-loop Systems. If the loop transfer function is plotted on the polar plane for all values of ω from plus infinity to minus infinity, and if this plot does not enclose the $-1 + j0$ point, then the closed-loop system is stable. The following section indicates, by means of sketched curves, the graphical interpretation of Nyquist's stability criterion on the polar plane. Succeeding sections give a simplified explanation of the physical meaning of the criterion, and explain its interpretation on the logarithmic plots.

6-3. Interpretation of Typical Polar Plots. In normal computation of transfer-function curves, only positive values of ω are used. A typical curve is shown as a solid-line curve in Fig. 6-1a. The curve for negative frequencies is shown as a broken line. It may be seen that the curve for negative frequencies is the mirror image, in the real axis, of the positive-frequency curve. This is true in general, and therefore no calculations are needed for negative frequencies, nor is it usually necessary to plot the negative-frequency curve.

The two curves of Fig. 6-1a form a closed loop on the polar plane, and the enclosed area is the crosshatched area. The $-1 + j0$ point is not enclosed, and therefore the system represented is stable. The enclosed area may be determined by imagining that the curve is drawn by a tracing point which starts at $\omega = 0$, traverses the positive-frequency portion of the curve to $\omega = +\infty$, then starts at $\omega = -\infty$ and traverses the negative-frequency portion, ending again at $\omega = 0$. The enclosed area is always to the right of such a tracing point.

It is apparent that the negative-frequency part of the locus is not needed for interpretation of Fig. 6-1a; in fact, it is seldom necessary to draw the negative-frequency portion. Figure 6-1b, c, d, and e show other typical plots of the positive-frequency transfer-function locus, and the enclosure of the $-1 + j0$ point is readily seen. It should be noted that the portion of the curve near the $-1 + j0$ point usually gives sufficient

---

* See Thaler, G. J., and R. G. Brown, "Servomechanism Analysis," McGraw-Hill Book Company, Inc., New York, 1953.

information to determine stability, so that it is not even necessary to plot the entire positive-frequency locus. Using the tracing-point concept, and assuming that the point moves from low to high frequencies, it may be noted that, for a stable system, the $-1 + j0$ point is to the left of the tracing point as it traverses that portion of the positive-frequency locus which is adjacent to the $-1 + j0$ point.

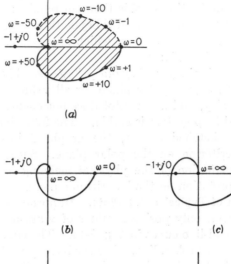

(a)

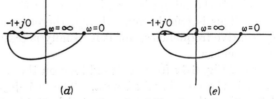

(b)   (c)

(d)   (e)

FIG. 6-1. Interpretation of stability from the polar plot.
(a) Polar plot of transfer function for positive and negative frequencies, stable system. (b) Stable. (c) Unstable. (d) Stable. (e) Unstable.

All the transfer-function plots in Fig. 6-1 have a finite value for frequency $\omega = 0$, as evidenced by the curves. Apparently, then, none of the transfer-function equations corresponding to these plots could have a factor $j\omega$ in the denominator. The majority of servomechanisms, however, have such a factor in the denominator, and a typical polar plot is shown in Fig. 6-2a. Such a plot does not close on itself when drawn on a finite plotting surface, but closes at infinity. It is then necessary to draw an auxiliary line to close the plotted curve so that the location of the enclosed area becomes apparent.

Returning to Fig. 6-1a and the tracing-point concept, it is seen that the closed curve is traversed in a *clockwise* direction, starting at $\omega = 0$

on the positive-frequency section. It can be shown that this procedure is correct for the open type of transfer-function plot. Thus the curve of Fig. 6-2a may be closed by drawing a circular arc in a clockwise direction from the low-frequency end of the negative-frequency locus to the low-frequency end of the positive-frequency locus, as shown. Since the $-1 + j0$ point is not enclosed, the system is stable.

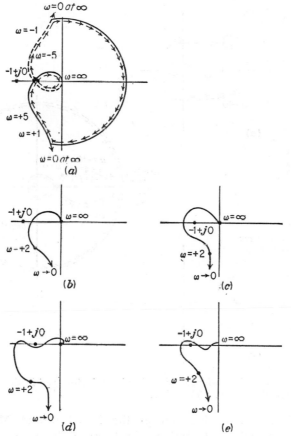

FIG. 6-2. Polar plots of transfer functions having a factor $(j\omega)$ in the denominator. (a) Both positive and negative frequencies shown, stable system. (b) Stable. (c) Unstable. (d) Stable. (e) Unstable.

It is seen that in this case also the negative-frequency part of the locus and the closing circular arc need not be drawn for most tests; only in exceptional cases will they be needed. Figure 6-2b, c, d, and e shows other typical plots for transfer functions having a $j\omega$ factor in the denominator. These are plotted for positive frequencies only, and the stability is readily determined.

Occasionally a servomechanism has a transfer function with a $(j\omega)^2$

factor in the denominator.   The plot of such a transfer function does not form a closed loop, and it must be closed by an added line in order to determine stability.   Again it may be shown that a suitable closing curve is a circular arc drawn clockwise from the low-frequency end of the negative-frequency locus to the low-frequency end of the positive-frequency locus.   Several polar loci of this type are shown in Fig. 6-3.

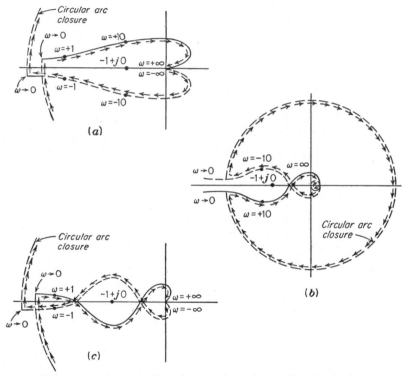

FIG. 6-3. Polar plots of transfer functions having a factor $(j\omega)^2$ in the denominator. (a) Unstable.   (b) Stable.   (c) Stable.

6-4. A Simplified Explanation of the Physical and Mathematical Meaning of the Stability Criterion.   In Chap. 5, it was shown that the magnitude of the ratio θ_C/θ_R (for sinusoidal motion) can be determined from the transfer-function plot by means of M circles.   When a family of M circles is drawn, it is seen that the center of the circle approaches the $-1 + j0$ point as the value of M increases, and this point in itself is a circle of zero radius having an M value of infinity.   Thus, if the transfer-function curve passes through the $-1 + j0$ point, M_p is infinite, i. e., $|\theta_C/\theta_R| = \infty$.   This does not mean that $|\theta_C|$ is infinite, but that $|\theta_C|$ may have a finite value even if $|\theta_R|$ is zero.   In other words, the output may oscillate when there is no input.

When a transfer-function curve passes through the $-1 + j0$ point, the KG vector to this point is $\theta_C/E = +1\underline{/180°}$. Using this fact and the block diagram of Fig. 4-13a, it is readily seen that the closed-loop system can oscillate, because the magnitudes of θ_C and E must be identical, and there are two phase shifts of 180°, one in the system represented by KG, and the second in the error detector where θ_C is *subtracted* from θ_R. At the frequency for which these conditions occur, the signal circulating around the closed loop reinforces itself at the error terminals, E. Since each time the signal goes around the loop it arrives at E undiminished in amplitude and exactly in phase, the input signal, θ_R, may be disconnected, and the circulating signal will continue without interruption. Conversely, if the system is at rest and some disturbance occurs, the system will fall into oscillation at the critical frequency. Such self-oscillations or auto-oscillations are not desired in servomechanisms; the system is usually considered to be unstable.

Instead of starting with the M circles, one may note that

$$\frac{\theta_C}{\theta_R} = \frac{KG}{1 + KG} \tag{6-1}$$

For the case where the transfer-function curve passes through the $-1 + j0$ point, the KG vector to this point is $KG = -1$. Thus,

$$\left|\frac{\theta_C}{\theta_R}\right| = \left|\frac{-1}{1-1}\right| = \frac{1}{0} = \infty \tag{6-2}$$

Furthermore, the characteristic differential equation of the system may be obtained from Eq. (6-1) by noting that

$$\theta_C(1 + KG) = \theta_R KG \tag{6-3}$$

Therefore the characteristic equation is

$$\theta_C(1 + KG) = 0 \tag{6-4}$$

To study this point further, note that the general algebraic form for the transfer function of a physical system may be written as

$$\frac{\theta_C}{E} = KG = K\frac{(j\omega\tau_a + 1)(j\omega\tau_b + 1) \cdots}{(j\omega)^N(j\omega\tau_1 + 1)(j\omega\tau_2 + 1) \cdots} \tag{6-5}$$

where K is a constant, N is restricted to 0, 1, 2, 3, . . . , and the equation may contain quadratic factors. Substituting Eq. (6-5) in Eq. (6-4),

$$\theta_C\left[1 + K\frac{(j\omega\tau_a + 1)(j\omega\tau_b + 1) \cdots}{(j\omega)^N(j\omega\tau_1 + 1)(j\omega\tau_2 + 1) \cdots}\right] = 0 \tag{6-6}$$

From Eq. (6-6), the characteristic equation of the system is

$$\theta_C[(j\omega)^N(j\omega\tau_1 + 1)(j\omega\tau_2 + 1) \cdots + K(j\omega\tau_a + 1)(j\omega\tau_b + 1) \cdots] = 0 \tag{6-7}$$

If Eq. (6-7) is expanded and manipulated, the roots of the characteristic equation may be found. For the case of a specific transfer function with plot passing through the $-1 + j0$ point, two of the roots thus determined will be conjugate imaginary numbers (real part = zero). It is well known that such roots indicate a transient response with undamped sinusoidal variation.

In view of the preceding statements, the stability of systems represented by curves such as those in Figs. 6-1a and b, 6-2a and b, and 6-3b may be explained by noting that:

1. All points on the curve have a finite M value; thus the frequency response can never be infinite.

2. Where there is a KG vector with a phase of 180°, its magnitude is less than unity, and so the signal fed back is not sufficient to sustain itself if the input signal is removed.

3. If the characteristic equation is formed and solved for the roots, it will be found that the real part of each root is negative, so that any transient oscillations are damped out.

For cases which encircle the $-1 + j0$ point and are therefore unstable, such as the curves of Figs. 6-1c and e, 6-2c and e, and 6-3a, the M-circle explanation does not work, since all points on the curve apparently have a finite M value even though the system is unstable and will oscillate. It is easily seen, however, that:

1. The KG vector with a phase of 180° has a magnitude greater than unity. Thus each time the signal traverses the closed loop, the error signal is increased and the output is increased, so that the output variation must eventually become infinite unless limited by some nonlinearity in the system.

2. If the characteristic equation is formed and the roots determined, at least one root will have a positive real part.

There are some special cases, such as the curves of Figs. 6-1d, 6-2d, and 6-3c, for which the only applicable comment is that solving their characteristic equation yields roots each of which has a negative real part. The M-circle explanation may be used but, since it proved invalid for the case of an enclosed critical point, it is not trustworthy. It may also be noted that for each of the curves mentioned there are KG vectors with a phase of 180° and a magnitude greater than unity, so that an increasing signal might be expected. Yet such is not the case; the systems are stable, and transient oscillations are damped out.

A much more complete and satisfactory explanation of the stability criterion may be obtained by using complex variable theory. Such treatment, however, is beyond the scope of this text.

6-5. Determining the Existence of Roots with Positive Real Parts—Routh's Criterion. There are a number of methods for finding the roots of a characteristic equation. Any of these is applicable to the equation of a servomechanism. When working with transfer-function methods, the engineer frequently does not need the numerical values of the roots, but would like a quick check to determine whether positive roots (or complex roots with positive real parts) exist. Such methods have been developed by Routh and by Hurwitz. The method outlined here (without proof) is essentially that due to Routh.

A characteristic equation as obtained from

$$\frac{\theta_C}{\theta_R} = \frac{KG}{1 + KG} \qquad (6-1)$$

has the algebraic form

$$A(j\omega)^M + B(j\omega)^{M-1} + C(j\omega)^{M-2} + \cdots = 0 \qquad (6-8)$$

To apply Routh's criterion, the coefficients are written alternately in two horizontal rows:

$$\begin{array}{cccc} A & C & E & G \quad \cdots \\ B & D & F & H \quad \cdots \end{array} \qquad (6-9)$$

Additional rows, 3, 4, 5, etc., are formed from these two rows by applying a definite arithmetic procedure. Each row is terminated when all succeeding numbers would be zero, and $M + 1$ rows must be formed to check M roots. The resulting array of numbers is triangular in shape because the number of terms in each row decreases as new rows are formed. The final array appears as:

$$\begin{array}{cccc} A & C & E & G \\ B & D & F & H \\ X_1 & X_2 & X_3 & \\ Y_1 & Y_2 & Y_3 & \\ Z_1 & Z_2 & & \end{array} \qquad (6-10)$$

The X, Y, Z rows are formed as follows:

$$\begin{aligned} X_1 &= \frac{BC - AD}{B} & Y_1 &= \frac{DX_1 - BX_2}{X_1} \\ X_2 &= \frac{BE - AF}{B} & Y_2 &= \frac{FX_1 - BX_3}{X_1} \\ X_3 &= \frac{BG - AH}{B} & Y_3 &= \frac{X_1H - B0}{X_1} \\ Z_1 &= \frac{Y_1X_2 - X_1Y_2}{Y_1} & Z_2 &= \frac{Y_1X_3 - X_1Y_3}{Y_1} \end{aligned} \qquad (6-11)$$

When the array has been completed, the existence of positive real roots is determined by inspecting the signs of the numbers in the left-hand column. If all signs are the same, there are no positive real roots. If there are changes in sign, then the number of positive real roots is equal to the number of changes in sign.

Numerical Example:

$$(j\omega)^5 + 8(j\omega)^4 + (j\omega)^3 + 12(j\omega)^2 + 18(j\omega) + 6 = 0$$

Routh's array is

1	1	18
8	12	6
-0.5	17.25	0
$+288$	6	0
$+17.26$	0	0
6	0	0

Inspecting the left-hand column, there are two changes in sign: from $+8$ to -4, and from -4 to $+288$. Therefore two roots are positive or have positive real parts.

6-6. Stability from Decibel vs. Log ω Plots. If logarithmic methods are used for analysis and design, interpretation of stability from the logarithmic plots is necessary. The needed interpretation is supplied with the help of the concept of *phase margin*. Phase margin may be defined as the negative of the additional negative phase shift required to make the phase angle of the transfer function $-180°$ at any given frequency. The terms *positive* and *negative* phase margin are frequently encountered. A positive phase margin means that a *negative phase shift* is required to make the phase angle $-180°$, whereas a negative phase margin means that a *positive phase shift* is required.

For the purpose of interpreting stability, phase margin need be defined at one frequency only; this is the frequency at which the magnitude of the transfer-function vector is unity, or, in logarithmic terms, when the magnitude is 0 db. The concept of phase margin and its use in interpreting stability are illustrated graphically in Fig. 6-4.

If the *KG* locus is plotted on polar coordinates and if a circle of unity radius and center at the origin is added, the circle intersects the locus at a frequency ω, at which the magnitude of the *KG* vector is unity. This is shown in Fig. 6-4a. The phase margin is then the angle between the *KG* vector at ω and the negative x axis, because this is the angle through which the vector would have to be shifted to make the phase angle $-180°$ at frequency ω. It is a positive phase margin because the required phase shift is clockwise, or negative.

Note that the *KG* locus of Fig. 6-4a does not enclose the $-1 + j0$ point, and the system is therefore stable. If the point is shifted clockwise through the angle corresponding to the phase margin, then the point ω coincides with the $-1 + j0$ point. When the $-1 + j0$ point is on the locus, it is considered to be enclosed, and the system is unstable.

Thus a physical interpretation of phase margin is the amount by which the unity KG vector has to be shifted to make a stable system unstable (or vice versa for an initially unstable system).

Figure 6-4b shows a decibel vs. log ω plot equivalent to the polar locus of Fig. 6-4a. It is seen that the magnitude curve crosses the 0-db axis

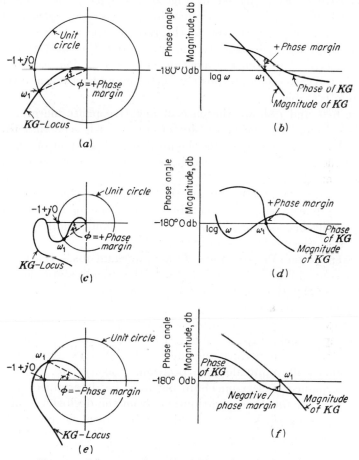

Fig. 6-4. Interpretation of stability with phase margin.

at ω_1, but the phase-shift curve crosses at some higher frequency. Thus if the magnitude crossover is located at ω_1, the phase angle of the locus may be read and the phase margin determined. The reason for making the $-180°$ phase-angle axis correspond to the 0-db magnitude axis lies in the fact that the phase margin may then be read directly as the height of the phase-angle curve above (or below) the magnitude-crossover point. The phase margin is so marked in Fig. 6-4b.

It may also be noted from Fig. 6-4b that the phase-crossover point lies to the right of (i. e., at a higher frequency than) the gain crossover. This provides an easy test for stability but one that must be used cautiously. In general, it may be said that on the decibel vs. log ω plot a system is stable if the phase crossover lies to the right of the gain crossover. However, it is possible to have several phase crossovers (or gain crossovers), as indicated in Fig. 6-4c and d. The polar plot of Fig. 6-4c shows a positive phase margin and a stable system. In Fig. 6-4d there is a phase crossover to the right of the gain crossover, but there are also phase crossovers to the left, so that the stability condition is not perfectly clear from the location of crossover points. The phase margin, however, is seen to be positive at the gain crossover, and therefore the system is stable.

Figure 6-4e and f shows the case of negative phase margin, i. e., an unstable system. On the polar plot of curve e it is seen that the locus encloses the $-1 + j0$ point. On the decibel vs. log ω plot of curve f it is seen that the phase crossover is to the left of the gain crossover and that the phase margin is negative.

Interpretation of stability from the decibel vs. phase-angle plot is available by noting the phase margin. The curves of Fig. 6-4 could be plotted on decibel vs. phase-angle coordinates and readily interpreted. This is left to the student as an exercise.

6-7. Steady-state Performance of Servomechanisms. If a servomechanism is controlling a mechanical load, the steady-state performance desired is usually that of maintaining a constant position, a constant velocity, a constant acceleration, or some combination of these, such as a constant velocity or acceleration with definite position correspondence between input and output. When the load is not mechanical, the required steady-state performance normally involves quantities which are mathematically equivalent to position, velocity, etc. The steady-state performance of servomechanisms may be determined accurately from the transfer-function equation and from the decibel vs. log ω plot. For certain applications, it may be determined from the polar plot. The above statements concern the response of the system to an input command signal. If disturbances are applied to the load, external to the closed loop, interpretation is more involved and is beyond the scope of this text.

The generalized form of the transfer-function equation is

$$KG = \frac{\theta_c}{E} = \frac{K(j\omega\tau_a + 1)(j\omega\tau_b + 1) \cdots [(j\omega)^2\tau_c + j\omega A + 1]}{(j\omega)^N(j\omega\tau_1 + 1)(j\omega\tau_2 + 1) \cdots [(j\omega)^2\tau_3 + j\omega B + 1]} \quad (6\text{-}12)$$

Several general remarks concerning this equation are necessary before formulating specific rules for interpretation. The equation expresses the ratio of the output *position*, θ_c, to the *position displacement*, or error, E, between the output and input. The output position is always a finite quantity and therefore, if there is to be zero error $(E = 0)$, the transfer function must evaluate as infinity. Likewise, if the error is to be constant and finite $(E = K)$, the transfer function must evaluate as some constant number. Equation (6-12) does not directly apply to cases where the output is to be a velocity or an acceleration, and it must be manipulated to permit interpretations for these conditions.

In order to interpret the steady-state performance of the system, some numerical value must be substituted for the $j\omega$ terms in Eq. (6-12). The value used for $j\omega$ must correspond to the time condition $t = \infty$, i. e., steady-state performance is desired and steady state is obtained at $t = \infty$. Therefore, the value used must be mathematically compatible with conditions at $t = \infty$. The proper value to use is $j\omega = 0$.

This statement can be proved by expanding the generalized equation for the error in a power series and applying the final-value theorem of the Laplace-transformation theory. Such a treatment is beyond the scope of this text. However, if the above rule is applied to the transfer functions of specific physical systems and the mathematical answer interpreted in terms of the expected physical performance, it is readily seen that the mathematical procedure gives the correct physical answer. Such an analysis is made in several of the following sections of this chapter.

The application of this may be summarized very simply, knowing the transfer function of the system, $\theta_c/E = KG$, where the algebraic form of KG is as in Eq. (6-12), and desiring to know the steady-state error characteristics of the system:

1. If the input signal is a command for a constant output *position* (or analogous quantity), substitute $j\omega = 0$ in the expression for KG and obtain a numerical answer.

2. If the input signal is a command for a constant output *velocity* (or analogous quantity), first multiply the transfer function by $j\omega$, obtaining $j\omega KG$; then substitute $j\omega = 0$ in the expression for $j\omega KG$ and obtain a numerical answer.

Because of the algebraic form of the transfer functions, only three types of numbers are to be expected from each of the above manipulations. These are zero, a positive finite constant, and infinity. The interpretation is

$$KG = \frac{\theta_c}{E} = 0; K; \infty; \qquad \text{for } j\omega = 0$$

If the numeric is 0, then $E = \infty$ since $\theta_c \neq 0$
If the numeric is K, then E is finite since θ_c is finite
If the numeric is ∞, then $E = 0$ since θ_c is finite

Similar interpretations result for $j\omega KG$ and $(j\omega)^2 KG$. In each case the interpretation is physical and specifies the magnitude of the *position error*, E, between input and output for the type of steady-state output operation being investigated.   If the steady-state error is either zero or infinite, the value of the system is immediately apparent.   On the other hand, if the error is a constant, the value of the system and its usefulness depend on the magnitude of the steady-state error.   The numbers obtained in this fashion are usually called "error coefficients."

6-8. Classification of Systems.   In order to study conveniently the steady-state performance of servomechanisms, it is desirable to classify them into groups which have comparable steady-state performance.   It will be seen that the exponent, N, in the denominator of the general transfer-function equation is a controlling factor in steady-state performance.   For this reason, the following classification is chosen:

Type 0 system = those for which $N = 0$
Type 1 system = those for which $N = 1$
Type 2 system = those for which $N = 2$
Etc.

6-9. Steady-state Performance of Type 0 Systems.   The basic transfer-function equation of a type 0 system has no $j\omega$ factor in the denominator, because $N = 0$, and is therefore of the form

$$KG = \frac{\theta_c}{E} = \frac{K(j\omega\tau + 1)}{(j\omega\tau_1 + 1)(j\omega\tau_2 + 1)} \tag{6-13}$$

Substituting $j\omega = 0$, this evaluates to

$$\frac{\theta_c}{E} = K \tag{6-14}$$

from which

$$E = \frac{\theta_c}{K} \tag{6-15}$$

and is some constant error.   It is seen that, if a type 0 system is used, the error cannot be zero, i. e., the output quantity does not reach the exact steady-state value desired, though it may approach this value by making K a large number.   Numerical evaluation of the error is obtained if the transfer-function equation is known quantitatively.

An example of a type 0 system is a voltage regulator used to maintain the output of a generator close to that of a reference.   An approximate schematic diagram is shown in Fig. 6-5.

Note that the field of the generator is driven (through the amplifier) by the difference between the reference voltage and the actual output voltage.   The output voltage can never be as great as the reference, because if it were, then $E = V_R - V_C = 0$, and no field current would be supplied to the generator. Since it is not possible for the generator to produce an output without excitation, the error E must always have a finite value other than zero, i. e., $V_R \neq V_C$. Derivation of the transfer function of this system is left to the student as an exercise.

It may readily be shown that type 0 systems are of no value as positioning systems when subjected to a changing command signal. If the input to such a system is a constant rate of change, then the steady-state

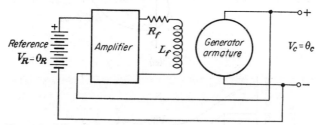

Fɪɢ. 6-5. Schematic diagram of a generator voltage regulator.

output performance is evaluated from

$$jωKG = \frac{jωθ_c}{E} = jω \frac{K(jωτ + 1)}{(jωτ_1 + 1)(jωτ_2 + 1)} \qquad (6\text{-}16)$$

Substituting $jω = 0$ in the right-hand side, this becomes

$$\frac{jωθ_c}{E} = 0 \qquad (6\text{-}17)$$

from which

$$E = \frac{jωθ_c}{0} = ∞ \qquad (6\text{-}18)$$

In physical terms, the input rate of change is not duplicated by the output, and so the position error becomes very large.

This concept may also be illustrated qualitatively with the voltage regulator of Fig. 6-5. If the command signal V_R is increased gradually at a constant rate, the output voltage also increases, but not at the same rate, and therefore the difference between these voltages $E = (V_R - V_C)$ also increases.

From Eq. (6-13) the general shape of the polar transfer-function locus and the decibel vs. log $ω$ locus may be determined. They are shown in the sketches of Fig. 6-6. From the polar plot, it is seen that the type 0 system is characterized by an intercept on the positive x axis at frequency $ω = 0$. The length of the vector from the origin to this intercept is the value of K needed in Eq. (6-15). From the decibel vs. log $ω$ plot, it is seen that the slope of the lowest-frequency asymptote is 0 db/octave. This is characteristic of type 0 systems. The decibel value of this asymptote is also the gain constant K expressed in decibels.   Thus the type 0 system may be recognized from the shape of the polar or logarithmic plot, and the numerical value of K needed to compute the steady-state error may also be obtained from the plots.

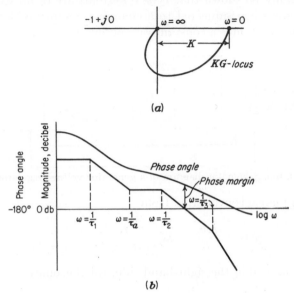

(a)

(b)

FIG. 6-6. Characteristics of a type 0 system.   (a) Polar plot.   (b) Decibel vs. log ω plot.

6-10. Steady-state Performance of Type 1 Systems.   The basic transfer-function equation of a type 1 system is characterized by a single $j\omega$ factor in the denominator and thus is of the form

$$KG = \frac{\theta_c}{E} = \frac{K_v(j\omega\tau_a + 1)}{j\omega(j\omega\tau_1 + 1)(j\omega\tau_2 + 1)} \qquad (6\text{-}19)$$

Substituting $j\omega = 0$, Eq. (6-19) becomes

$$\frac{\theta_c}{E} = \frac{K_v}{0} = \infty \qquad (6\text{-}20)$$

or

$$E = \frac{\theta_c}{\infty} = 0 \qquad (6\text{-}21)$$

Thus a type 1 system, when used as a positioning system, has no position error and inherently produces the exact position required by the command signal.   The gun-director servomechanism discussed in previous chapters is an example of a type 1 system.

If the input to a type 1 system is operated at constant velocity, the steady-state performance is evaluated from

$$j\omega KG = \frac{j\omega\theta_c}{E} = \frac{K_v(j\omega\tau_a + 1)}{(j\omega\tau_1 + 1)(j\omega\tau_2 + 1)} \tag{6-22}$$

Substituting $j\omega = 0$ in the right-hand side,

$$\frac{j\omega\theta_c}{E} = K_v \tag{6-23}$$

and

$$E = \frac{j\omega\theta_c}{K_v} = \frac{V_c}{K_v} \tag{6-24}$$

where V_c is the output velocity and is also a constant when the system is in steady state.

From Eq. (6-24) it is seen that, when a type 1 system is operated as a "velocity" system, the *position error*, E, is a constant in the steady-state condition. In order for this to be true, the output velocity must be exactly the same as the input velocity; otherwise, a constant-position displacement between input and output could not exist.

That such a position-displacement error or "velocity-lag" error must exist may be seen from the block diagram of Fig. 6-7 which is a simpli-

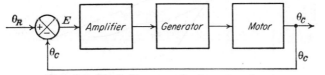

FIG. 6-7. Block diagram of a type 1 system.

fied functional diagram for the gun-director servo. From Fig. 6-7 it is seen that the motor, M, must run at constant speed if the output, θ_c, is to operate at constant velocity. Then the generator must supply a constant voltage output; the amplifier must supply constant current to the generator field and, therefore, there must be a constant signal, E, applied to the input of the amplifier. But E is the position displacement between input and output, or the position error. Thus it is obvious that a position error must exist in a type 1 system if the output is to operate at constant velocity.

Figure 6-8 shows a polar plot and a decibel vs. log ω plot for a type 1 system. On the polar locus the $\omega = 0$ end of the curve goes to infinity along the negative imaginary axis. This is characteristic of type 1 systems. Thus, from the polar plot, the type 1 system may be recognized. This identification ensures that the system has no steady-state error if used for static positioning. It also ensures that there will be a velocity-lag error if the system is operated at constant velocity. However, there is no way to compute the velocity-lag error from the polar plot.

On the decibel vs. log ω plot the identifying characteristic of the type 1 system is the -6 db/octave slope of the lowest-frequency asymptote. This -6 db/octave slope is due to the $j\omega$ factor in the denominator. Thus, if a decibel vs. log ω plot is inspected and the slope of the lowest-frequency portion is -6 db/octave, this identifies the system as type 1. The static-position error is therefore zero, and there is a velocity-lag

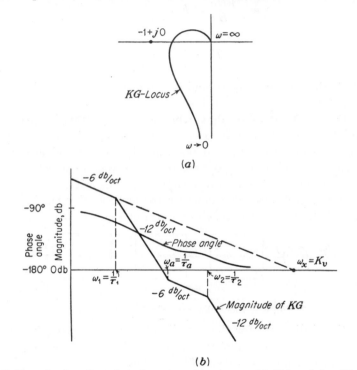

(a)

(b)

FIG. 6-8. Transfer function plots for a type 1 system.   (a) Polar plot.   (b) Decibel vs. log ω plot.

error if the system is operated at constant velocity. Moreover, the velocity constant K_v, which is the gain constant of the system, may be determined from the plot by extrapolating this -6 db/octave slope to the 0-db axis and reading the frequency ω_x at the intercept.   Then

$$K_v = \omega_x \tag{6-25}$$

and

$$E = \frac{V_c}{\omega_x} \tag{6-26}$$

To justify this statement, consider the logarithmic form of the transfer-function equation:

$$20 \log_{10} \left| \frac{\theta_C}{E} \right| = 20 \log_{10} |K_v| + 20 \log_{10} |j\omega\tau_a + 1| \cdots$$
$$- 20 \log_{10} |j\omega| - 20 \log_{10} |j\omega\tau_1 + 1| - 20 \log_{10} |j\omega\tau_2 + 1| \quad (6\text{-}27)$$

The problem is to evaluate K_v, knowing the *left*-hand side of the equation. (This is known because the plot is available.) It is necessary to know that the plot represents a type 1 system, but this is determined by checking the slope of the lowest-frequency asymptote to make sure it is -6 db/octave. Then it must be realized that the steady-state performance (and therefore K_v) are related to the transfer-function response at lowest frequencies. With this in mind, a very small value of $j\omega$ is selected and substituted in Eq. (6-27). When evaluated, all terms containing time constants approach unity, so that their logarithm approaches zero and the terms may be neglected. The remaining terms are then used to evaluate K_v, i. e., the equation reduces to

$$20 \log_{10} \left| \frac{\theta_C}{E} \right| - 20 \log_{10} |K_v| - 20 \log_{10} |j\omega| \quad (6\text{-}28)$$

If the proper frequency, ω_x, is selected to make the left-hand side of Eq. (6-28) equal to 0 db, then

$$0 = 20 \log_{10} |K_v| - 20 \log_{10} |\omega_x|$$
$$20 \log_{10} |K_v| = 20 \log_{10} |\omega_x| \quad (6\text{-}29)$$
$$K_v = \omega_x$$

The logarithmic plot of Eq. (6-28) is a straight line of -6 db/octave slope, and selection of a frequency, ω_x, which satisfies Eq. (6-29) is equivalent to finding the point where this line intersects the 0-db axis. Thus, when a complete locus of a type 1 system is available, the lowest-frequency -6 db/octave slope may be extrapolated to the 0-db axis and the intersection locates ω_x, which is numerically equal to K_v. The velocity-lag error is then found by dividing the known system velocity by ω_x, as indicated by Eq. (6-26).

6-11. Steady-state Performance of Type 2 Systems. The basic transfer function of a type 2 servomechanism is of the form

$$KG = \frac{\theta_C}{E} = \frac{K_a(j\omega\tau_a + 1) \cdots}{(j\omega)^2(j\omega\tau_1 + 1)(j\omega\tau_2 + 1) \cdots} \quad (6\text{-}30)$$

This equation may be analyzed by the same methods as are used with type 0 and type 1 systems. It is seen that a type 2 system inherently has no error when operating as a static-positioning system or when operating at constant velocity. There is a position-lag error, or "acceleration error," when the system is operated at constant acceleration.

If a polar plot of a type 2 system transfer function is made, the $\omega = 0$ end of the curve goes to infinity along the negative real axis. This is the identifying characteristic of a type 2 polar plot. If a decibel vs. log ω plot is made, the lowest-frequency asymptote has a -12 db/octave slope; this is the identifying characteristic of a type 2 decibel vs. log ω plot.

The acceleration error of a type 2 system may be determined from its equation as

$$E = \frac{A_c}{K_a} \tag{6-31}$$

where A_c is the known output acceleration and K_a is the system gain constant. K_a may be evaluated from the decibel vs. log ω plot by extrapolating the initial -12 db/octave slope to the 0-db axis and determining the intercept frequency, ω_a. Then $K_a = \omega_a{}^2$. Proof of this is left to the student.

6-12. Transient Performance of Servomechanisms from Transfer-function Plots. The important features of the transient response of a servomechanism are the peak overshoot, the oscillating frequency, and the speed of response, as previously pointed out. The peak transient overshoot is related to the height of the resonance peak of the frequency response, and the transient oscillating frequency is very nearly the same as the resonant frequency, as also previously discussed. The transient speed of response is difficult to interpret in terms of the frequency response or transfer-function data, but it has been established that, for a given height of resonance peak, systems with high resonant frequencies respond quickly, while those with low resonant frequencies respond slowly.

The M circles and M contours provide a convenient means for determining the height of the resonance peak and the resonant frequency from the polar plot and the decibel vs. phase-angle plot. Methods for utilizing these tools have been presented, and no further discussion seems necessary.

On the decibel vs. log ω and phase-angle vs. log ω plot, interpretation of transient performance is, at best, qualitative. The phase-margin concept provides a ready indication of stability, as well as empirical limits of 30° to 60° as corresponding roughly to excessive overshoot and critical damping, respectively. At present, however, it is not possible readily to evaluate the resonance peak or the resonant frequency.

The empirical limits of 30° to 60° for phase margin may be explained from the polar plot, and only one assumption is necessary. The necessary assumption is that the gain continues to decrease for frequencies above the gain-crossover frequency. This is true for a large number of systems.

Consider Fig. 6-9. Two KG curves have been sketched on the polar plot such that curve KG_a has a phase margin of 60° and curve KG_b has a phase margin of 30°. The phase margins are indicated at points a and

b, respectively. For both curves the gain is decreasing as the loci pass through these points. M circles have been added, and it is readily seen that, for curve KG_a, M_p is slightly greater than 1.0, and for KG_b, M_p is approximately 2.0. The first corresponds approximately to critical damping, and the second to a slightly excessive overshoot.

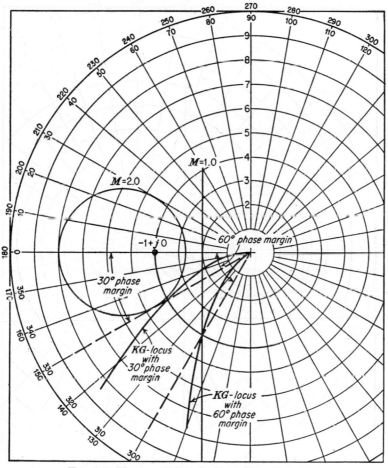

FIG. 6-9. Phase-margin criteria on the polar plot.

It is fairly obvious that considerable variation is possible, and of course no numerical correlation could be expected between phase-margin angles and values of M_p. Yet a little consideration of Fig. 6-9 indicates that for most type 0 and type 1 systems, if the phase margin is between 30° and 60°, an M_p greater than 2.0 would be unusual.

If the basic requirement of continuously decreasing gain is not met, the empirical limits of 30° to 60° phase margin cannot be used. This can be shown quite readily by sketching a few hypothetical transfer-function curves. Figure 6-10 shows polar plots of three transfer-function curves, each of which has approximately 30° phase margin. From the M circles shown, only curve A has the expected M_p of approximately 2; curves B and C have considerably larger resonance peaks. Figure 6-11

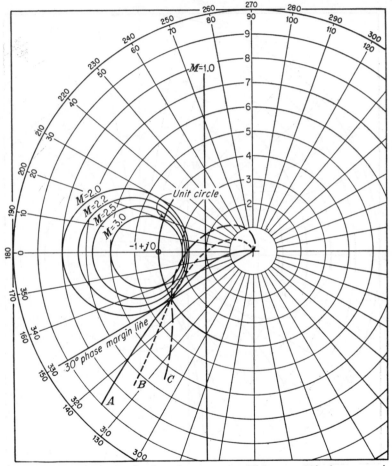

Fig. 6-10. Hypothetical transfer function curves. All have a 30° phase margin but various M_p's.

shows essentially the same curves on decibel vs. log ω and phase-angle vs. log ω coordinates. In this case, there are no M circles to aid in interpretation, but it can be seen that the rates of attenuation are not the same in the three cases shown. It is not possible to specify the expected M_p from the logarithmic plots, but it is possible to define a quantity, *gain margin*, which aids in predicting satisfactory transient performance. The gain margin is marked on Fig. 6-11a, b, and c, and may be defined verbally as the number of decibels by which the gain must be changed to put the system at the limit of stability. In terms of the decibel vs. log ω plot, the gain margin is the amount by which the magnitude curve must be raised (or lowered) to make the gain crossover coincide with the phase crossover. In terms of the polar plot, the gain margin is the number (expressed in decibels) by which the actual gain must be multiplied to

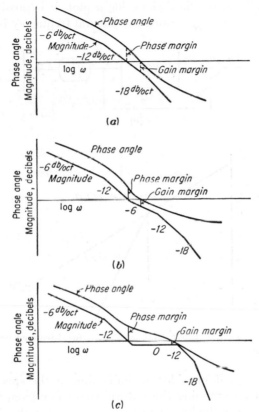

FIG. 6-11. Decibel vs. log ω plots of curves A, B, and C on Fig. 6-12.

make the polar plot pass through the $-1 + j0$ point. Note that gain margin may be either positive or negative. If the gain must be raised to make the system unstable, the gain margin is positive.

The gain-margin concept is generally used in conjunction with the phase-margin concept, since neither is a complete criterion in itself. If both the phase margin and the gain margin are adequate, transient performance should be satisfactory. Of course the words "adequate" and "satisfactory" cannot be defined specifically, since the type of performance desired of a system varies with the application. Thus use of the phase-margin–gain-margin criterion is empirical and depends on experience. In most applications, if the phase margin is between 40° and 60° while the gain margin is positive and between 10 db and 20 db, the transient overshoot will be small and there probably will be only one overshoot and one undershoot. This is generally considered satisfactory transient performance.

Although it is not possible to evaluate the resonance peak or the resonant frequency from the decibel vs. log ω plot, it is possible to estimate the natural frequency, ω_n. Since the natural frequency is related to the

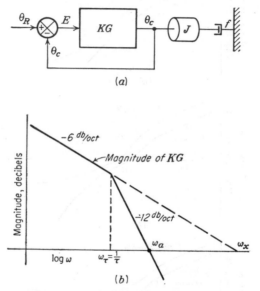

(a)

(b)

FIG. 6-12. Sketches used to prove that $\omega_a \cong \omega_n$. (a) Idealized servo system. (b) Decibel vs. log ω plot.

resonant frequency, it provides an indication of the speed of response. The method for determining the natural frequency from the decibel vs. log ω plot is to locate the lowest-frequency asymptote having a -12 db/ octave slope, extrapolate this to the 0-db axis, and read the frequency at the intercept, which is approximately the natural frequency.

That the intercept of the lowest-frequency -12 db/octave asymptote with the 0-db axis approximates the natural frequency for simple systems may be shown as follows:

Consider the idealized system of Fig. 6-12a, in which it is specified that the drive torque at the load shaft is directly proportional to the error signal, E. Applying Newton's law,

$$KE = J \frac{d^2\theta_c}{dt^2} + f \frac{d\theta_c}{dt} \qquad (6\text{-}32)$$

and

$$E = \theta_R - \theta_C \tag{6-33}$$

Thus

$$K\theta_R = J \frac{d^2\theta_C}{dt^2} + f \frac{d\theta_C}{dt} + K\theta_C \tag{6-34}$$

$$\frac{K}{J} \theta_R = \frac{d^2\theta_C}{dt^2} + \frac{f}{J} \theta_C + \frac{K}{J} \theta_C \tag{6-35}$$

where $K/J = \omega_n^2$, by definition of the natural frequency of the system.

The transfer function of the system may be derived by the usual methods and is

$$\frac{\theta_C}{E} = \frac{K}{j\omega(j\omega J + f)} = \frac{\omega_n^2 \tau}{j\omega(j\omega\tau + 1)} \tag{6-36}$$

where $\tau = J/f$.

For values of ω large enough that $j\omega \gg 1$, Eq. (6-36) reduces to

$$\frac{\theta_C}{E} = \frac{\omega_n^2 \tau}{(j\omega)^2 \tau} = \frac{\omega_n^2}{(j\omega)^2} \tag{6-37}$$

Expressing both sides of the equation in decibels,

$$20 \log_{10} \left| \frac{\theta_C}{E} \right| = 20 \log_{10} |\omega_n^2| - 20 \log_{10} |(j\omega)^2| \tag{6-38}$$

It is readily seen that the slope of the curve is -12 db/octave, since ω_n is a constant. If a value of ω is selected such that

$$20 \log_{10} \left| \frac{\theta_C}{E} \right| = 0 = 20 \log_{10} |\omega_n^2| - 20 \log_{10} |(j\omega_a)^2| \tag{6-39}$$

then obviously

$$\omega_n = \omega_a \tag{6-40}$$

For Eq. (6-38) to be zero, the value of ω_a must be the value at which the -12 db/octave line intersects the 0-db axis, as shown in Fig. 6-12b.

It may also be shown that

$$\omega_n = \omega_a = \sqrt{\omega_r \omega_x} \tag{6-41}$$

where ω_r is the corner frequency between the -6 db/octave slope and the -12 db/octave slope, and where ω_x is the intercept frequency for the -6 db/octave slope. These points are shown in Fig. 6-12b. Proof of Eq. (6-41) is left to the student.

PROBLEMS

6-1. Check each of the following differential equations for positive real roots or roots with positive real parts:

a. $\ddot{x} + 6\dot{x} + 12x = 0$

b. $\dddot{x} + 6\dot{x} + 12x = 0$

c. $\dddot{x} - 2\ddot{x} + 6\dot{x} + 12x = 0$

d. $\ddddot{x} + 3\dddot{x} + 2\ddot{x} + \dot{x} + 14x = 0$

6-2. Check the stability of the closed-loop systems represented by the following direct-transfer functions:

a. $KG = \dfrac{10}{(j\omega + 1)(6j\omega + 1)}$

b. $KG = \dfrac{10}{j\omega(j\omega + 1)(6j\omega + 1)}$

c. $KG = \dfrac{10}{(j\omega)^2(j\omega + 1)}$

d. $KG = \dfrac{10(3j\omega + 1)}{j\omega(j\omega + 1)(6j\omega + 1)(0.1j\omega + 1)}$

e. $KG = \dfrac{10}{(6j\omega + 1)(j\omega + 1)(0.5j\omega + 1)(0.1j\omega + 1)}$

f. $KG = \dfrac{10(j\omega + 1)}{(j\omega)^2}$

g. $KG = \dfrac{j\omega + 1}{(j\omega)^2}$

h. $KG = \dfrac{1}{j\omega(0.5j\omega + 1)(0.1j\omega + 1)(0.02j\omega + 1)}$

6-3. For each of the transfer functions of Prob. 6-2, determine the steady-state error for a step-displacement input of 1 radian.

6-4. For each of the transfer functions of Prob. 6-2, determine the steady-state position error (velocity-lag error) and the steady-state velocity error for a ramp input of 1 rad/sec.

6-5. What value of gain will make the system of Prob. 3-3 unstable?   (See Prob. 5-6.)

6-6. What gain will make the system of Prob. 3-6 unstable?   (See Prob. 5-10.)

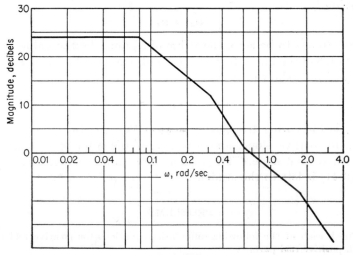

FIG. 6P-1

6-7. What is the gain increase (in decibels) required to make the system of Prob. 3-7 unstable?   (See Prob. 5-11.)

6-8. Repeat Prob. 6-7 for the system of Prob. 3-8.   (See Prob. 5-13.)

6-9. Determine the value of gain required to make the system of Prob. 3-9 unstable. (See Prob. 5-14.)

6-10. What are the gain and phase margins for the system of Prob. 3-22?   What gain is required to make the system unstable?   (See Prob. 5-15.)

6-11. What are the gain and phase margins for the system of Prob. 3-13?   What gain increase (in decibels) is required to make the system unstable?   (See Prob. 5-16.)

6-12. A servo system with unity feedback has a direct transfer-function asymptotic plot as shown in Fig. 6P-1.   What is the numerical transfer function?   Is the system stable?

6-13. Repeat Prob. 6-12 for the plot of Fig. 6P-2.

6-14. Repeat Prob. 6-12 for the plot of Fig. 6P-3.

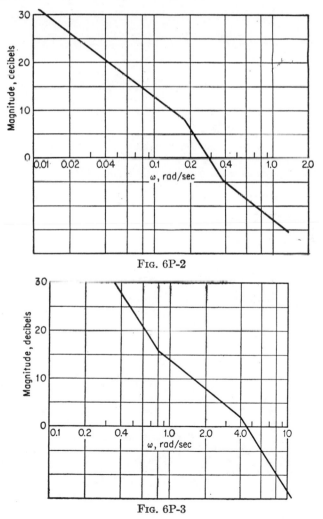

Fig. 6P-2

Fig. 6P-3

REFERENCES

Bode, H. W., "Network Analysis and Feedback Amplifier Design," D. Van Nostrand Company, Inc., New York, 1945.

Graham, R. E., Linear Servo Theory, *Bell System Tech. J.*, October, 1946.

Nyquist, H., Regeneration Theory, *Bell System Tech. J.*, January, 1932.

Routh, E. J., "Advanced Rigid Dynamics," vol. 2, St. Martin's Press, Inc., New York, 1930.

Thaler, G. J., and R. G. Brown, "Servomechanism Analysis," McGraw-Hill Book Company, Inc., New York, 1953.

CHAPTER 7

METHODS OF MEETING
PERFORMANCE SPECIFICATIONS

7-1. Specifications Involved in System Design. The automatic-control problem is invariably one of design. A load of definite dimensions and characteristics exists, usually without much possibility of altering it, and the desired performance is pretty well defined. In many cases the command signal also exists, though some variation is frequently possible here, and in some cases it is desired to use certain specific pieces of auxiliary equipment. The problem is, then, to select devices to drive the load and measure its performance, and to design whatever additional apparatus is necessary to produce the specified performance. In many applications, particularly for aircraft and military apparatus, additional complications are introduced by space and weight limitations, expected variations in temperature and climatic conditions, limitations in the type of power to be used, etc. This chapter is concerned only with performance specifications.

In general, the primary performance specification is that of a required steady-load condition with definite tolerances. The second might be a required response time or response speed, usually with an upper limit on the allowable time. A third item might specify the maximum magnitude of overshoot, if any is permissible, and possibly the number of overshoots and undershoots allowed. The form in which this information is supplied to the designer and the completeness of the information vary considerably with the customer and his understanding of the problems involved.

7-2. The Preliminary Design. The normal procedure in beginning a design is to select components for the drive (a motor) and for the output measurement. Either of these selections may involve considerable work, depending on the specific problem. The selection of a measuring device is not discussed here, except to note that factors to be considered are the accuracy and speed required in taking the measurement, and that comparison of the resultant measurement with the command signal is necessary. The selection of a motor (here assumed to be an electric motor) depends on the steady-state power required, and on the necessary transient accelerations and velocities which the motor must supply. The manufacturer's rating of the motor selected may be considerably greater than the steady-state power requirements, because of the transient velocity and acceleration requirements.

Having selected the motor, means must be provided for supplying it with power. In an instrument-type system where the motor is small, the power may be supplied directly from an electronic amplifier; for larger motors, an amplidyne generator* or equivalent rotating amplifier may be used. The field of this generator must be energized; perhaps this may be accomplished with an electronic amplifier. In order to design the amplifier, the error-detection system must be devised, i. e., some method must be devised for comparing the output signal with the command signal and for producing an electrical signal indicative of the difference to feed into the amplifier. The gain of the amplifier is then designed so that a definite amount of error produces full output.

The preceding general discussion of preliminary design is brief because every design problem is different, and it is difficult to outline a general approach in any detail. What has been stated, however, is sufficient to indicate two important points: The preliminary design is aimed largely at satisfying steady-state requirements, and at providing accelerations and velocities which make possible the desired response speed. Up to this point no consideration is given to such items as the transient overshoot and the resonant frequency, and the response speed and steady-state error have not been quantitatively determined.

It is hardly to be expected that such a selection of components would result in a system having both satisfactory steady-state performance and acceptable transient performance. Thus, all performance requirements must be checked; this is done from the transfer-function plots. In general, neither transient nor steady-state requirements are met satisfactorily by the preliminary design. At times only slight adjustments are necessary to obtain satisfactory performance, but usually the system must be compensated, i. e., additional components must be inserted to change the system so that all specifications can be met.

7-3. Effects of Gain Adjustment and Compensation. Generally the only available adjustment in a single-loop system is a gain adjustment, and this, of course, is in the amplifier†, if one is used.

On the other hand, for certain cases the steady-state error is inherently zero, as when a type 1 system is used for static positioning. In such

---

* Relays may be used, and the system would then be called a relay servomechanism. Such systems are nonlinear. While methods are available for analysis, they are beyond the scope of this text.

† The amplifier gain is not the system gain, but is one of the factors which enters into the system gain.

applications the gain can theoretically be set entirely on the basis of transient performance. It should be noted, however, that positioning systems sometimes have specifications as to permissible error during changes in position, and this may place a lower limit on the gain, i. e., if the gain is too low, large errors may exist while changing from one steady-state position to another. Also, if the load itself is subject to random disturbances, the system should be "stiff," i. e., a relatively high gain should be used so that errors due to load disturbances are quickly corrected.

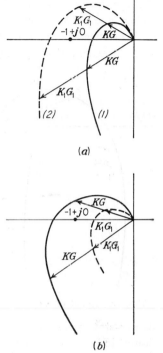

(a)

If, as is usually the case, gain adjustment is not capable of satisfying both steady-state and transient specifications, then compensating devices must be used. Compensating devices, in general, are filters. They reshape the transfer-function locus so that the gain required for steady-state performance may be used. These characteristics may be illustrated readily on the polar plot, as shown in the following paragraphs. In actual design, the use of logarithmic methods is preferable, but discussion of these methods is reserved for a later chapter.

Consider the polar plot of Fig. 7-1a, assuming that it is a type 1 system used at approximately constant velocity. There will be a velocity-lag error, of course, and it may further be assumed that for the gain of curve 1 the velocity-lag error is excessive. If this is so, the gain must be increased to obtain the required steady-state performance. Assume that the gain is doubled by doubling the amplifier amplification. This makes each KG vector twice as long, and, as may be seen, the

(b)

Fig. 7-1. Effect of gain adjustment.
(a) Type 1 system; gain too low for steady-state requirements.
(b) Type 1 system; gain too high, system unstable.

resulting locus (curve 2) encloses the $-1 + j0$ point, so that the gain adjustment makes the system unstable. The maximum allowable gain increase for proper transient performance would probably be no more than 10 to 15 per cent; if this is insufficient for the steady-state requirements, then compensation must be added.

Figure 7-1b shows a similar plot for which the initial gain setting is excessive and the system is unstable. Stability can readily be obtained by decreasing the gain. Curve 1 shows the initial unstable condition, while an approximate 50 per cent reduction in gain gives curve 2, which is stable.   If the system is to be used for positioning, and velocity-lag error is not important, such gain reduction is satisfactory, providing the system remains stiff enough to oppose any expected load disturbances.

Compensation is used when gain adjustment alone cannot satisfactorily meet steady-state and transient requirements.   The commonest types of compensation devices are high-pass and low-pass filters.   Both of these devices reshape the polar locus, and in general permit the use of higher gain than would be permissible with uncompensated systems. Both are used because of the effect produced in the range of frequencies near the resonant frequency of the system, but each produces a different effect, as will be shown.

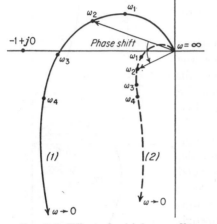

FIG. 7-2. Effect of a high-pass filter.

High-pass filters are used primarily because of the phase shift produced in the critical range of frequencies. In general, they cause a phase *lead*, or counterclockwise rotation of the higher-frequency vectors, together with attenuation at the lower frequencies.   Figure 7-2 shows the general effect obtained on the polar locus; curve 1 is the uncompensated locus, and curve 2 is the resultant locus after insertion of a high-pass filter.   The frequencies ω_1, ω_2, ω_3, and ω_4 are seen to be shifted in a counterclockwise direction.   The steady-state performance is appreciably affected because of the attenuation at low frequencies, and so the gain must be increased.   Normally the gain can be increased sufficiently that the steady-state performance for the same resonance peak, M_p, is better than it would be with the uncompensated system.   At the same time, the resonant frequency is increased so that a faster system normally results.   This is due to the positive phase shift.

Low-pass filters are used primarily because they attenuate at high frequencies.   In general, they produce a phase *lag*, or clockwise rotation of the KG vector.   They are used primarily in situations where large increases in gain are needed to meet steady-state requirements, since phase-lead (high-pass) networks usually will not permit very large gain increases.   They may also be used where a low resonant frequency is desired.   Figure 7-3 shows qualitatively the result of using a low-pass filter.   Frequencies ω_1, ω_2, ω_3, and ω_4 are shifted clockwise from curve 1 to curve 2, but, what is more important, the magnitudes are greatly attenuated.   Since the lower frequencies are not appreciably affected, the steady-state performance is virtually unaffected, and all additional gain increases directly improve the steady-state performance. The new resonant frequency, however, is considerably lower than in the uncompensated system, and the transient response will be slower.

In some systems it is necessary to use both high-pass and low-pass filters, or a single band-elimination filter. This is done to permit high gain for steady-state performance and at the same time to obtain a higher resonant frequency with attendant increases in speed of response. Detailed discussion of this is beyond the scope of this text.

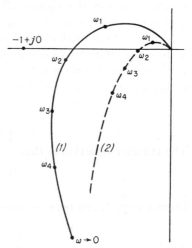

FIG. 7-3. Effect of a low-pass filter.

7-4. Physical and Mathematical Interpretation of Compensation. While it is easy to see the effect of phase lead and phase lag on the transfer-function curve, and thus on the frequency response of the system, it is desirable to investigate the effects of such devices in terms of the time performance of the system, i. e., in terms of the differential equation. It is then possible to interpret their effect in terms of physical phenomena which give a better insight into the purposes of these devices.

Figure 7-4 shows two high-pass and two low-pass filters. Types a and c are used in feedback paths (discussed in Chap. 10) but never in series

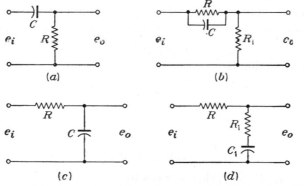

FIG. 7-4. Filters used in the compensation of servos. (a) High pass. (b) High pass. (c) Low pass. (d) Low pass.

paths, while types b and d are commonly used in the series compensation of servomechanisms. Type a cannot be used in series because it completely blocks d-c signals. If a servomechanism using such a device in its series path was at steady state, but the output was not in correspondence with the input, a d-c error signal would not get through.   Type c cannot be used in series because it completely shorts out high frequencies and the system would not respond to rapid changes in command.   Type b, however, passes d-c signals although it attenuates them, and likewise type d passes high frequencies.

Mathematical analysis of circuit b shows that its output, e_o, is approximately the sum of two components.   One component is proportional to the input signal and the other component is proportional to the derivative of the input signal.   To prove this, assume that

$$e_o = Ae_i + B\frac{de_i}{dt} \tag{7-1}$$

The transfer function is then

$$\frac{e_o}{e_i} = A + j\omega B \tag{7-2}$$

From Chap. 4, the transfer function of the network is

$$\frac{e_o}{e_i} = \alpha\,\frac{j\omega\tau + 1}{j\omega\alpha\tau + 1} \tag{7-3}$$

where $\tau = RC$.   Now α is always less than unity, and if $\omega RC \ll 1$, Eq. (7-3) reduces to

$$\frac{e_o}{e_i} = \alpha + j\omega\alpha\tau \tag{7-4}$$

This, of course, is true only over a limited range of frequencies.

In like manner it can be shown that the phase-lag circuit d has an output which is approximately the sum of some factor times the input signal and another factor times the integral of the input signal.   Thus,

$$e_o = Ae_i + B\int e_i\,dt \tag{7-5}$$

The transfer function is

$$\frac{e_o}{e_i} = A + \frac{B}{j\omega} \tag{7-6}$$

The transfer function of circuit d is

$$\frac{e_o}{e_i} = \frac{j\omega R_1 C_1 + 1}{j\omega(R + R_1)C_1 + 1} \tag{7-7}$$

and if $\omega(R + R_1)C_1 \gg 1$, this reduces to

$$\frac{e_o}{e_i} = \frac{R_1}{R + R_1} + \frac{1/(R + R_1)C_1}{j\omega} \tag{7-8}$$

This relationship also is valid only over a limited range of frequencies. Having thus indicated that the essential function of phase-lead and phase-lag devices is to produce approximately the derivative and the integral of the input signal, the physical effect of such devices may be seen qualitatively by assuming the use of true differentiators and integrators. The effect of these on system performance is readily seen from the differential equation of the system.

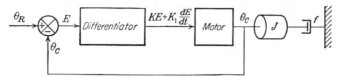

FIG. 7-5. Idealized servo with differentiating compensator.

Figure 7-5 shows the block diagram of an idealized servomechanism with a series-differentiating compensator. The differential equation of the system may be obtained by applying Newton's law at the output:

$$K_m\left(KE + K_1\frac{dE}{dt}\right) = J\frac{d^2\theta_c}{dt^2} + f\frac{d\theta_c}{dt} \tag{7-9}$$

Substituting $E = \theta_R - \theta_c$,

$$K_mK\theta_R + K_mK_1\frac{d\theta_R}{dt} = J\frac{d^2\theta_c}{dt^2} + (f + K_mK_1)\frac{d\theta_c}{dt} + K_mK\theta_c \tag{7-10}$$

From these equations two features of the series derivative device may be seen. The left-hand side of Eq. (7-9) is the torque applied to drive the load. It consists of two components: one proportional to the instantaneous error; the other, to the rate of change of the error. Now, if dE/dt is defined to be positive when the error is increasing, it is seen that the derivative device tends to anticipate the error. If there is a rapid change in the input, an error is produced; the torque due to the error itself is not large until the input has achieved considerable displacement, but the torque due to the rate of change of error can be quite large, and thus a large correction torque is applied in anticipation of the error which is being produced by the rapidly changing input.

As the output is displaced by the drive torque, the error decreases and the sign of the derivative term reverses, decreasing the drive torque and thus limiting the overshoot. This is equivalent to additional damping. Such physical interpretation is available from Eq. (7-10) where the effect of the derivative term is seen in the coefficient $f + K_mK_1$. The dimensions of this coefficient are the same as the dimensions of f, which is the viscous-friction term. Viscous friction tends to damp the transient oscillations by opposing the velocity of the load, and the addition of a derivative device produces the same damping effect as adding viscous friction.

Such derivative damping does not dissipate energy, however, as may readily be seen from the nature of the circuits involved.

Figure 7-6 shows the block diagram of an idealized servomechanism with a series-integrating compensator. The differential equation of the system is

$$K_m \left(KE + K_2 \int_0^t E\,dt \right) = J\frac{d^2\theta_c}{dt^2} + f\frac{d\theta_c}{dt} \tag{7-11}$$

Substituting $E = \theta_R - \theta_c$,

$$K_m K\theta_R + K_m K_2 \int_0^t \theta_R\,dt = J\frac{d^2\theta_c}{dt^2} + f\frac{d\theta_c}{dt} + K_m K\theta_c + K_m K_2 \int_0^t \theta_c\,dt \tag{7-12}$$

From these equations it may be seen that the integrator improves the steady-state performance but makes the transient performance more com-

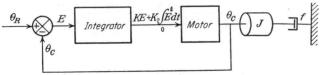

Fig. 7-6. Idealized servo with integrating compensator.

plex and the system more oscillatory. Equation (7-11) shows that the drive torque has a component due to the error itself and another component due to the time integral of the error. The integral term enables the system completely to eliminate steady-state errors. For example, assume that the system is operated at constant velocity. If the integrator is not present, the system comes to equilibrium with a velocity-lag error, owing to the fact that the load friction sets up a retarding torque and there must be an error to permit the system to establish a counterbalancing drive torque. With the integral device, however, if any error exists, its time integral sets up a torque. This permits the error itself ultimately to reach zero, after which the integrator supplies the necessary signal so that a drive torque may be maintained to counteract the friction drag.

The change in the transient response may be seen from the right-hand side of Eq. (7-12), where the addition of the integral term makes the characteristic equation a cubic. In general, the addition of a third root makes a system less stable, though this is not necessarily true. The effect of the integral term on the transient performance of the system may be seen qualitatively from the sketched error-vs.-time curve of Fig. 7-7, which assumes that a constant-velocity input signal is suddenly applied. The error then increases gradually while the output is being accelerated. The drive torque is the sum of the instantaneous error and the integral of the error, which is the crosshatched area under the curve. This torque accelerates the output until it overshoots at point a. The instantaneous error then reverses, but the integral already established does not reverse. The torque counteracting the overshoot is thus the difference between the two components, so that the overshoot is greater than it would be if the integrator was not present. The effect of the integral term is decreased during the overshoot, because the area under the error curve is negative. The overshoot is gradually eliminated by

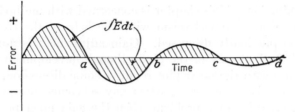

FIG. 7-7. Transient effects in a system with an integrating device.

the combination of increasing error torque and decreasing integral torque until an undershoot occurs at point b. The integral torque then increases again. This procedure is repeated until the net area under the curve is just sufficient to counteract the load torque so that the steady-state error is eliminated. It is thus seen that the integral term, while improving steady-state performance, tends to produce larger and more numerous transient overshoots and undershoots.

It should not be assumed that the filter networks of Fig. 7-4 can produce true derivative and integral effects, for they cannot. However, they generally do a sufficiently good job so that it is not economical to use the relatively complex systems necessary for true integration or differentiation. In particular, it should be noted that the phase-lag filter of Fig. 7-4d cannot completely eliminate steady-state error. However, in most practical cases where it is used to reduce velocity-lag error, it is possible to reduce the error to approximately that value which would be produced by noise and other disturbances, so that a true integrator would have essentially no advantage in terms of steady-state performance.

CHAPTER 8

GAIN ADJUSTMENT OF SERVOMECHANISMS

8-1. Introduction. This chapter is concerned with methods of adjusting the gain of a servomechanism with the help of the three types of transfer plots previously discussed. Gain adjustment is not a particularly difficult task on any of the plots, though development of a simple method for use with the polar plot requires some discussion. However, gain adjustment is a necessary part of any servomechanism design. If steady-state error is not a problem, then the gain must be adjusted to provide proper transient performance. When steady-state errors must be controlled, the gain must also be adjusted. Finally, if compensation is required to meet steady-state and transient specifications, the gain of the compensated system must be adjusted.

Steady-state errors cannot be checked from the polar plot or from the decibel vs. phase-angle plot. Thus, gain adjustments on these plots are entirely a matter of adjusting transient performance. If the steady-state error must be checked, this is done from the transfer-function equation or by setting up the decibel vs. log ω plot.

On the decibel vs. log ω plot the steady-state error is readily checked. The transient performance can be estimated, but M_p and ω_r are not available. Thus, for an accurate check on the resonance peak and the resonant frequency, it is necessary to plot either a polar locus or a decibel vs. phase-angle curve.

If the gain is to be adjusted only to obtain the desired transient performance, a single plot—either polar or decibel vs. phase angle—is sufficient. Likewise, only a single plot of decibel vs. log ω is required when the steady-state performance is the determining factor. If both the steady-state and the transient performances are to be considered in the gain adjustment, two plots must be used. The decibel vs. log ω plot would probably be used first, because the steady-state performance is given directly, and the transient performance can be estimated from the phase margin. Transient performance can then be checked more accurately from a polar plot or a decibel vs. phase-angle plot.

8-2. Gain Adjustment with the Polar Plot. In the following discussion it is assumed that the steady-state performance of the servomecha-

134

nism either need not be considered or is being checked by additional computations.   The only point considered is the adjustment of the system to obtain a specified value of M_p.

Figure 8-1 shows the higher-frequency portion of the KG locus for a type 1 system; however, the method of gain adjustment applies equally

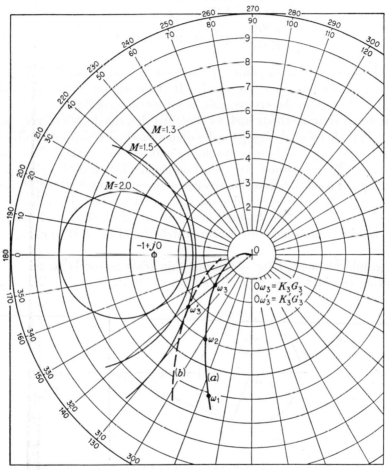

FIG. 8-1. Basic principles of gain adjustment on the polar plot.
(a) Original locus.   (b) After gain adjustment.

well for a type 0 system, since the difference in the loci is primarily in the low-frequency range.   Assume that the gain is to be adjusted to obtain a resonance peak $M_p = 1.3$.   The fundamental problem is to increase the gain of the system until one point on the locus is tangent to the $M = 1.3$ circle.   This may be done by trial and error.   First, the original KG locus is drawn.   Then a guess is made (from inspection of the curve) as to which frequency will be tangent when the gain is increased. For Fig. 8-1 the guess is that ω_3 will be tangent. Since an increase in gain increases the length of each KG vector but does not shift its phase, a straight line is drawn from the origin through ω_3 to the $M = 1.3$ circle. Then

$$O\omega_3 = K_3G_3 \tag{8-1}$$

$$O\omega_3' = K_3'G_3' \tag{8-2}$$

$$\frac{K_3'G_3'}{K_3G_3} = \text{gain-increase factor} \tag{8-3}$$

As a check, several other points on the locus should be multiplied by this factor, and the new locus sketched. If there are no intersections with the $M = 1.3$ circle, the system gain is adjusted accordingly.

Trial-and-error methods such as that just described are not very accurate. It is therefore desirable to develop a method which inherently has greater accuracy. This may be done, and several methods have been proposed. These methods are based on the obvious fact that, instead of changing the locus, it is possible to adjust the scale to which the M circles are drawn. In order to produce the same desired condition of tangency to a given M circle, the factor by which the M-circle scale is changed must be the reciprocal of the factor which would be used to change the locus.

A graphical method for obtaining this scale factor is based on the following considerations: Fig. 8-2 shows an M circle with a line drawn

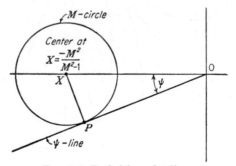

FIG. 8-2. Definition of ψ line.

tangent to it from the origin. This line, hereafter called the "ψ line," lies at an angle ψ from the negative x axis. From the figure it may be seen that this angle is defined by

$$\psi = \sin^{-1}\frac{XP}{0x} = \sin^{-1}\frac{M/(M^2-1)}{M^2/(M^2-1)} = \sin^{-1}\frac{1}{M} \tag{8-4}$$

Table 8-1 gives a series of values for M and ψ.

TABLE 8-1

M	ψ
1.1	65.2°
1.2	56.5°
1.3	50.2°
1.4	45.6°
1.5	41.8°
1.8	33.7°
2.0	30°
2.5	23.6°
3.0	19.5°
3.5	16.6°
4.0	14.5°

On Fig. 8-1 it is possible to draw many circles which have their center on the negative x axis and which are tangent to the ψ line. Each of these would correspond to an M circle having the same M value but plotted to a different scale, i. e., the physical distance from the origin to the center of each circle varies but the coordinate of the center of this circle is the same, since it is defined by the value of M, and this corresponds to a change in the scale of the plot.

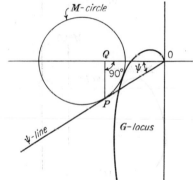

The graphical method for setting the gain utilizes this fact, and the method of construction is shown in Fig. 8-3. The procedure is as follows:

1. Derive the transfer function of the system, KG; then replace the gain constant K with unity, i. e., assume unit gain. Plot the G locus.

2. Draw the ψ line corresponding to the desired value of M_p.

3. By trial and error, draw in a circle which is tangent to both the ψ line and the G locus.

FIG. 8-3. Graphic construction for gain setting.

4. Locate the point, P, at which the circle is tangent to the line. From this point, draw a line which is perpendicular to the x axis, thus locating point Q.

5. Read the distance $0Q$, using the scale to which the G locus was plotted.

6. The gain constant which the system must have in order to obtain the desired M_p is

$$K = \frac{1}{0Q}$$ (8-5)

Proof of Eq. (8-5) is left to the student.

For normal type 0 or type 1 systems the preceding method of gain adjustment can readily be used to obtain any desired value of M_p.   However, for type 2 systems or for those type 0 and type 1 systems whose loci cross the negative x axis more than once, it is not always possible to obtain a specific value of M_p, and other complications arise.   Figure 8-4a and b show typical plots where such conditions exist.   It is apparent that

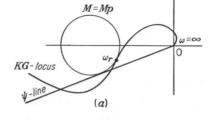

(a)

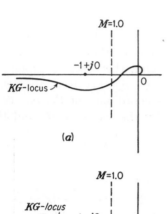

(a)

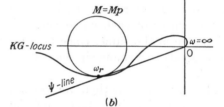

(b)

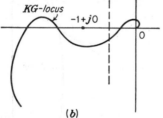

(b)

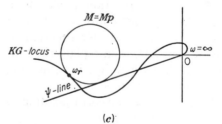

(c)

FIG. 8-4. Systems for which several values of gain produce the same M_p.
(a) Type 2 system.
(b) Type 1 system.

FIG. 8-5. Effect of gain setting on a Type 2 system.
(a) Type 2 system; M_p at high frequency.
(b) Type 2 system; M_p at intermediate frequency.
(c) Type 2 system; M_p at low frequency.

certain M values are not readily used with such systems.   For example, $M = 1$ is impossible with a type 2 system, and it can be obtained with the system of Fig. 8-4b only if a very low gain is used.

For transfer-function loci of the type illustrated in Fig. 8-4, the M circle must fit in the loop of the curve.   Thus, if the gain is high, the right-hand side of the M circle becomes a tangent to the locus at a high-frequency point, and if the gain is reduced, the tangency may move to the bottom of the circle or to the left-hand side, but it always occurs at a lower frequency.   This is illustrated in Fig. 8-5.   The gain for a desired M_p may be set just as for normal type 0 or type 1 systems, but it is necessary to plot enough of the transfer-function locus to be sure that some other portion of the locus does not intersect the M circle, i. e., it is necessary to make sure that the desired M_p is possible.

8-3. Gain Adjustment on the Inverse Polar Plot.   When the inverse transfer function is plotted, the gain-setting procedure is as follows:

1. Draw the ψ line ($\psi = \sin^{-1} 1/M$) in the *second* quadrant, since the critical portion of the locus is in the second quadrant when the inverse function is used.

2. With the center on the negative x axis, draw a circle which is tangent to both the ψ line and the locus.

3. If the G locus has been plotted (i. e., $K = 1$), then the x coordinate of the center of the circle, read from the scale to which the locus was plotted, is the required gain for the specified M_p.   If some other value of gain was used in plotting the locus, the coordinate of the center of the circle is the number by which this gain must be multiplied to obtain the required system gain.

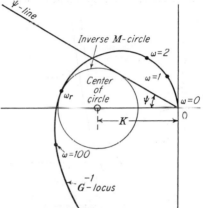

Fig. 8-6. Gain adjustment on the inverse polar plot.

4. The point of tangency between the locus and the M circle is the resonant frequency.

The gain-setting procedure for the inverse-polar locus is shown in Fig. 8-6.

8-4. Gain Adjustment on the Decibel vs. Phase-angle Plot.   On the decibel vs. phase-angle plot, steady-state performance is not available, so that gain adjustment involves only the setting of transient performance to a specified M_p.   To do this, the M contour for the desired M_p must be drawn.   The G locus is then plotted and its position adjusted so as to be tangent to the M contour.

Figure 8-7 shows a decibel vs. phase-angle plot of a G locus with M contour added.   The G locus as shown does not intersect the M contour. To set the gain, the entire G locus is shifted upward (parallel to the db axis) until some point on the locus is tangent to the M contour.   The magnitude of this shift is then measured at any convenient point.   In Fig. 8-7 the magnitude of the changes is A db, as shown by the length of line $0A$.   Thus the desired M_p is attained by *adding* (or subtracting) a number of decibels to the system gain response.   This is equivalent to multiplying the system transfer function by a gain constant K, where the value of K is defined by

$$A \text{ db} = 20 \log_{10} K \tag{8-6}$$

Transposition of the G locus is not a very convenient manipulation. An easier approach is to make a template and move it. Since individual G loci are not likely to be repeated in different problems, it is advisable to make templates of the M contours rather than the locus itself. Templates of the M contours can be used not only for gain setting, but as an easy means of putting the M contours on a plot when the frequency response is to be checked or when compensation is to be designed.

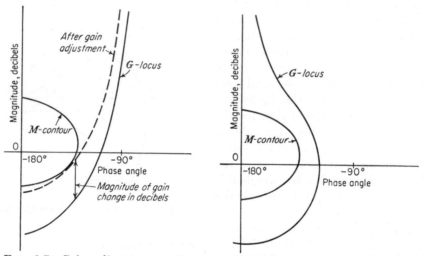

FIG. 8-7. Gain adjustment on the decibel vs. phase-angle plot.

FIG. 8-8. Type 2 locus on the decibel vs. phase-angle plot.

When type 2 systems are encountered, the G locus appears on the decibel vs. phase-angle plot approximately as shown in Fig. 8-8. As may be seen from the location of the M contour, there are at least two values of gain which provide the desired M_p. The general remarks made in discussing Figs. 8-4 and 8-5 are applicable here also.

8-5. Gain Adjustment on the Decibel vs. Log ω Plot. On the polar plot and the decibel vs. phase-angle plot, the gain may be adjusted to transient specifications but not to steady-state specifications, whereas the reverse is true for the decibel vs. log ω plot. Actually, when the final gain adjustment is made on a system, the decibel vs. log ω plot is not used, because the final adjustment of gain normally is concerned with transient performance. For preliminary gain adjustments, however, as an aid to estimating whether steady-state and transient specifications are compatible and also as an aid to determining the amount and type of compensation to be used, the decibel vs. log ω plot can be valuable.

Figure 8-9 shows a simplified transfer-function plot on decibel vs. log ω coordinates. Curve a shows what might be an initial (and stable) plot, using asymptotes. The intercept at ω_a indicates the gain constant of the system and therefore the velocity-lag error. There is also sufficient phase margin at the intercept x for good transient performance. The natural frequency of the system may also be read from the intercept of the -12 db/octave asymptote. Thus the steady-state error, the approximate transient performance, and the natural frequency are determined at a glance.

When the steady-state error is excessive, the gain is set by using a straightedge and moving the -6 db/octave asymptote parallel to itself

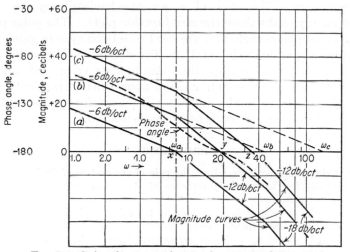

FIG. 8-9. Gain adjustment for steady-state performance.

until its intercept (extrapolated) indicates satisfactory steady-state performance. The change in gain is then determined readily from the number of decibels through which the asymptote has been shifted. If such a gain adjustment results in a location such as curve b, the steady-state performance is indicated by ω_b, and the transient performance may be checked by adding the higher-frequency asymptotes and checking the phase margin and natural frequency.

In the case of curve b in Fig. 8-9, the intercept at y indicates a barely stable system with negligible phase margin. To provide satisfactory transient performance, some compensation would be necessary. It is obvious, however, that a reasonable amount of phase lead at the frequency of the gain and phase crossovers can readily supply adequate phase margin. Thus, adjusting the gain on the decibel vs. log ω plot not only indicates the approximate gain for satisfactory steady-state performance but also indicates the type of compensation required, the frequency range where such compensation will be most effective, and the approximate magnitude of the phase shift needed.

Curve c in Fig. 8-9 shows a possible location of the asymptotes for a system in which the steady-state error must be kept quite small. From the intercept of the -12 db/octave asymptote at point Z, it is seen that the system is unstable, and has a large negative phase margin. In such a case, it is obvious that compensation is required. There may be some doubt, however, as to the type of compensation to use. The magnitude of the phase margin indicates that appreciable phase shift would be required if phase-lead compensation is used, so that it may be preferable to use phase-lag compensation.

8-6. Summary. The gain of a servomechanism may be readily adjusted on any of the three transfer-function plots. The polar plot and the decibel vs. phase-angle plot are used to set the system gain which is required for a specified value of M_p. The decibel vs. log ω plot may be used to set the gain for a specified steady-state error and, after such adjustment, indicates the stability and approximate transient performance of the system. It also indicates the need for compensation and may be used in selecting the type of compensation.

PROBLEMS

8-1. *a.* Using polar methods, adjust the gain of the system of Prob. 3-3 to obtain a resonance peak for the frequency response of $M_p = 1.5$. (See Prob. 5-6.) What is the resonant frequency?

b. Read off the phase margin, and compute the gain margin in decibels.

c. Plot the frequency-response curve.

8-2. Repeat Prob. 8-1 on M-N-contour paper. ((See Prob. 5-8.)

8-3. *a.* For the system of Prob. 3-4, adjust the gain to obtain a resonance peak (for the frequency response) of $M_p = 2.0$. (See Prob. 5-9.)

b. Read off the phase margin and the resonant frequency. Compute the gain margin in decibels.

c. Plot the frequency-response curve.

8-4. *a.* What gain is required for the system of Prob. 3-6 if $M_p = 1.3$ is desired? (See Prob. 5-10.)

b. What are the resonant frequency, phase margin, and gain margin?

c. What is the steady-state velocity-lag error if the system is to operate at 15 rpm?

8-5. *a.* For the system of Prob. 3-7, what gain is required for $M_p = 2.0$? (See Prob. 5-12.)

b. What are the resonant frequency, phase margin, and gain margin?

8-6. *a.* What gain is required for the system of Prob. 3-8 if the steady-state velocity-lag error is to be 0.3° when the system operates at 5 rpm? (See Prob. 5-13.)

b. Is the system stable under these conditions? If so, what are M_p, the resonant frequency, the phase margin, and the gain margin?

c. If the gain is adjusted to give $M_p = 1.3$, what is the velocity-lag error for 5-rpm operation?

8-7. *a.* For the system of Prob. 3-9, what gain is required to obtain an M_p of 1.4? (See Prob. 5-14.)

b. What are the resonant frequency, the phase margin, and the gain margin?

c. What is the velocity-lag error if the system is operated at 3 rpm?

d. What gain is required to reduce this velocity lag to one-fourth of its value?   Is the system stable for such a gain?   What is M_p?

8-8. *a.* The system of Prob. 3-12 is to operate at a constant velocity of 6 rpm. The maximum permissible velocity-lag error is 0.5°.   What gain is required?   (See Prob. 5-15.)

b. Is the system stable for this gain?   If so, what is M_p?

c. What gain is required if M_p is to be 2.0?   For this gain, what is the velocity-lag error when operating at 6 rpm?

8-9. What gain is required to produce an M_p of 1.5 for the system of Prob. 3-13? (See Prob. 5-16.)   What are the resonant frequency, gain margin, and phase margin?

8-10. Repeat Prob. 8-9, including the system modification indicated in Prob. 3-14.

8-11. Consider the transfer function of Prob. 5-1, part *g*.   What value of gain will stabilize the system?   Is $M_p = 3.0$ possible?   Compute two values of gain which will give $M_p = 4.0$.   Which of these values is preferable?   Why?

8-12. Repeat Prob. 8-11 for the transfer function of Prob. 6-2, part *g*.

8-13. Compute the gain required for $M_p = 2.0$ for the transfer function of Prob. 6-2, part *d*.

8-14. Compute the gain required for a velocity-lag error of 0.5° at 10 rpm for the transfer function of Prob. 6-2, part *h*.   Is the system stable?   If so, what is M_p? What gain is required for $M_p = 1.5$?   What is the velocity-lag error at 10 rpm for this gain?

CHAPTER 9

SERIES COMPENSATION OF SERVOMECHANISMS

9-1. Introduction. As discussed in this chapter, series compensation means the addition of components in cascade with the main amplification channel of a servomechanism. The illustrations and discussions are restricted to electric filter networks, but theoretically any device which has the proper transfer-function characteristics may be used. In practice, if an electronic amplifier is employed, compensation with electric networks is usually the simplest and most economical solution to the compensation problem. For certain types of electric systems, electric networks are not ideal; for example, they do not always provide adequate compensation when a two-phase induction motor is used for a drive (carrier-frequency servomechanisms), and they may be replaced by other devices.

In systems which are primarily mechanical, pneumatic, or hydraulic, electrical compensation would obviously add undesirable complications. In such cases, nonelectric devices are used. The design of nonelectric compensators is considerably more complicated than the design of electric filters, and frequently it is more economical and more effective to use such a device in a feedback path rather than in series. Economy and simplicity also dictate the use of feedback compensation for purely electrical servos in many cases. Feedback compensation is discussed in Chap. 10.

9-2. Situations Requiring Compensation. The general purpose of compensation is, of course, to permit simultaneous satisfaction of steady-state and transient specifications. An implication of this general purpose is that gain adjustment is almost invariably required in conjunction with compensation. Thus, while gain adjustment is not stressed in this chapter, its use is implied at all times.

There are, in general, two situations in which compensation is required. The first is the case where the system is inherently unstable, and compensation is required to stabilize it. The second is the more general case in which the system is stable but compensation is required to obtain the desired performance. This second case has many variations, some of which are discussed in this chapter.

Systems which are type 2 or higher are usually inherently unstable, i. e., no value of gain will stabilize them.   For such systems the need of a compensating device for stabilization is obvious.   Figure 9-1 shows a type 2 polar locus and the effect of compensation used to stabilize it. It will be noted that phase-*lead* compensation must be used.   If specifications require a definite value of M_p, this affects the specific design of the compensator, but not the general principle.

Type 0 and type 1 systems are inherently stable in the sense that stable operation may always be obtained if the gain is sufficiently reduced. Type 1 systems inherently have no static-position error, so that when such a system is used for positioning, compensation theoretically is not required.   However, high gain is usually required to provide stiffness in opposition to load disturbances, and thus compensation may be necessary to control transient oscillations. A phase-lead device is normally used. When a type 0 system is used, or when a type 1 system is used as a velocity control, steady-state error is inherent, and the gain used is controlled by the permissible error. Compensation is generally required to control the transient performance,

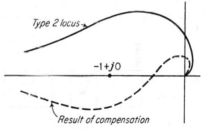

Fig. 9-1. Stabilization of a type 2 system by compensation.

but the choice of phase lead or phase lag depends on the specific problem.

In the following paragraphs the detailed discussion of series (or cascade) compensation is begun by considering a type 2 system.   This is done because the compensation requirements for a type 2 system are simple and clear-cut, i. e., there is no need to choose between phase lead and phase lag; a phase-lead compensator must be used.   Thus it is possible to concentrate on the required characteristics of the compensator itself. Once the problem has been solved for a type 2 system, the additional problems which arise for type 1 and type 0 systems can be approached with less difficulty.

9-3. An Idealized Type 2 System.   A possible application for a type 2 system is the case of a servomechanism which is to control the position of a load when the load is moving at constant velocity, and for which no steady-state velocity-lag error is permissible.   There will, of course, be position errors during the transient period; no servomechanism as yet designed can eliminate transient position errors for rapidly varying inputs. For steady-state requirements of no velocity-lag error, a type 1 system cannot be used because inherently it must have some velocity-lag error, but a type 2 system is theoretically satisfactory in steady state.   It should be pointed out, however, that in practice the type 2 system probably would not give perfect performance because of noise and other extraneous signals in the amplification process, and a properly designed type 1 system can be made to operate at very small velocity-lag errors, so that the choice between type 2 and type 1 is not as clear-cut as might be expected.

Figure 9-2a shows the schematic diagram of a system that might be used to obtain zero velocity-lag error. The block diagram of the system

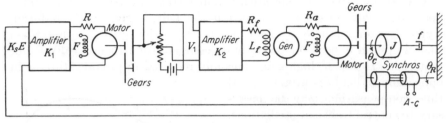

(a)

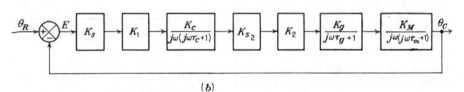

(b)

Fig. 9-2. Type 2 servomechanism. (a) Schematic diagram. (b) Block diagram.

is shown in Fig. 9-2b. Derivation of the transfer functions shown in the blocks is left to the student as an exercise. The direct transfer function of the system is

$$KG = \frac{\theta_c}{E} = \frac{K_{s1}K_1K_cK_{s2}K_2K_gK_m}{(j\omega)^2(j\omega\tau_c + 1)(j\omega\tau_g + 1)(j\omega\tau_m + 1)} \tag{9-1}$$

where K_{s1} = synchro sensitivity, volts/rad
K_c = gain of control motor, rad/sec/volt
K_{s2} = potentiometer sensitivity, volts/rad
K_2 = gain of second amplifier
K_1 = gain of first amplifier
K_g = gain of generator, volts/amp
K_m = gain of drive motor, rad/sec/volt
τ_c = time constant of control motor
τ_g = time constant of generator field
τ_m = time constant of drive motor and load

From a physical point of view, the operation of the system may be explained as follows: The control motor at the input of the system is a positioning device which merely sets the magnitude and the polarity of the voltage applied to the generator field. When the potential divider supplying this voltage is set at some specific point, the generator field current is constant and therefore the speed of the output motor is constant. The synchro error detector compares the instantaneous *position* of the load with a reference position on the input. If position correspondence does not exist (even though input and output velocities are equal), an error signal is fed to the input amplifier, and the control motor changes the position of the potentiometer tap. This changes the output velocity, allowing position correspondence to be reestablished. The system, as shown in Fig. 9-2, is unstable, and the problem of compensation will be discussed.

It should be noted that with the synchro error detector shown it is possible that a rapid acceleration of the input would cause one or more complete rotations before the output could respond. This would destroy the original position correspondence, since the synchros would indicate zero error at their nearest alignment point. Such difficulties can be taken care of by a somewhat more complicated synchro system known as a "two-speed" system. This is not discussed here.

In order to discuss the compensation in concrete terminology, it is desirable to use numbers with Eq. (9-1). Therefore the following assumptions are made:

1. The system gain, which is the numerator of Eq. (9-1), is arbitrarily set at unity, since gain adjustment will be necessary in any event.

2. The control motor would normally be small because it has essentially no load to drive, and thus it is likely to have a small time constant. Therefore assume $\tau_c = 0.05$.

3. The generator and drive motors must have about the same ratings, and will be larger machines than the control motor. Their time constants will therefore be larger, but not necessarily equal to each other. It is therefore assumed that $\tau_g = 0.08$ and $\tau_m = 0.1$.

With these numerical values, the transfer function of the system is

$$KG = \frac{\theta_c}{E} = \frac{1}{(j\omega)^2(0.05j\omega + 1)(0.08j\omega + 1)(0.1j\omega + 1)} \tag{9-2}$$

9-4. Designing Phase-lead Compensation for the Type 2 System from a Decibel vs. Log ω Plot. The decibel vs. log ω plot generally gives more qualitative information about performance than the polar plot or the decibel vs. phase-angle plot, and therefore the preliminary investigations of compensation requirements will be made on the decibel vs. log ω plot. From this investigation the desired *gain* may be set approximately, the range of frequencies needing compensation is determined, and the approximate magnitude of the required phase shift is noted. Selection of the compensating device is then undertaken, and the changes caused in the loci are added to the decibel vs. log ω plot. If the result is qualitatively satisfactory, final adjustments for transient response may be made on the polar plot or on the decibel vs. phase-angle plot.

Figure 9-3 shows an asymptotic plot of the magnitude curve and a calculated plot of the phase-angle curve. It is noted that the magnitude intercept is at a higher frequency than the phase intercept, and therefore the system is unstable. Furthermore, reduction in gain will not interchange the intercepts, and so compensation must be used. The initial slope is -12 db/octave; thus there is no steady-state velocity-lag error.

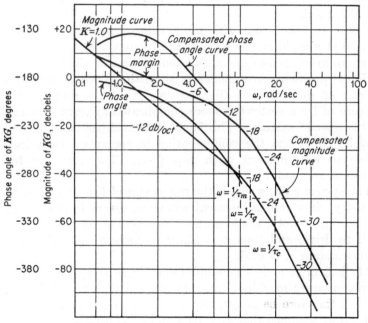

FIG. 9-3. Calculated curves—compensation of a type 2 system.

The intercept of the -12 db/octave slope with the 0-db axis gives the approximate natural frequency, however; this is seen to be 1 rad/sec. This is rather low, and to make the system stiffer a higher natural frequency might be desirable. The problem of stabilizing the original system is discussed first; then the natural frequency will be raised, and the additional problems thus encountered will be discussed.

In Fig. 9-3 the phase margin at the gain crossover is approximately $-8°$. Thus only a small positive phase shift is required to stabilize the system. If it is further required that the resonance peak should be less than $M_p = 2.0$, a positive phase margin greater than $30°$ must be established. For this, the phase-lead compensator must produce a positive phase shift of at least $38°$ at the frequency of the gain crossover, assuming that the introduction of the compensator causes no shift in this crossover point. If the gain-crossover point is changed by the compensator, the phase shift required at the new crossover must be computed and the compensator designed accordingly.

A typical phase-lead compensator is the electric filter network shown in Fig. 4-3 in Chap. 4. A single section might be incorporated in the amplifier of the servo system and can produce adequate phase shift if the component values are properly selected. The transfer function of the compensator is given in Eq. (4-28) and is

$$\frac{e_o}{e_i} = \alpha \frac{j\omega\tau + 1}{j\omega\alpha\tau + 1} \tag{4-28}$$

where $\alpha = R_1/(R + R_1)$ and $\tau = RC$.

The amount of phase shift produced by this network depends only on the value of α. Curves showing the effect of α on the maximum phase

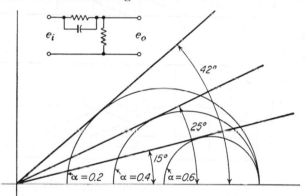

FIG. 9-4. Relationship between α and the maximum phase shift obtainable with the phase-lead circuit shown.

shift produced are given in Fig. 9-4. The frequency range over which the phase shift is effective depends primarily on the value of τ. Plots of the logarithmic transfer characteristics of this network are shown in Fig. 9-5 for $\alpha = 0.1$ and for several values of τ. Note that the filter attenuates the low frequencies. This attenuation is normally compensated for by increasing the system gain. In order to minimize manipulation and focus attention on the compensation procedure, it is assumed in this text that the system gain is increased by a factor $1/\alpha$. This may be done in practice, though it is not a necessary manipulation. The net result of such a procedure is to keep the original system asymptotes (low-frequency) in their original location, and permits direct addition of the compensator asymptotes.

The effect of cascading such a filter with the servo system is readily seen from Fig. 9-5. First of all, the magnitude asymptote has a slope of +6 db/octave. When the compensator is introduced, its transfer function multiplies the servo transfer function, and thus the asymptote is added to the system asymptotes shown in Fig. 9-3. Since this must occur in the region of the gain crossover in order to stabilize the system, and since the system asymptote in this region has a slope of -12 db/ octave, the net effect is to change the slope to -6 db/octave. If the lower corner frequency of the compensator is set at some frequency below that of the system gain crossover, then the compensator moves the gain crossover to a higher frequency. Since the phase margin of the uncompensated system is more negative at higher frequencies, the phase shift required of the compensator becomes greater.   On the other hand, if the

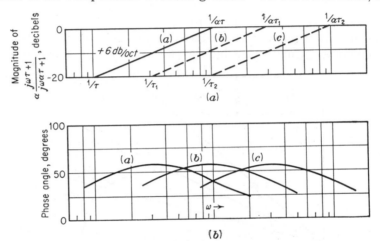

(a)

(b)

FIG. 9-5. Logarithmic curves for the phase-lead circuit.   (a) Asymptotic plot of the magnitude of the transfer characteristic of a simple phase-lead filter for $\alpha = 0.1$.   (b) Phase-angle characteristic of a simple phase-lead filter for $\alpha = 0.1$.

lower corner frequency of the compensator is set at a frequency very near the original gain crossover, little or no change is made in the gain crossover, but the maximum available phase shift is not utilized.   The design of the compensator is thus a trial-and-error procedure, and a realistic approach is to estimate the required phase shift, select a compensator which produces somewhat more than the necessary amount, and try several locations of the lower corner frequency until the desired phase margin is obtained.

A first trial of this procedure is added to Fig. 9-3.   One section of phase-lead network is assumed with $\alpha = 0.1$, so that the compensator characteristics are identical with those shown in Fig. 9-5.   The lower corner frequency is arbitrarily selected as $\omega = 0.6$ in Fig. 9-3.   The asymptotes are then added to obtain the compensated magnitude curve, and the phase angles are added to obtain the compensated phase-angle curve.   The addition of the compensator moves the gain crossover from $\omega = 1.0$ to $\omega = 1.65$.   At this frequency the net phase margin is positive and is about 43°. This seems to be adequate. A better solution (more phase margin) might be obtained by further trials. This is left to the student as an exercise.

9-5. Designing the Compensation by Polar Methods. Figure 9-6 shows a polar plot of the transfer function of an uncompensated type 2 system. It is readily seen that the system is unstable, that phase-lead compensation is required, and that the system may be stabilized with very little compensation. When a magnitude circle for $M = 2.0$ is added, however, it is apparent that appreciable phase shift is required if the resonance peak is to be made less than 2.0.

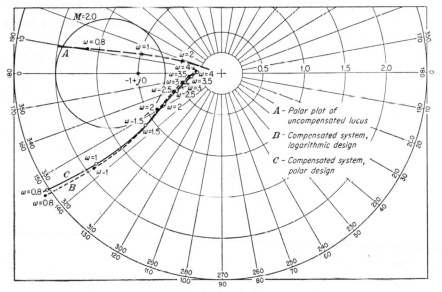

FIG. 9-6. Polar loci (calculated) for a type 2 system.

In order to design the compensation, it is necessary to estimate the amount of phase shift required and the frequency at which this phase shift must be produced. Such an estimate can be made by inspection of the polar locus, provided the basic effects of phase-lead compensators are understood. One basic characteristic of phase-lead compensators is that they attenuate low frequencies more than high frequencies, and the phase shift produced is greatest over a range of *intermediate* frequencies. (The terms "high," "low," and "intermediate" as used here are relative, and should not be associated with fixed numerical values.) Since attenuation at low frequencies is usually undesirable, it is normal practice to increase the system gain so that the low-frequency gain after compensation is essentially the same as it was before compensation, though there are exceptions to this. However, if the gain is so increased, the net effect on the polar vectors is this: The vectors that are phase-shifted usually *increase* in length, and the higher the frequency the greater this increase.

In terms of the polar locus of Fig. 9-6, the estimate of the required phase shift and its frequency might be based on reasoning such as the following:

1. Since an M of 2.0 or less is required, all frequencies lying within the M circle must be phase-shifted sufficiently to move them outside the circle. Thus values of ω of 0.8 and 1.0 must receive appreciable phase shift.

2. The higher-frequency vectors will be increased in length. Thus vectors for values of ω in the range from 1.0 to about 10.0 must be phase-shifted also, or the increase in length will move the tips of some of these vectors into the M circle.

3. In order to make a specific guess, a definite compensator is required, and so one must be selected at this point. If it proves unsatisfactory, another may be tried. For this problem, the phase-lead network of Fig. 4-3 will be tried. With this compensator in mind, it is noted that the angle between the vector to $\omega = 2.0$ and the radial line tangent to the bottom of the M circle is about 50°. Thus, if maximum phase shift is required for this frequency, the compensator must have $\alpha = 0.1$.

4. If maximum phase shift is obtained at $\omega = 2.0$, the compensated vector at this frequency will have a net phase angle of about $-145°$, and no matter how much the vector length increases, the tip of the vector cannot fall inside the $M = 2.0$ circle. Vectors at higher frequencies have less phase shift and are increased in length by a greater factor, and their tips may fall inside the $M = 2.0$ circle. The frequency selected for maximum phase shift must be chosen so that this does not happen. However, any such selection is a guess, based partly on experience.

5. Conclusion: Try the network of Fig. 4-3, use $\alpha = 0.1$, and set maximum phase shift at about $\omega = 2.0$.

In order to write the transfer function of the compensator, the value of τ must be determined. For this filter, maximum phase shift occurs at the geometric mean of the two corner frequencies, which are $1/\tau$ and $1/\alpha\tau$, and which are defined graphically by the logarithmic asymptotes of Fig. 9-5. The value of τ is then determined from

$$\omega \text{ (for } \Phi_{max}) = 2.0 = \sqrt{\frac{1}{\tau}\frac{1}{\alpha\tau}} = \frac{1}{\tau}\sqrt{\frac{1}{\alpha}}$$

$$= \frac{\sqrt{10}}{\tau}$$

$$\tau = \frac{\sqrt{10}}{2} = 1.595$$

It may be noted, however, that $1/\tau = 0.626$, and in Sec. 9-4, working with logarithmic methods, $1/\tau = 0.60$. Since there is little difference between these numbers, it is readily seen that the result of compensation design from the polar plot is essentially the same as from the decibel vs. log ω plot. Further to verify this point, the polar loci for both compensators are plotted on Fig. 9-6, and it is seen that the results are nearly identical. In both cases the resonance peak has been kept below 2.0. If desired, the gain could be increased slightly without exceeding this limit.

It may be concluded that phase-lead compensation can be designed for the type 2 system from the polar plot or the decibel vs. log ω plot with about the same accuracy. However, the choice of numerical values is more readily determined from the decibel vs. log ω plot.

9-6. The Type 2 System with Increased Gain. The type 2 system studied in the preceding sections has a relatively low gain. In many

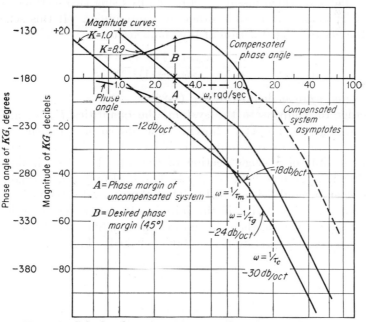

Fig. 9-7. Calculated curves—compensation of a type 2 system.

applications a higher gain might be required. If the gain is increased appreciably, the compensation problem becomes considerably more difficult. In Fig. 9-7 the original asymptotes are shown, and also a new set of uncompensated asymptotes with gain crossover at 3 rad/sec. These new asymptotes correspond to a gain increase of 19 db, which results in a K of 8.9. The phase-angle curve remains unchanged by the gain increase.

Once more, to stabilize the system, the phase must be shifted so that the phase crossover occurs at a higher frequency than the gain crossover. Furthermore, if transient performance is important, sufficient phase margin must be provided at the gain crossover. Let it be assumed that M_p must not exceed 2.0; then a positive phase margin of 45° should be sufficient to meet the transient requirements. Inspection of Fig. 9-7 shows that the existing phase margin (length A) is −36°. The desired phase margin (length B) is plus 45°. Therefore a total phase shift of 81° seems necessary at a frequency of 3 rad/sec.

It is readily seen from Fig. 9-7 that the compensator used for the low-gain system will not work here. It might be used to stabilize the system but it could never provide the phase margin needed for an M of 2.0. Obviously, the compensator to be used must be capable of producing fairly large phase shifts. If the gain crossover is not changed by the compensator, the phase shift required to satisfy specifications is about 81° at 3 rad/sec, which might be obtained by using two sections of filter in cascade, isolated from each other by an amplifier. If this scheme is used, the net transfer function of the compensator is

$$\frac{e_o}{e_i} = \frac{K_a \alpha^2 (j\omega\tau + 1)^2}{(j\omega\alpha\tau + 1)^2} \qquad (9\text{-}3)$$

where α and τ are as defined in Eq. (4-28).

In order to compensate the system, the quantities K_a, α, and τ in Eq. (9-3) must be properly chosen. The choice of α depends on the maximum phase shift required. The effect of varying α on the available phase shift of a single section of the filter has been indicated in Fig. 9-5, and large phase shifts may be obtained only if α is small. For the problem at hand, let $\alpha = 0.1$. Then the over-all attenuation of the compensator is $\alpha^2 = 0.01$. If the initial −12 db/octave slope is to be kept at a fixed location, then the gain of the amplifier should counteract the attenuation. Therefore $K_a = 100$ is selected. Figure 9-8 shows the decibel vs. log ω and phase-angle vs. log ω plots.

Before manipulation of Fig. 9-7 is undertaken, considerable help can be obtained by studying the compensator curves of Fig. 9-8. Note that the asymptote from the lower corner frequency has a slope of +12 db/octave. When this asymptote is added to the −12 db/octave asymptote of the system, the resulting curve is a horizontal line with 0 db/octave slope. Thus, if the lower corner frequency is placed at a frequency below the gain crossover (below 3 rad/sec, in this case), the new magnitude curve will be located above the 0-db axis, and the gain crossover will be shifted to a much higher frequency. This might not be objectionable for some systems, but in this case the phase angle of the uncompensated system is changing very rapidly, and any shift of the gain crossover to a higher frequency means that additional phase lead is required of the compensator. If the specified compensator has its lower corner frequency below 3 rad/sec, it cannot even stabilize the system.

Thus, if the compensator of Fig. 9-8 is to be used, its lower corner frequency must be above 3 rad/sec. More information can be obtained by consulting the compensator phase-shift curves in Fig. 9-8b. Here it is seen that maximum phase shift is obtained at some frequency between the two corner frequencies (actually at their geometric mean); the phase

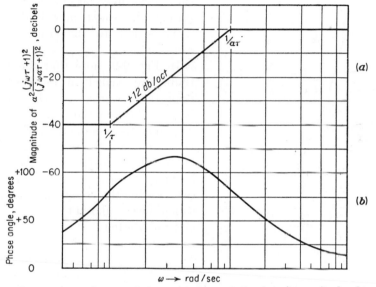

Fig. 9-8. Compensator characteristics. (a) Asymptotic plot of magnitude of transfer function of two phase-lead sections cascaded with an isolating amplifier. Amplifier gain = 1.0. (b) Phase-shift characteristics.

shift obtainable at the corner frequencies is about two-thirds of the maximum phase shift, and below the lower corner frequency the available phase shift decreases rapidly.

Since the compensator must be designed with lower corner frequency above the system-gain crossover frequency, and since it is at the gain-crossover frequency that maximum phase lead is desired, it seems logical to place the lower corner frequency of the compensator only slightly above 3 rad/sec. This is done in Fig. 9-7, using 3.5 rad/sec as the lower corner frequency for the compensator. The asymptotes and phase-angle curve for the compensated system are shown. It is seen that the compensation provides a phase margin of 40° instead of the desired 45°. This is not serious, since the relationship between M_p and the phase margin is not definite. It should also be noted that the gain margin at the new phase crossover is quite small, appearing to be about 4 db from the asymptotic plot.   This is not very desirable, since a slight increase in system gain would make the system unstable.   If gain increases are very unlikely, the compensator could be used, provided the actual value of M_p is acceptable.   Therefore the next step is to check the value of M_p; this is done most easily by replotting the data of Fig. 9-7 on an M-contour chart, as shown in Fig. 9-9.   The peculiar shape of this curve is due to the fact that the decibel values of the points plotted were obtained directly from the asymptotes of Fig. 9-7.   A smoother and more accurate curve may be obtained by computing the exact magnitude curve. This is left to the student as an exercise.

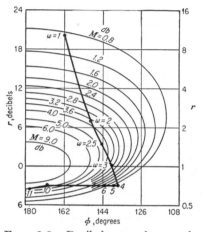

FIG. 9-9.   Decibel vs. phase-angle plot of the compensated locus of Fig. 9-7.

In Fig. 9-9, note that the M contours are scaled in decibels.   The important contour for this problem is the 6.0-db contour, since 6 db corresponds to a numeric ratio of 2.0. It is seen that the compensated locus crosses this contour, but only at a few frequencies near $\omega = 10$.   For accurate results, the true magnitude curve should be calculated for these frequencies and plotted.   Without performing these calculations, inspection of Fig. 9-7 indicates that the true magnitude curve lies below the asymptotes for the frequencies specified.   Therefore it may be safely estimated that the resonance peak is less than 2.0, and the specifications have been met.

It may be concluded that two sections of phase-lead compensation as computed, together with an isolating amplifier gain of 100, will stabilize the high-gain type 2 system and will keep the resonance peak below 2.0. It should not be concluded that this compensator is optimum, since no other possibilities have been investigated, nor should it be concluded that the specified compensator is completely satisfactory, since the gain margin is rather small and instability might result if the system gain is subject to fluctuations.

9-7. Summary and Comments.   The calculations and comments in Secs. 9-4, 9-5, and 9-6 have shown:

1. A type 2 system may be stabilized and its resonance peak limited to a specified value by means of a phase-lead compensator.

2. The compensator may be designed by logarithmic or polar methods. Essentially the same difficulties are encountered with either method, but the logarithmic approach seems simpler and less laborious.

3. The compensation design was considerably more difficult for the system with a high gain.

While not stated previously, it should be noted that it is not the high gain which causes difficulties, but the amount of negative phase shift which must be overcome. For the system studied in Sec. 9-6, the increase in gain caused a large increase in negative phase margin. This made it necessary to use two sections of filter, and the attenuation characteristic of the filter caused an undesirably small gain margin. Other systems, having different phase-shift characteristics, might be operable at considerably higher gains without being difficult to compensate.

9-8. A Type 1 System for Static Positioning. Type 1 systems are commonly used for positioning during motion (as with gun directors),

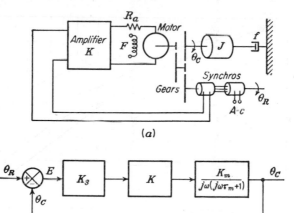

(a)

(b)

Fig. 9-10. Type 1 static-positioning system. (a) Schematic diagram. (b) Block diagram.

or for static positioning. Figure 9-10a is a schematic diagram of a simple type 1 system which might be used for static positioning. The block diagram of the system is shown in Fig. 9-10b. The transfer function is

$$KG = \frac{\theta_C}{E} = \frac{K_s K K_m}{j\omega(j\omega\tau_m + 1)} \tag{9-4}$$

Derivation of the transfer function is left to the student.

When a type 1 system is used for static positioning, the steady-state error is inherently zero, so that the gain is set to provide sufficient stiffness against load disturbances and to provide reasonable response speed when a change in position is made. Under such conditions, it is sometimes necessary to compensate the system to prevent undesirable transient overshoots. Phase-lead compensation would be used, partly because it is the high-frequency part of the locus which must be reshaped, and partly because the resonant frequency of the system must be maintained at a high value to obtain a fast response. For the system of Fig. 9-10, assume that the over-all gain is set at 10 for purposes of stiffness, $\tau_m = 0.5$, and the resonance peak is to be kept at $M_p = 1.5$ or less. The transfer-function equation of the system is then

$$KG = \frac{\theta_c}{E} = \frac{10}{j\omega(0.5j\omega + 1)}$$ (9-5)

9-9. Compensation of a Type 1 Static-positioning System with Decibel vs. Log ω Plot.
The decibel vs. log ω and phase-angle vs. log ω plots of Eq. (9-5) are shown in Fig. 9-11. It is seen that the system can never be unstable, because the phase shift is never more negative than $-180°$.

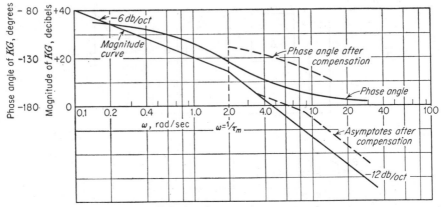

FIG. 9-11. Calculated curves for type 1 system.

However, the phase margin at the gain crossover is only 20°, which indicates a badly underdamped system. A phase margin of about 45° is needed if $M_p = 1.5$ is required, and thus a phase lead of approximately 25° should be added as compensation.

A phase lead of 25° is readily obtained with a single section of the filter of Fig. 4-3, and so this network is selected. For a maximum phase shift of 25°, choose $\alpha = 0.4$. To compensate for this attenuation at the lower frequencies, the gain is raised by a factor $1/\alpha = 2.5$. The transfer function of the compensator, including the factor for the gain increase, is

$$\frac{e_o}{e_i} = K_a\alpha \frac{j\omega\tau + 1}{j\omega\alpha\tau + 1} = \frac{j\omega\tau + 1}{0.4j\omega\tau + 1}$$ (9-6)

To complete the compensation design, a suitable value of τ must be determined. The first step in determining τ is to inspect the uncompensated loci and estimate the effect of the compensator loci:

1. If the lower corner frequency of the compensator is set at less than 4.5 rad/sec, the gain crossover is changed to a higher frequency.

2. The phase angle of the uncompensated system changes slowly over the range of frequencies near the gain crossover, and a reasonably small change in the location of the gain crossover has no objectionable effects.

3. Therefore it seems advisable to utilize the maximum phase shift of the compensator. This means that the lower corner frequency of the compensator should be located below 4.5 rad/sec, which will change the gain crossover. The new gain crossover should be located at a frequency for which the compensator gives approximately maximum phase shift.

For the compensator selected, the low and high corner frequencies are $1/\tau$ and $1/0.4\tau$, respectively. The maximum phase shift is obtained at the geometric mean of these frequencies. Inspection of the asymptotic plot of Fig. 9-5 shows that this geometric-mean frequency is located slightly below the geometric center of the asymptote. Thus, if the lower corner frequency is located arbitrarily on Fig. 9-11 and the asymptotes drawn, and if the new gain crossover is then located at about the center of the compensator asymptote, the compensation should be satisfactory.

The result of following this procedure is shown in Fig. 9-11. The lower corner frequency was arbitrarily set at 3.5 rad/sec and the asymptotes added. The phase-angle curve was computed, and the phase margin at the new gain crossover is about 45°. The compensated asymptotes in Fig. 9-11 represent a first trial. It may be noted that the new gain crossover is not at the geometric mean of the compensator corner frequencies, and a larger phase margin might be obtained by changing the corner frequency. This is left to the student as an exercise.

9-10. Checking the Type 1 Static-positioning System with the Decibel vs. Phase-angle Plot. To check the resonance peak and the resonant frequency of the system as compensated in Fig. 9-11, the locus has been replotted on decibel vs. phase-angle coordinates in Fig. 9-12. It is seen that the locus falls outside the $M = 1.5$ contour so that the resonance peak will be less than 1.5. If desired, the gain might be raised by 4.0 db. This would provide a still stiffer system, with a resonance peak of 1.5 and a resonant frequency $\omega_r \cong 7$.

9-11. Designing Phase-lead Compensation for the Type 1 Static-positioning System on the Polar Plot. Since the type 1 system of Fig. 9-10 is to be used for static positioning and the steady-state error is inherently zero, the transient performance may be set directly from the polar plot. In this case, a minimum gain of 10 has been set, and the maximum M_p is to be 1.5. Therefore the uncompensated locus will be plotted first, using the full gain of 10. This is shown in Fig. 9-13. The $M = 1.5$ circle is added, and it is seen that the locus enters the circle. The problem is to reshape the locus, using a phase-lead device, so that it does not enter the circle; at the same time, the low-frequency gain must be maintained to preserve stiffness and speed of response.

In order to select the compensator, the plot of Fig. 9-13 must be inspected and certain facts obtained from it. Frequency points from about $\omega = 2.8$ to $\omega = 5.5$ lie inside the M circle. These must be shifted counterclockwise, and therefore a phase-lead device which produces some phase shift at frequencies as low as 3 rad/sec is needed. But phase-lead devices normally attenuate the low frequencies, so that the gain must be increased to counteract this attenuation. Thus phase shift must be

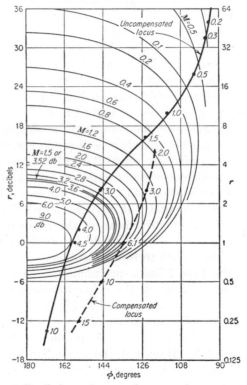

FIG. 9-12. Decibel vs. phase-angle curves for type 1 system.

obtained above 5.5 rad/sec or the increased gain will move these frequencies inside the circle. The KG vectors at high frequencies will be lengthened by almost the entire gain increase, and therefore maximum phase shift should be set at some frequency such as $\omega = 6$.

A phase-lead device of the type shown in Fig. 4-3 is suitable and will be used. To set the value of α, the required maximum phase shift must be known. This is determined by assuming that $\omega = 6$ (for which maximum phase shift is required) will be the point of tangency on the compensated locus, and that it will be tangent to the M circle at some arbitrary point, as shown in Fig. 9-13. The vectors from this point to the origin and from the original $\omega = 6$ point to the origin are drawn and the phase angle between them determined. From Fig. 9-13 this maximum phase shift, Φ_{max}, is seen to be 24°. Therefore $\alpha = 0.4$ is a suitable value.

To compensate for the attenuation at low frequencies, the gain must be increased by the reciprocal of α, i. e., $K_a = 2.5$. The equation for the compensator is then

$$\frac{e_o}{e_i} = \frac{j\omega\tau + 1}{0.4j\omega\tau + 1} \tag{9-7}$$

This is seen to be the same equation that was obtained from the decibel vs. log ω analysis. To determine τ, it may be noted that the phase shift

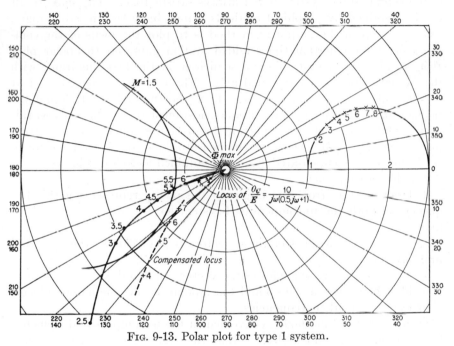

FIG. 9-13. Polar plot for type 1 system.

required at $\omega = 6$ is about 25°. Therefore,

$$25° = \tan^{-1} 6\tau - \tan^{-1} 2.4\tau \tag{9-8}$$

which is the difference in phase between the numerator and denominator of Eq. (9-7) at frequency $\omega = 6$. Furthermore, the value of τ depends on the low-frequency end of the band which is to be phase-shifted, and so the approximate value of τ is known. Thus Eq. (9-8) may be solved for τ by trial and error. Assuming that $\tau = \frac{1}{3}$,

$$\tan^{-1} 2 - \tan^{-1} 0.8 = 63.4° - 38.6° = 24.8°$$

which is close enough, and the desired value is $\tau = \frac{1}{3}$.

The equation of the compensated system thus becomes

$$KG = \frac{\theta_c}{E} = \frac{10(0.333j\omega + 1)}{j\omega(0.1333j\omega + 1)(0.5j\omega + 1)} \tag{9-9}$$

The locus of the compensated system may then be computed and added to Fig. 9-13, as shown. It is seen that the purpose of the compensation has been accomplished, and the system gain can be increased slightly without exceeding a resonance peak of 1.5.

The procedure of computing the compensated locus from the equation of the compensated system is not always satisfactory. The same result can be obtained by graphical methods, which have certain advantages. The first step in the graphical method is to plot the locus of the compensator (filter equation times added system gain) on the polar plot. It is readily shown that this is a semicircle in the first quadrant, with the diameter on the positive real axis. The intercepts are $e_o/e_i = 1$ at $\omega = 0$, and $e_o/e_i = 2.5$ at $\omega = \infty$. Thus the center is at 1.75 and the radius is 0.75. Specific points (frequencies) must then be located on this locus. Only those in the important band of frequencies need be computed from Eq. (9-7). Once the compensator locus has been determined, the locus of the compensated system is obtained as follows:

1. Select a frequency.
2. Draw vectors from the origin to the points representing this frequency on both the uncompensated-system locus and the compensator locus.
3. Measure the lengths of these vectors to the scale of the plot, and multiply them.
4. Measure the phase angles of the vectors, and add.
5. Plot the results of steps 3 and 4 as a point on the compensated locus.
6. Repeat for other frequencies.

Such a graphical method is convenient if the uncompensated locus has been obtained experimentally, so that the system equation is not specifically known. When the system equations are known, the graphical method of computation is not needed, but the addition of the compensator locus to the plot may be helpful. Specifically, if the original estimates on the compensator were not good enough, so that the desired result is not obtained, the plot of the compensator locus is helpful in deciding what changes are required. Inspection of the plots shows the maximum phase shift available from the compensator; if this is deemed inadequate, the value of α must be reduced. If the maximum available phase shift is sufficient but is not obtained at the proper frequency, inspection of the compensator locus shows the direction in which the frequency points must be shifted, and this leads to a better selection of the values of τ.

9-12. A Type 1 System for Dynamic Positioning. A common servo-mechanism application is the control of an output position during periods when the position is continuously changing. Perhaps the best-known application of this type is the gun-director servo, which must move the load continuously but must keep the output position closely aligned with the command signal. A type 1 servomechanism may be used for such control applications, because the velocity-lag error may be kept within reasonably small limits, and the stability is usually better than that of a type 2 system.

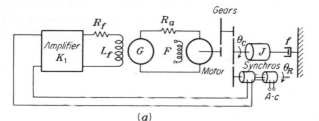

(a)

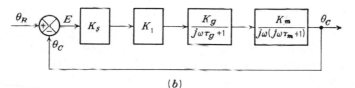

(b)

Fig. 9-14. Type 1 dynamic-positioning system. (a) Schematic diagram. (b) Block diagram.

Figure 9-14a shows a possible schematic diagram for such a system, and Fig. 9-14b shows the block diagram. The actual load is represented schematically by its inertia and friction. The transfer-function equation of the system is

$$KG = \frac{\theta_C}{E} = \frac{K_s K_1 K_m K_g}{j\omega(j\omega\tau_m + 1)(j\omega\tau_g + 1)} \tag{9-10}$$

The performance specifications for such a system depend on the purpose for which it is intended. If the problem is to track slowly moving targets, the normal load velocity will be small and the gain need not be high in order to obtain a small velocity-lag error. On the other hand, in an application like antiaircraft fire control, the target velocity is high and thus the normal load velocity is high. To obtain high velocities with reasonable lag error requires a high-gain system. For a lower-gain system, whatever compensation is needed can probably be obtained with a phase-lead device, but when the gain is high, use of a phase-lag device may be necessary. Both of these problems are considered in the following sections.

To make the phase-lead and phase-lag requirements more obvious, it is assumed that the same basic system may be used for both applications. The motor time constant is arbitrarily chosen as $\tau_m = 0.5$, and the generator time constant is chosen as $\tau_g = 0.2$. The gain will be set separately for each problem. The transfer-function equation thus becomes

$$KG = \frac{\theta_c}{E} = \frac{K}{j\omega(0.5j\omega + 1)(0.2j\omega + 1)} \qquad (9\text{-}11)$$

9-13. A Type 1 System at Low Velocities. *Computing Gain.* For slowly moving targets the required output velocity may be specified in this case as 2 rpm, or $\pi/15$ rad/sec. The permissible velocity-lag error at this velocity may be 2°, and the gain may be computed from

$$\frac{j\omega\theta_c}{E} = \frac{\text{output velocity}}{\text{error}} = K \qquad (9\text{-}12)$$

$$K = \frac{\pi/15}{2/57.3} = 6 \qquad (9\text{-}13)$$

The transfer-function equation thus becomes

$$KG = \frac{\theta_c}{E} = \frac{6}{j\omega(0.5j\omega + 1)(0.2j\omega + 1)} \qquad (9\text{-}14)$$

Use of the Decibel vs. Log ω Plot. The asymptotes of Eq. (9-14) may be sketched rapidly on the decibel vs. log ω plot by noting that the gain, 6, is numerically equal to the frequency of the 0-db intercept of the -6 db/octave slope. This fixes the initial asymptote. The -12 db/octave slope starts at the first corner frequency, which is

$$\omega = \frac{1}{\tau_m} = 2 \text{ rad/sec}$$

and the -18 db/octave slope starts at the second corner frequency, which is $\omega = 1/\tau_g = 5$ rad/sec. The asymptotes are shown in Fig. 9-15. The phase angles must then be computed and the phase-angle curve added. This also is shown in Fig. 9-15.

Inspection of Fig. 9-15 shows that the system is slightly unstable. There is a negative phase margin of about 5° at the asymptote crossover. If the true magnitude curve were plotted, the phase margin would be approximately zero. To stabilize the system and keep M_p at a reasonable magnitude, the phase margin should be about 40°. This can be accomplished with a single phase-lead network of the type used in previous examples. Let $\alpha = 0.2$; then the gain increase must be $K_a = 5$.

The asymptotes of the phase-lead compensator are added, choosing the lower corner frequency at $\omega = 2.5$. This fixes the time constant of the compensator at $\tau = 0.4$. The transfer function of the compensator thus becomes

$$\frac{e_o}{e_i} = \frac{0.4j\omega + 1}{0.08j\omega + 1} \tag{9-15}$$

The phase angles due to the compensator must then be computed and added to Fig. 9-15. Inspection of Fig. 9-15 shows that the compensator moves the asymptote crossover to $\omega = 5$ and provides a phase margin of about 25° at this point. The crossover of the true magnitude curve

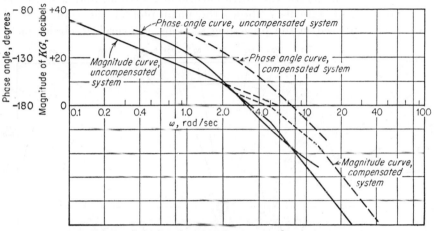

FIG. 9-15. Calculated curves for type 1 dynamic system.

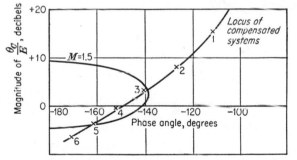

FIG. 9-16. Decibel vs. phase-angle curves for type 1 dynamic system.

would be at a lower frequency, so that a true phase margin of about 30° is expected. This is a rather small phase margin, and it might be desirable to recompute the compensation for a smaller value of α, or for a different lower corner frequency. This is left to the student as an exercise.

Checking M_p on the Decibel vs. Phase-angle Plot. To find the actual resonance peak of the compensated system as adjusted in Fig. 9-15, the locus may be replotted on decibel vs. phase-angle coordinates and checked against the M contours. An M contour for $M = 1.5$ is selected for this purpose. The resultant plot is shown in Fig. 9-16. It may be seen from the figure that the resonance peak is considerably greater than $M = 1.5$. To reduce the resonance peak to $M_p = 1.5$, the gain might be reduced by 3 db. If this is not permissible, the compensation should be redesigned.

Checking M_p and ω_r on the Polar Plot. Compensation for the system may be designed on the polar plot, if desired. First, the required gain must be computed as indicated previously. The rest of the design procedure is the same as for the static-positioning system, and will not be repeated here. Figure 9-17 shows the polar plot of the compensated system as computed in the preceding sections. Several M circles have

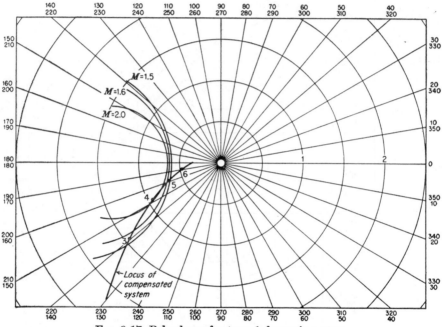

FIG. 9-17. Polar locus for type 1 dynamic system.

been added. It may be seen that the resonance peak is slightly greater than 2.0, and the resonant frequency is $\omega_r = 4$.

9-14. A Type 1 System at High Velocities. *Computing the Gain.* For a target which moves at high speed, such as an aircraft, a servomechanism might be required to operate at an output velocity of 15 rpm (or higher), which is equivalent to $\pi/2$ rad/sec. The velocity-lag error would have to be reduced, and might be $\frac{1}{2}°$. Thus the required system gain is

$$K = \frac{\text{output velocity}}{\text{error}} = \frac{\pi/2}{0.5/57.3} = 180 \qquad (9\text{-}16)$$

The transfer-function equation then becomes

$$KG = \frac{\theta_c}{E} = \frac{180}{j\omega(0.5j\omega + 1)(0.2j\omega + 1)} \qquad (9\text{-}17)$$

Use of the Decibel vs. Log ω Plot.   The asymptotes for Eq. (9-17) may be drawn on the decibel vs. log ω plot, using the methods previously described.   The phase-angle curve must be computed and added.   These curves are shown in Fig. 9-18.   It is readily seen that the high gain makes the system unstable, and the phase margin at the gain crossover is roughly $-57°$.

It might be possible to stabilize the system with phase-lead compensation, though the phase shift required would be about 100°.   However, the phase shift would have to be most effective at frequencies above the

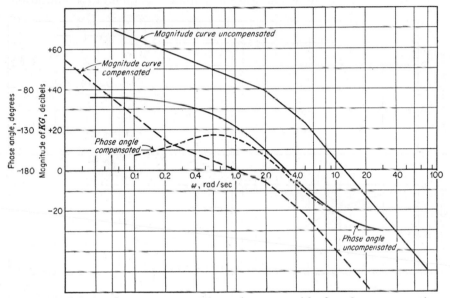

FIG. 9-18. Calculated curves—type 1 dynamic system with phase-lag compensation.

gain crossover.   This is not necessarily objectionable, but it might result in negative phase margins at lower frequencies and thus a conditionally stable system.   (A conditionally stable system is one that may be made unstable by either a gain increase or a gain decrease.)   In any event, phase-lag compensation seems more suitable and will be used here to illustrate the manipulations involved.

A network suitable for phase-lag compensation is shown in Fig. 9-19a. Its asymptotic gain characteristics are shown in Fig. 9-19b, and its phase-angle characteristics in Fig. 9-19c.   The transfer function of the network is

$$\frac{e_o}{e_i} = \frac{j\omega\tau_1 + 1}{j\omega\tau_2 + 1} \qquad (9\text{-}18)$$

where $\tau_1 = R_1 C_1$ and $\tau_2 = (R_1 + R_2)C_1$.

In using such a network for compensation, the general objective is to utilize the attenuation characteristic, i. e., the -6 db/octave slope, to move the gain crossover to some frequency lower than the phase crossover.   To do this, the first corner frequency must be located at a rather low frequency.   Furthermore, it is generally desired to leave the phase crossover at essentially its original location, and thus the second corner frequency should occur at a frequency several octaves below the phase-crossover frequency.   Both of these conditions indicate that the phase-lag network should be designed for frequencies far below the phase-cross-over frequency, but do not indicate any limit.   A qualitative limitation

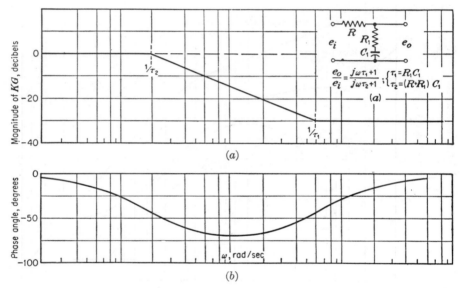

FIG. 9-19. Asymptotic characteristics of phase-lag network.   (a) Asymptotic magnitude curve.   (b) Phase-angle curve.

exists, owing to the fact that the use of a phase-lag device will move the -12 db/octave slope to a lower frequency, reducing ω_n, and thus make the system sluggish.   It is desirable, therefore, to design the phase-lag network for operation at as high a frequency as is consistent with the previously stated general objectives.   If such a design does not provide satisfactory transient performance, a phase-lead network may be added to raise the resonant frequency and thus increase the response speed. Such double compensation is not considered in this text.

The first step in designing the compensation is to determine the amount of attenuation which the compensator must produce.   This is done by selecting the desired location for the new gain crossover.   The compensator must reduce the gain to 0 db at this frequency, and therefore the required attenuation in decibels is simply the decibel gain of the uncompensated system at the frequency selected for the gain crossover. Selection of the gain-crossover point is based on the phase-angle characteristic and the desired phase margin. In this case, assume that 45° phase margin is desired. If no phase shift were produced by the compensator, this phase margin could be obtained at 1.3 rad/sec; but some negative phase shift will be introduced by the compensator, and a more logical gain crossover is therefore at an ω of 1.0. The gain at this frequency is 45 db, and therefore the compensator must attenuate that amount at $\omega = 1.0$. Since the chosen compensator attenuates at 6 db/octave, the corner frequencies of the compensator must be separated by at least $45\!\!/\!\!6 = 7.5$ octaves in order to produce the required attenuation.

The ratio of the two corner frequencies of the compensator must be $2^{7.5} = 181$. This is a very high ratio, and would not be used in practice[*] because of limitations in the physical equipment. However, it will be used in this illustration to show the principles involved.

Having determined the ratio of the corner frequencies, it is only necessary to select one of them to complete the compensation design. The second is immediately determined and the result checked on the plot. The higher corner frequency is the one selected, because it must be located far enough below the uncompensated phase crossover to assure that the phase crossover is not appreciably changed by the compensation. For the network chosen, a reasonable assumption is that the higher corner frequency should be 4 octaves below the phase-crossover frequency. The phase-crossover frequency is 3.4 rad/sec, and so the desired corner frequency is $3.4/2^4 = 0.212$ rad/sec, which is rounded off to 0.22 rad/sec for convenience. The time constant is then $\tau_1 = 1/0.22 = 4.55$ and the larger time constant is $4.55 \times 2^{7.5} = 4.55 \times 181 = 824 = \tau_2$.

The transfer function of the compensator becomes

$$\frac{e_0}{e_i} = \frac{4.55j\omega + 1}{824j\omega + 1} \tag{9-19}$$

and the transfer function of the system is

$$KG = \frac{\theta_C}{E} = \frac{180(4.55j\omega + 1)}{j\omega(824j\omega + 1)(0.5j\omega + 1)(0.2j\omega + 1)} \tag{9-20}$$

The asymptotes and phase-angle curve of the compensated system are shown in Fig. 9-18. From these curves it is seen that the phase shift introduced at the original phase crossover is about 5°, which is satisfactory. The desired phase margin of 45° was not obtained, the actual phase margin being about 40°. This is reasonably close, and it is advisable to check M_p and ω_r to determine whether the compensation is satisfactory.

* See Brown, G. S., and D. P. Campbell, "Principles of Servomechanisms," p. 215, John Wiley & Sons, Inc., New York, 1948.

Checking Transient Performance on the Decibel vs. Phase-angle Plot.   In the case of phase-lag compensation, it is particularly important to check the M_p and ω_r of the system.   The value of M_p has no more significance than for phase-lead compensation, but ω_r is quite important, because phase-lag compensation tends to reduce ω_r and make the system sluggish. Thus a check on the speed of response by determining ω_r is desirable.

M_p and ω_r may be found either by the decibel vs. phase-angle method or by a polar plot.   The former is used here for convenience, and the curve is shown in Fig. 9-20.   It is seen that the compensated locus is tangent to the $M = 3.2$ db contour somewhere between $\omega = 1.0$ and $\omega = 1.5$.   Thus the resonance peak is less than $M_p = 1.5$, and the resonant frequency is approximately 1.2 rad/sec. The value of M_p is apparently satisfactory, and unless ω_r is too low, the compensator has accomplished its purpose.

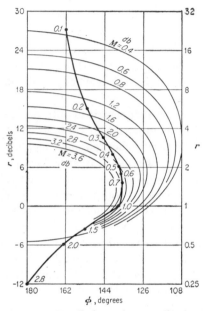

FIG. 9-20. Decibel vs. phase-angle plot for compensated system.

Designing Phase-lag Compensation on the Polar Plot.   The problem of designing phase-lag compensation on the polar plot is somewhat different from that of designing phase-lead compensation, owing to the fact that the attenuation at high frequencies is the important feature of the compensation, and the phase shift is something that the system must accept.   In designing phase-lead compensation, the procedure used previously was to plot the polar locus for the full gain required by steady-state conditions, then select the compensator, and determine its constants by inspecting the plot.   With phase-lag compensation, this usually is not a desirable procedure, because the high gains encountered require a compressed scale, and interpretation of the plot is difficult.

A procedure which is satisfactory for many phase-lag compensator designs is as follows:

1. Plot the uncompensated locus for an assumed gain of unity ($K = 1$).

2. Construct an M circle for M equal to or less than the desired resonance peak, using the construction method usually applied to gain adjustment.

3. Determine the resonant frequency, ω_r, and note that the phase lag

introduced at this frequency should be 5° or less.   Also compute the
gain which would produce this resonant frequency.

4. From the gain computed in step 3 and the gain required for steady-
state performance, compute the factor by which the gain setting of step 3
must be increased.

The information thus obtained permits the choice of the time constants
in the compensating device.   The methods used to interpret the information depend largely on the type of phase-lag device selected.   In this

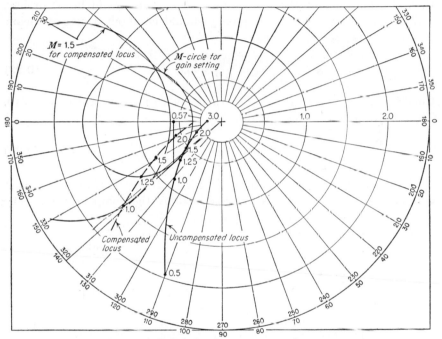

FIG. 9-21. Polar plot for compensated system.

illustration, the phase-lag compensator chosen is the simple circuit of
Fig. 9-19.

The polar plot of the transfer function is shown in Fig. 9-21, and an
M circle for $M = 1.5$ has been constructed.   The gain required for this
resonance peak is

$$K = 1/0.57 = 1.75$$

and the resonant frequency at this gain is $\omega_r = 1.5$.   Since the gain
necessary to meet the steady-state error requirement is 180, this system
gain must be increased by a factor of 103.   It is apparent, however, that
the vectors at frequencies above 1.5 rad/sec cannot be multiplied by any
factor greater than unity, or the resonance peak will be excessive.   Thus,
while the low frequencies must be multiplied by a factor of 103, there

must be a compensator which attenuates, or nullifies, this entire gain for the higher frequencies.

The ratio of the time constants in the chosen compensator may be computed from this information, i. e., since the compensator must attenuate by a factor of $\frac{1}{103}$ at $\omega = 1.5$, it follows that

$$\left| \frac{j1.5\tau_1 + 1}{j1.5\tau_2 + 1} \right| = \frac{1}{103} \tag{9-21}$$

It is also known that the phase shift at $\omega = 1.5$ should be 5° or less, and thus the higher corner frequency should be about 3 octaves below $\omega = 1.5$. This evaluates τ_1 as

$$\tau_1 = \frac{1}{0.2} = 5.0 \tag{9-22}$$

Combining Eqs. (9-21) and (9-22), the second time constant is $\tau_2 = 519$. Then the system transfer function is

$$KG = \frac{\theta_C}{E} = \frac{180(5j\omega + 1)}{j\omega(519j\omega + 1)(0.5j\omega + 1)(0.2j\omega + 1)} \tag{9-23}$$

The compensated curve is shown in Fig. 9-21. It is readily seen that a resonance peak of 1.5 was not attained by the compensation. The

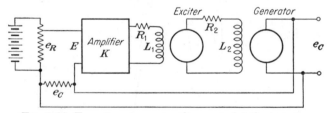

FIG. 9-22. Type 0 system—a voltage-regulated generator.

difficulty lies in the negative phase shift produced by the compensator. To correct this deficiency, a redesign of the compensator would be required. This is left to the student as an exercise.

9-15. A Simple Type 0 System. Figure 9-22 shows a voltage-regulated generator excited by a smaller generator. The input to the system, e_R, is a reference voltage derived from some d-c source. This is compared with the output voltage, e_C, by the potentiometer arrangement. The difference between the input and output voltages, $E = e_R - e_C$, is fed into the amplifier. The system is connected so as to reduce this error to zero. It is obvious from physical reasoning that the output voltage can never exactly equal the input voltage because, if this happened, there would be no signal fed into the amplifier, no exciter voltage, and, therefore, no output voltage.

The transfer function of the system is

$$\frac{e_C}{E} = \frac{K}{(j\omega\tau_y + 1)(j\omega\tau_x + 1)} \qquad (9\text{-}24)$$

where $\tau_y = L_2/R_2$ and $\tau_x = L_1/R_1$. The student should verify this by deriving the transfer function of the system.

Inspection of Eq. (9-24) shows that the system is type 0. Furthermore, the phase angle of the system approaches $-180°$ as ω approaches infinity and therefore the system can never be unstable. Any problem of compensation must arise as a compromise between steady-state error and transient performance. If the steady-state error is to be small, the system gain must be high and the transient performance of the regulator may have an undesirable resonance peak. Whether phase-lead or phase-lag compensation is required depends on the magnitude of the gain used, i. e., on the permissible steady-state error. It should be noted, however, that the transfer function of Eq. (9-24) does not include the effect of any load; it is a relationship involving only the open-circuit voltage. Thus the following illustrations express only the variations in the open-circuit voltage when the input, e_R, is changed. A discussion of the effect of load variations is beyond the scope of this text.

To permit the computation of a numerical illustration, the following values are assumed arbitrarily:

$$\tau_y = 0.5 \qquad \tau_x = 0.25 \qquad K = \left|\frac{e_C}{E}\right|_{\omega \to 0} = 100$$

$e_C = 100$ volts $\qquad E = 1.0$ volt (specified for steady state)

The transfer function of the system thus becomes

$$\frac{e_C}{E} = \frac{100}{(0.5j\omega + 1)(0.25j\omega + 1)} \qquad (9\text{-}25)$$

Use of the Decibel vs. Log ω Plot. Equation (9-25) may be plotted on decibel vs. log ω coordinates, as shown in Fig. 9-23. It is seen that the phase margin at the gain crossover is only 12°, and the resonance peak is likely to be excessive. The use of phase-lead compensation seems an obvious choice, since a reasonable amount of phase lead should produce ample phase margin not only at the gain crossover but at all lower frequencies.

A single section of the phase-lead network of Fig. 4-3 should be satisfactory. If an additional 30° phase lead is sufficient, $\alpha = 0.3$ is a reasonable value. The gain of the system must then be increased by a factor of 3.33 to counteract the attenuation. The choice of the compensator time constant is made so that the maximum phase lead of the compensator is obtained at the new gain crossover. This is done graphically in Fig. 9-23

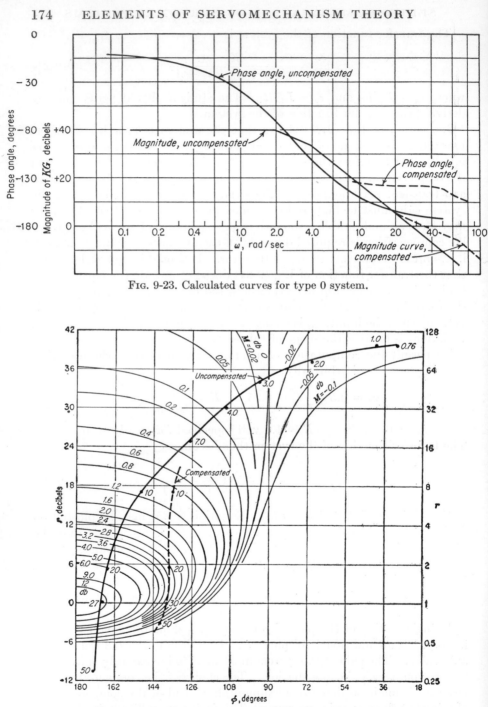

FIG. 9-23. Calculated curves for type 0 system.

FIG. 9-24. Decibel vs. phase-angle curves for type 0 system.

by drawing the compensator asymptote so that it crosses the 0-db axis at about the middle of its geometric length.

From Fig. 9-23, the equation of the compensator is

$$\frac{e_o}{e_i} = K_a \alpha \frac{j\omega\tau_1 + 1}{j\omega\alpha\tau_1 + 1} = \frac{0.05j\omega + 1}{0.015j\omega + 1} \tag{9-26}$$

It is seen that the phase-lead compensation has moved the gain crossover from $\omega = 27$ to $\omega = 36$ but has provided a phase margin of 42° at the asymptotic gain crossover.

Checking M_p and ω_r on the Decibel vs. Phase-angle Plot. The height of the resonance peak and the resonant frequency may be checked by an

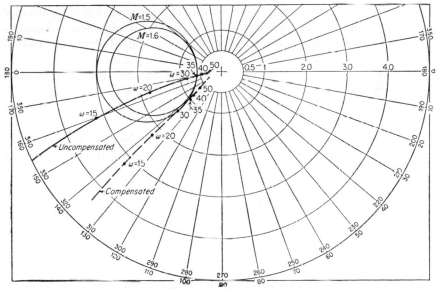

Fig. 9-25. Polar loci for type 0 system.

M-contour study on the decibel vs. phase-angle plane. The required curves are shown in Fig. 9-24. It is seen from the figure that M_p is about 3.2 db, which corresponds to a ratio of less than 1.5, and ω_r is about 28 rad/sec. The high value of ω_r indicates that the speed of response will be quite high.

Designing Compensation from the Polar Plot. The design of phase-lead compensation for a type 0 system requires essentially the same operations on the polar plot as were used with the type 1 static-positioning system in Sec. 9-11. Therefore the manipulations are not repeated here. Figure 9-25 shows the polar plot of the uncompensated system and also the compensated plot using the compensation determined by logarithmic methods. M circles have been added to check the transient performance.

It is seen from Fig. 9-25 that the resonance peak is somewhere between

$M = 1.5$ and $M = 1.6$. The resonant frequency is approximately $\omega_r = 32$. These results agree with the M-contour analysis of Fig. 9-25, as they should. It is perhaps easier to see from Fig. 9-25 that the resonance peak could be still further reduced.

9-16. Phase-lag Compensation of a Type 0 System. In some cases, a type 0 system is to be used, but the steady-state error is to be kept very small. Rather high gains must be used in such cases, and it is likely that the system will contain more time constants than are shown in Eq. (9-25). The additional time constants would make the possible phase shift greater than 180°, and this fact combined with the high gain may make the system unstable.

Whether the additional time constants are present or not, it is usually possible to control the transient performance with phase-lead compensation. However, if phase-lead compensation is used, the attenuation at low frequencies must be overcome by additional gain increases, and such very high gain systems are generally undesirable from an economic point of view and because of the possibility of parasitic oscillations, etc. Thus, it is usually desirable to compensate such a system with a phase-lag device.

To illustrate the procedures involved in designing the compensator, a type 0 system as in Fig. 9-22 is assumed, but the output voltage and error requirements are changed. Assume

$$|e_C| = 1,000 \text{ volts} \qquad |E| = 0.5 \text{ volt} \qquad K = \left|\frac{e_C}{E}\right|_{\omega=0} = 2,000$$

The transfer function is then

$$KG = \frac{e_C}{E} = \frac{2,000}{(0.5j\omega + 1)(0.25j\omega + 1)} \qquad (9\text{-}27)$$

9-17. Designing Phase-lag Compensation for the Type 0 System on the Decibel vs. Log ω Plot. The asymptotes and phase-angle curve for Eq. (9-27) are shown in Fig. 9-26. It is seen that the gain crossover is at a frequency of 122 rad/sec, and there is a positive phase margin of about 5°. Thus the system is stable, but transient oscillations will have appreciable amplitude and duration. The problem is to improve this transient performance without altering the steady-state accuracy. A resonance peak of about 1.5 should obtain with a phase margin of 40° to 45°. While this phase margin can undoubtedly be obtained with a phase-lead device, it is assumed that a phase-lag compensator is more suitable.

The basic principle in designing a phase-lag compensator is to utilize its attenuation characteristic to shift the gain crossover, but at the same time the phase shift produced by the compensator must not appreciably change the phase angle at the new gain crossover. Inspection of Fig.

9-26 shows that a phase margin of 49° would be obtained by shifting the gain crossover to a frequency of 6.0 rad/sec. This seems reasonable, since the phase shift of the compensator will probably reduce this phase margin by 5° or 6°, thus leaving a net phase margin within the estimated limits of 40° to 45°.

To obtain a gain crossover at 6.0 rad/sec, the system gain must be attenuated 52 db, and this, of course, is the job of the compensator. If a single phase-lag section is used, attenuating at 6 db/octave, the attenuation requires nearly 9 octaves, which is excessive. It is therefore decided

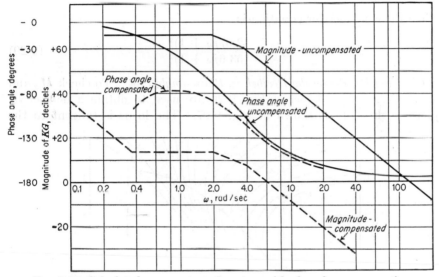

FIG. 9-26. Calculated curves—type 0 system with phase-lag compensation.

to attenuate at 12 db/octave by using two phase-lag sections (see Fig. 9-19) in cascade, but separated by an isolating amplifier of unity gain. The transfer function of the combination is

$$\frac{e_o}{e_i} = \frac{(j\omega\tau_1 + 1)^2}{(j\omega\tau_2 + 1)^2} \tag{9-28}$$

The smaller of these time constants is τ_1, which determines the higher corner frequency on the asymptotic plot. It is estimated that the higher corner frequency should be 4.0 octaves below the new gain crossover to keep the phase shift reasonable. This makes

$$\omega_1 = \frac{6.0}{2^4} = \frac{6.0}{16} = 0.375 \text{ rad/sec}$$

and

$$\tau_1 = \frac{1}{\omega_1} = \frac{1}{0.375} = 2.67$$

The asymptotes in Fig. 9-26 are altered in accordance with these computations, and the new phase-angle curve is plotted (the corner at $1/\tau_2$ is not shown). The resulting phase margin is 45° and should be adequate. Therefore τ_2 is calculated to complete the compensator design.

$$\omega_2 = {}^{52}\!/_{12} = 4.333 \text{ octaves below } \omega_1$$

$$\omega_2 = \frac{\omega_1}{2^{4.33}} = \frac{0.375}{20.1} = 0.01865 \text{ rad/sec}$$

$$\tau_2 = \frac{1}{\omega_2} = 53.6$$

Then the compensator equation is

$$\frac{e_o}{e_i} = \frac{(2.67j\omega + 1)^2}{(53.6j\omega + 1)^2} \tag{9-29}$$

Checking Results on the Decibel vs. Phase-angle Plot. To check M_p and ω_r, the compensated loci of Fig. 9-26 are used to obtain a decibel vs. phase-angle plot, as shown in Fig. 9-27. The locus is tangent to the

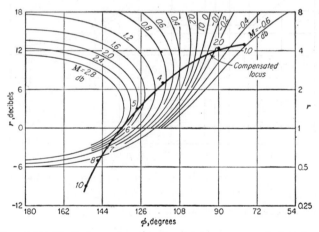

FIG. 9-27. Decibel vs. phase-angle plot for compensated system.

contour for $M = 2.4$ db, and this corresponds to a magnitude ratio of less than 1.4. Thus the compensator has obtained the desired value of M. By inspection of Fig. 9-27, the resonant frequency is 6 rad/sec.

Use of the Polar Plot. Checking the M_p and ω_r of the compensated system with a polar plot and M circles is a relatively simple task, and will not be attempted here. Instead, the procedures involved in designing phase-lag compensation from the polar plot will be illustrated.

The gain required for the desired steady-state performance is known to be 2,000. As a first step, the locus for the uncompensated system with full required gain is plotted on Fig. 9-28 as curve A. (No M cir-

cles are shown because the scale used does not permit a clear picture.)
Inspection shows that the use of phase-lead compensation is a possibility
requiring a phase shift of perhaps 50° over a frequency band located
somewhere near $\omega = 100$ (estimated).   The attenuation normal to such
a phase-shift compensator is appreciable, so that considerable additional
gain would be required.   Also, the resonant frequency would obviously
be quite high.   Neither of these conditions is particularly desirable, and
so the possibility of using phase-lag compensation is investigated.

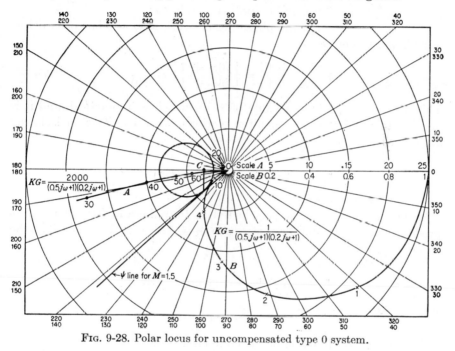

FIG. 9-28. Polar locus for uncompensated type 0 system.

Phase-lag compensation affects primarily the low-frequency portion of
the locus, and it is desirable to have most of the low-frequency range on
the plot for preliminary investigations.   Therefore, curve B is added to
Fig. 9-28, using a different scale, and showing the polar locus for unity
gain.   From curve B it is seen that if the system were operated with
unity gain, it would be badly overdamped and very sluggish.   Assuming
that $M_p = 1.5$ is desired, the gain which will produce such a resonance
peak may be determined by the usual gain-adjustment procedure, as
shown in Fig. 9-28.   The gain required is $K = 1/0.12 = 8.34$.

If the desired steady-state performance is to be obtained, the low frequencies must be amplified much more than this; by another factor
$K' = 2,000/8.34 = 240$.   The high frequencies, that is, the range of
frequencies near and above the point of tangency with the M circle,

must not be multiplied by this additional gain or the locus at these frequencies will enter the M circle and increase M_p. Thus the attenuation of the phase-lag network must approach a value of $\frac{1}{240}$ at a frequency of perhaps $\omega = 6$ in order to counteract the additional gain. Also, any appreciable phase lag at frequencies above $\omega = 6$ would rotate the locus into the M circle. Thus the characteristics required of the phase-lag device are determined roughly.

Assuming that the phase-lag network of Fig. 9-19 is to be used, the preceding information may be applied as follows:

1. The attenuation of the phase-lag network at $\omega = 6$ has been determined, and therefore

$$\left|\frac{j\omega\tau_1 + 1}{j\omega\tau_2 + 1}\right| = \left|\frac{j6\tau_1 + 1}{j6\tau_2 + 1}\right| = \frac{1}{240}$$

This, however, results in a value of τ_2/τ_1, which is impractical, and it is decided to use two cascaded filter sections, with a unity-gain isolating amplifier between them.

2. For the cascaded filter,

$$\left|\frac{(j\omega\tau_1 + 1)^2}{(j\omega\tau_2 + 1)^2}\right| = \left|\frac{(j6\tau_1 + 1)^2}{(j6\tau_2 + 1)^2}\right| = \frac{1}{240}$$

3. The value of τ_1 must be selected so that there is little phase shift produced at $\omega = 6$, and for this reason $\omega_1 = 1/\tau_1 = 6/2^4 = \frac{6}{16}$, i. e., the corner frequency is set at 4 octaves below $\omega = 6$.

4. From this, $\tau_1 = \frac{16}{6} = 2.67$, and the relationship for τ_2 becomes

$$|(j6\tau_2 + 1)^2| = 240|[j6(2.67) + 1]^2|$$

which may be solved for

$$\tau_2 = 41.3$$

5. The transfer function of the compensator is

$$\frac{e_o}{e_i} = \frac{(2.67j\omega + 1)^2}{(41.3j\omega + 1)^2}$$

6. The direct transfer function of the compensated system becomes

$$\frac{e_c}{E} = \frac{2,000(2.67j\omega + 1)^2}{(41.3j\omega + 1)^2(0.5j\omega + 1)(0.25j\omega + 1)}$$

The locus for the compensated system is plotted in Fig. 9-29. An M circle for $M = 1.5$ has been added. It is seen that the compensation has accomplished its purpose; M is slightly less than 1.5, and the resonant frequency is about 8.3 rad/sec.

9-18. General Comments. This chapter has presented in some detail the manipulations involved in adjusting system performance by series compensation. Both phase-lead and phase-lag compensation have been investigated. The choice between phase lead and phase lag is seen to be perfectly obvious in some cases, but in other cases either might have been used. It should also be noted that only one phase-lead network or one phase-lag network was used. Many other suitable networks are available, and the problem of which one to choose is beyond the scope of this text. It may be noted in general that phase-lead compensation raises the resonant frequency and increases the speed of response while the reverse is true of phase-lag compensation.

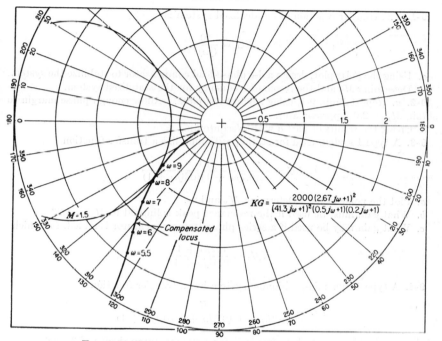

$$KG = \frac{2000\,(2.67\,j\omega+1)^2}{(41.3\,j\omega+1)^2(0.5\,j\omega+1)(0.2\,j\omega+1)}$$

Fig. 9-29. Polar locus for compensated type 0 system.

The decibel vs. log ω plot is by far the easiest to use for preliminary design, especially if asymptotic approximations are utilized for the gain curve. The results of such preliminary design should usually be checked, however. The decibel vs. phase-angle plot was used mostly to check the results of the decibel vs. log ω design. The design possibilities of the decibel vs. phase-angle plot were not investigated to any appreciable extent.

The polar plot is a convenient way to represent the transfer-function data. In particular, it is quite convenient for checking transient performance, since the M circles are easily added. Design of compensation on the polar plot is not as convenient as with the logarithmic plots, but may be carried out without excessive labor.

It should be noted that the methods used for the design of compensation were adapted to the rather simple specifications stated. In many cases the specifications are more complicated and more severe. Methods for adjusting or compensating a given system to given specifications usually have to be adapted to the problem at hand. The preceding illustrations should serve as a reasonable background which can be expanded and modified by experience.

PROBLEMS

9-1. The transfer function of an idealized system is

$$KG = \frac{10}{(j\omega)^2}$$

a. Using the polar plot, design a d-c phase-lead compensator to stabilize the system.
b. Determine M_p and the resonant frequency for the stabilized system.

9-2. *a.* Repeat Prob. 9-1, using asymptotic plots. Allow enough phase margin to obtain $M_p = 2.0$ (approximate).
b. Check the results of part *a* with M contours.

9-3. A type 1 system used for static positioning has a transfer function

$$KG = \frac{10}{j\omega(0.7j\omega + 1)(0.3j\omega + 1)}$$

a. Plot the polar locus. Determine M_p and ω_r.
b. What gain must be used if the resonance peak is limited to $M_p = 1.3$?
c. What gain may be used if a series phase-lead compensator is added, for which

$$K_cG_c = \frac{0.2j\omega + 1}{0.04j\omega + 1}$$

9-4. A type 1 dynamic-positioning system has a transfer function

$$KG = \frac{K}{j\omega(2j\omega + 1)(0.5j\omega + 1)(0.1j\omega + 1)}$$

If the permissible velocity-lag error is 5° for a steady-state velocity of 3 rpm,
a. Determine the required gain, K, from the decibel vs. log ω plot.
b. If the system is to be critically damped ($M_p = 1.0$ approximate), must it be compensated?
c. If compensation is necessary, select the required type (phase lead or phase lag) and design it approximately on the decibel vs. log ω plot.
d. Check the compensator design with M contours.

9-5. A type 0 system has a transfer function

$$KG = \frac{30}{(0.8j\omega + 1)(0.3j\omega + 1)(0.08j\omega + 1)}$$

A single phase-lead section of the type shown in Fig. 9P-1 is placed in series to compensate the system. If $\alpha = 0.2$, and the gain is raised to compensate for the attenuation at low frequencies,
a. Write the transfer function of the compensated system (in terms of τ, the time constant of the compensator).

b. Study the effect of the phase lead by means of a decibel vs. log ω and phase-angle vs. log ω plot. Use at least five values for τ.

c. Select a plot from part *b* for which you would expect the resonance peak to be $M_p = 1.5$ and check the value by means of both decibel vs. phase-angle and polar plots.

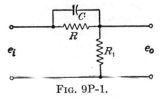

FIG. 9P-1.

9-6. In the system of Prob. 9-5 the gain must be raised from 30 to 100 to obtain the desired steady-state performance; to permit the gain increase, a single phase-lag section of the type shown in Fig. 9P-2 is placed in series.

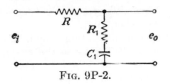

FIG. 9P-2.

a. Write the transfer function of the compensated system.

b. Study the effect of the phase-lag compensation on a decibel vs. log ω and a phase-angle vs. log ω plot.

c. Select one plot from part *b* and check M_p and W_r on both decibel vs. phase-angle and polar plots.

9-7. The system of Prob. 3-3 is to be operated at 10 rpm with a permissible velocity-lag error of 1.0°. The resonance peak is to be limited to 1.5, and it is desired that the resonant frequency be between 5 and 7 rad/sec.

a. Determine the type of compensation required.

b. Design a d-c filter to accomplish the compensation.

c. Check the transient specifications on the polar plot.

9-8. The system of Prob. 3-9 is to operate with a stiffness of 0.1 deg/ft-lb, i. e., a torque of 1 ft-lb applied to the load shaft must not cause the output shaft to move more than 0.1°. At the same time, the system M_p must not exceed 1.3.

a. Compute the gain required to obtain the desired stiffness.

b. Must the system be compensated to obtain the desired M_p?

c. If the answer to part *b* is "yes," design a d-c filter to accomplish the compensation.

9-9. The system of Prob. 3-12 is to be operated at a velocity of 15 rpm with a permissible velocity-lag error of 0.25° and a resonance peak (M_p) of 1.6.

a. Compute the required system gain.

b. Design a d-c filter to compensate the system.

9-10. The system of Prob. 3-13 is to operate with a stiffness of 0.5 deg/ft-lb. (See Prob. 9-8 for explanation.)

a. What gain is required?

b. Determine M_p and the resonant frequency.

c. Design a filter, of the type specified in Fig. 4P-3a, to reduce M_p to 2.0.

d. Design a filter, of the type specified in Fig. 4P-3b, to reduce M_p to 2.0.

9-11. The asymptotes of a transfer function are:

-6 db/octave below 1.3 rad/sec

−12 db/octave between 1.3 rad/sec and 14 rad/sec

−18 db/octave above 14 rad/sec

At $\omega = 0.1$, the asymptote has a magnitude of +56 db

Design a compensator to adjust the system to an M_p of 2.0 without changing the velocity-lag error characteristics.

9-12. The asymptotes of a transfer function are:

−12 db/octave below 0.35 rad/sec

−6 db/octave between 0.35 and 4.5 rad/sec

−12 db/octave between 4.5 and 13 rad/sec

−18 db/octave above 13 rad/sec

a. Using the M-contour chart, determine what range of gain values is possible for stable operation.

b. What is the smallest value of M_p possible in the range of stable operation?

c. Design a d-c filter network to reduce the minimum M_p to 1.3.

REFERENCES

CHESTNUT, H., Obtaining Attenuation-frequency Characteristics for Servomechanisms, *Gen. Elec. Rev.*, December, 1947.

CLARKE, J. G., Differentiating and Integrating Circuit, *Electronics*, November, 1944.

HALL, A. C., Application of Circuit Theory to the Design of Servomechanisms, *J. Franklin Inst.*, 1946.

McDONALD, D., Stabilizing Servomechanisms, *Electronics*, November, 1948.

SCHWARTZ, G. J., The Application of Lead Networks and Sinusoidal Analysis to Automatic Control Systems, *Trans. AIEE*, 1947.

TSCHUDI, E. W., Transfer Functions for *RC* and *RL* Equalizer Networks, *Electronics*, May, 1949.

CHAPTER 10

FEEDBACK COMPENSATION
OF SERVOMECHANISMS

10-1. Introduction. It was shown in Chap. 9 that the net effect of compensation devices (when used in series with the main transmission path) is to change the phase shift and attenuation of a system over a selected frequency range. There is no reason why this effect must be accomplished by placing some device in *series* with the main amplification channel. It is possible and practical to obtain a similar, even an identical, effect by placing a compensator in parallel with one or more of the components in the main transmission path. Energy may be fed through the compensator in either direction (feedback or feed forward), though the design of the compensator is determined by the chosen direction. Feedback compensation is more common and is the topic chosen for discussion here.

10-2. Desirability of Feedback Compensation. There are many reasons why the addition of one or more feedback loops may be a desirable method of compensating a servomechanism. Some of these are listed below:

1. The input to the compensator is at a higher power level than the output, and amplification may not be necessary.

2. Devices which absorb some power may be used, i. e., low-impedance networks.

3. If the system is not electrical in nature, a suitable series device may not be available.

4. Frequently the feedback compensator is more economical.

5. Feedback compensation often provides greater "stiffness" against load disturbances.

There are other reasons why feedback compensation may be used. Some of these are often peculiar to the application and cannot be readily classified. Others are concerned with performance features which are beyond the scope of this text. It should not be thought, however, that feedback compensation is always more desirable than series compensation. In many cases series compensation is quite satisfactory and very economical, especially in small instrument-type servos where it may often be superior to feedback compensation, at least from an engineering point of view.

Three illustrations of possible applications of feedback compensation are shown in the schematic diagrams of Fig. 10-1. These are introduced at this point to provide a physical picture of feedback-compensation arrangements. Each is treated in some detail later in the chapter.

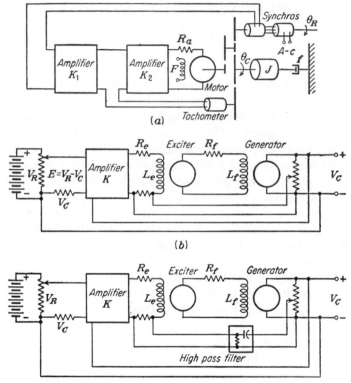

FIG. 10-1. Systems using feedback compensation. (a) Tachometer (velocity) feedback. (b) Feedback loop in voltage regulator system. (c) Feedback loop with high-pass filter.

10-3. Block-diagram Analysis of Feedback Loops. One result of adding a feedback compensator to a system is to change the system transfer-function equation and frequency-response equation. The algebraic nature of this change is somewhat more complicated than for a series compensator. The net effect is that the analytic design of a feedback compensator is made more difficult than that of an equivalent series device, and graphical computations are made more complex. It is, therefore, desirable to investigate these effects rather generally before attempting quantitative computations.

Figure 10-2a shows a simplified block diagram for an uncompensated single-loop servomechanism. The transfer functions of the individual blocks are represented by the symbols KG with appropriate subscripts. The transfer-function equation of the system is

$$\frac{\theta_C}{E} = K_1 G_1 K_2 G_2 K_3 G_3 \tag{10-1}$$

If compensation is required and feedback means are to be used, a feedback compensator $A_1 F_1$ might be added, as shown in Fig. 10-2b. The

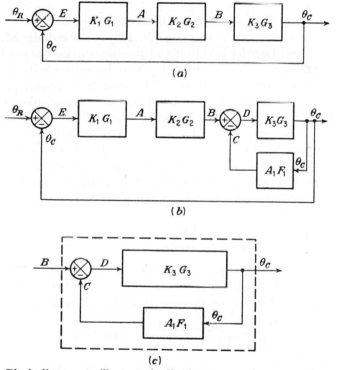

(a)

(b)

(c)

FIG. 10-2. Block diagram to illustrate feedback compensation. (a) Uncompensated system. (b) Feedback compensated system. (c) Detail of feedback loop.

error-detector symbol at the point where the feedback signal is introduced into the main path may mean either an addition or a subtraction, and the equation of the error detector must be known. Negative feedback (subtraction) is much more common and is the only type of feedback considered in this text.

The equations for the subordinate loop may be set up from Fig. 10-2c.

$$\frac{\theta_C}{D} = K_3 G_3 \tag{10-2}$$

$$\frac{C}{\theta_C} = A_1F_1 \tag{10-3}$$

$$\frac{C}{D} = K_3G_3A_1F_1 \tag{10-4}$$

$$\frac{\theta_C}{B} = \frac{K_3G_3}{1 + K_3G_3A_1F_1} \tag{10-5}$$

Equations (10-2) and (10-3) are, respectively, the transfer functions of the main-path component and the feedback component. Equation (10-4) is the loop transfer function. Equation (10-5) is the frequency-response function of the closed loop.

The component transfer functions must be known in order to analyze performance, and K_3G_3 must be known if A_1F_1 is to be designed. However, it is the loop transfer function and the frequency-response function which must be used directly with the Nyquist criterion to determine whether or not the system is stable. For example, if a polar plot of the loop transfer function is made, the closed loop will be unstable if the locus encloses the $-1 + j0$ point, but it will be stable if the $-1 + j0$ point is not enclosed. However, the addition of M and N circles to such a plot of the loop transfer function does not directly give the relationship between the input signal and the output signal of the closed loop.

It has been shown that the construction of the M and N circles is based on the fact that the vector on the polar plot is KG and the M circle is a locus of

$$\left| \frac{\theta_C}{\theta_R} \right| = \frac{|KG|}{|1 + KG|} = \text{constant} \tag{10-6}$$

The N circle then gives the phase angle between θ_C and θ_R. When there is a component in the feedback path, the loop-transfer-function plot has a vector length of $K_3G_3A_1F_1$, and therefore the M circle represents a locus of

$$\left| \frac{C}{B} \right| = \frac{|K_3G_3A_1F_1|}{|1 + K_3G_3A_1F_1|} = \text{constant} \tag{10-7}$$

which obviously is not the ratio of output to input. It may be noted, however, that if Eq. (10-7) is multiplied by the reciprocal of the feedback transfer function, the frequency-response function is obtained:

$$\frac{\theta_C}{B} = \frac{C}{B} \times \frac{\theta_C}{C} = \frac{1}{A_1F_1}\frac{K_3G_3A_1F_1}{1 + K_3G_3A_1F_1} = \frac{K_3G_3}{1 + K_3G_3A_1F_1} \tag{10-8}$$

This fact is used to advantage in some of the graphical manipulations with feedback compensation.

Thus, if the transfer functions of all components, including the feedback component, are known, the performance of the subordinate loop is readily calculated. Analysis of the feedback loop itself is, therefore, not particularly difficult. Analysis of the entire system is somewhat more complicated, however, and the *design* of a feedback loop to produce specified performance for the whole system is decidedly more difficult, as will be shown.

It must be realized that the entire subordinate loop (set up by the addition of a feedback component) is simply a single series component as far as the remainder of the system is concerned. This is indicated in Fig. 10-2c by enclosing the entire loop in a broken-line box. The transfer function of the box is

$$\frac{\theta_C}{B} = \frac{K_3 G_3}{1 + K_3 G_3 A_1 F_1} \tag{10-5}$$

which is the frequency response of the subordinate loop. The system transfer function is thus changed to

$$\frac{\theta_C}{E} = K_1 G_1 K_2 G_2 \frac{K_3 G_3}{1 + K_3 G_3 A_1 F_1} \tag{10-9}$$

The system transfer function of Eq. (10-9) is no longer a simple equation. The vector at a given frequency can no longer be determined by just multiplying magnitudes and adding angles. Instead, a vector multiplication and a vector addition are required in the denominator alone, and then the denominator must be combined with the numerator. In terms of system analysis (when all transfer functions are known), this simply means additional labor. In terms of designing the feedback network, however, the complications are serious because the feedback transfer function $A_1 F_1$ is not conveniently separated from the rest of the equation, and therefore its contribution to the system transfer function is not readily distinguished.

In designing compensation (either series or feedback), a certain amount of trial and error is usually unavoidable. It is therefore desirable to use methods which clearly show the effects of altering the compensator. There are several methods of accomplishing this for feedback compensation. Two of the methods are:

1. Use the inverse transfer function and polar plots of this function. For example, Eq. (10-9) may be rewritten as

$$\frac{E}{\theta_C} = \frac{1 + K_3 G_3 A_1 F_1}{K_1 G_1 K_2 G_2 K_3 G_3} = K_1^{-1} G_1^{-1} K_2^{-1} G_2^{-1} (K_3^{-1} G_3^{-1} + A_1 F_1) \tag{10-10}$$

where the superscript -1 indicates a reciprocal. Equation (10-10) shows that the feedback transfer function may be plotted as a separate curve which would then be added to $K_3^{-1} G_3^{-1}$ and the result multiplied by the inverse transfer functions of the elements outside the subordinate loop. The manipulation is laborious, but trends may be established and an optimum result obtained.   Note that inverse functions are not adaptable to logarithmic computations because of the addition.

2. In problems of compensation design it is generally true that the transfer function of the uncompensated system is known and the result to be obtained by compensation is known.   Thus, if it is decided to compensate by means of a subordinate loop around a given component, the frequency response of this subordinate loop can be specified.   The design problem is thus reduced to one of designing a feedback component which will produce a given frequency response between two points in the main transmission path.   This problem can be solved by either polar or logarithmic methods.

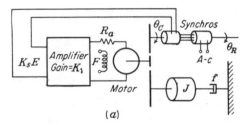

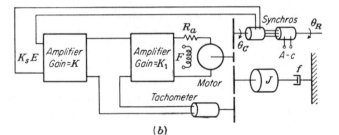

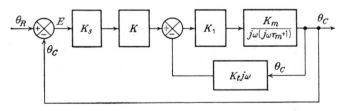

Fig. 10-3. Velocity feedback compensation.   (a) Positioning system—schematic. (b) Addition of tachometer feedback.   (c) Block diagram of compensated system.

10-4. Velocity Feedback Compensation—Type 1 System.

In order to illustrate and expand the concepts presented in the preceding sections, several numerical examples are worked out and explained in detail. Figure 10-3a shows a simplified schematic diagram for a positioning system which is to be operated with an input velocity signal. The steady-state error must be kept small, and so the system gain is high. It is desired to introduce damping (i. e., phase lead) to reduce the peak overshoot, and it is decided to accomplish this by using a tachometer to measure the output velocity and feed back a signal proportional to the velocity. The addition of the tachometer is shown in Fig. 10-3b, and the block diagram is shown in Fig. 10-3c.

The transfer function of the uncompensated system is

$$\frac{\theta_C}{E} = \frac{K_s K_1 K_m}{j\omega(j\omega\tau_m + 1)} \tag{10-11}$$

Assume that the gain is 15 and the time constant of the motor is 0.5. Then

$$\frac{\theta_C}{E} = \frac{15}{j\omega(0.5j\omega + 1)} \tag{10-12}$$

The polar plot of this transfer function is shown in Fig. 10-4 with M circles added. It is seen that the resonance peak is nearly $M = 3.0$ at approximately $\omega = 5.5$. If it is desired to reduce the resonance peak to about $M = 1.3$ without reducing the system gain, then phase-lead compensation may be used. The addition of the tachometric feedback loop is to reduce M_p to the desired value.

Upon addition of the tachometer and isolating amplifier, the system transfer function becomes

$$\frac{\theta_C}{E} = \frac{K_s K \dfrac{K_1 K_m}{j\omega(j\omega\tau_m + 1)}}{1 + \dfrac{K_1 K_m K_t j\omega}{j\omega(j\omega\tau_m + 1)}} = K_s K \frac{K_1 K_m}{j\omega(j\omega\tau_m + 1) + j\omega K_1 K_m K_t} \tag{10-13}$$

This may be manipulated into

$$\frac{\theta_C}{E} = \frac{K_s K K_1 K_m}{j\omega(j\omega\tau_m + 1 + K_1 K_m K_t)} = \frac{\dfrac{K_s K K_1 K_m}{1 + K_1 K_m K_t}}{j\omega\left(j\omega\dfrac{\tau_m}{1 + K_1 K_m K_t} + 1\right)}$$

$$= \frac{K'}{j\omega(j\omega\tau'_m + 1)} \tag{10-14}$$

The result of adding the tachometer is simply a change in the gain and the time constant of the system. Equation (10-14) has the same form as Eq. (10-11) so that special methods need not be used. To illustrate the basic principles, however, the desired result will be obtained using both the direct transfer function and the inverse transfer function.

The quantities which must be determined are the tachometer gain, K_t, which has dimensions of volts per radian per second, and the gain of the additional amplifier, K. The value of K_t may be increased, if necessary, by changing the gear ratio, and may be decreased either by placing a potential divider across the tachometer output, or by a gear change. The amplifier gain is adjustable also, of course. The restrictions on K and K_t are as follows:

1. The values of K and K_t must be such that $K' = 15$.

2. The values of K and K_t must make τ'_m less than τ_m by an amount sufficient to produce the desired phase lead.

There are at least two ways to approach the problem on the polar plane. One is to guess the amount of phase shift required at a specific frequency and evaluate τ'_m from this guess; then evaluate K_t and K from related equations, checking the result by another polar plot. A second method is to rewrite Eq. (10-14) in terms of a new variable, plot the resulting equation for unity gain, and set the gain for the specified M_p by the usual graphical methods. The values of τ'_m, K_t, and K are then determined from the proper equations. Both methods are used here to illustrate the techniques involved.

The first method requires a polar plot of the uncompensated-system transfer function as a starting point. Inspection of Fig. 10-4 shows that a phase lead of about 30° is desirable at $\omega = 5$, where the transfer-function angle is 158°. Subtracting 90° for the $j\omega$ term, the phase angle due to the time-constant term is 68°. Therefore, at $\omega = 5$,

$$\tan^{-1} 2.5 = \tan^{-1} 5\tau_m = 68° \tag{10-15}$$

and it is desired that

$$\tan^{-1} 0.781 = \tan^{-1} 5\tau'_m = 38° \tag{10-16}$$

Thus

$$5\tau'_m = \frac{5\tau_m}{1 + K_1 K_m K_t} = 0.781 \tag{10-17}$$

$$K_t = \frac{5\tau_m - 0.781}{0.781 K_1 K_m} \tag{10-18}$$

In order to evaluate K_t and τ'_m, the values of K_1 and K_m or their product must be known. In general, they would be known, but they have not yet been specified for this problem except implicitly in the over-all gain constant. It has been specified by Eq. (10-12) that

$$K_s K_1 K_m = 15 \tag{10-19}$$

A common value for the synchro sensitivity is 1.0 volt/deg:

$$K_s = 57.3 \text{ volts/rad} \tag{10-20}$$

Substituting in Eq. (10-19),

$$K_1 K_m = \frac{15}{K_s} = 0.262 \tag{10-21}$$

Then, from Eq. (10-18),

$$K_t = 8.4 \tag{10-22}$$

and from Eq. (10-17),

$$\tau'_m - 0.1562 \tag{10-23}$$

The remaining quantity to be determined is K, the gain of the amplifier. This may be found by equating the numerator of Eq. (10-14) to the

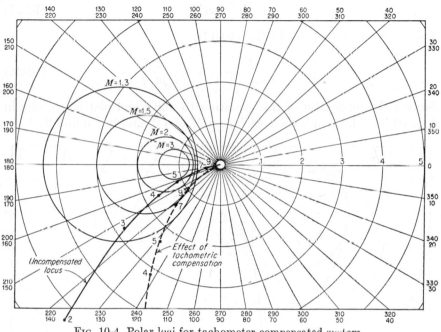

FIG. 10-4. Polar loci for tachometer-compensated system.

desired gain of 15. Thus,

$$\frac{KK_sK_1K_m}{1 + K_1K_mK_t} = 15 \tag{10-24}$$

But

$$K_1K_sK_m = 15 \tag{10-19}$$

thus

$$\frac{K}{1 + K_1K_mK_t} = 1.0 \tag{10-25}$$

from which $K = 3.2$.

The transfer function of the compensated system becomes

$$\frac{\theta_c}{E} = \frac{15}{j\omega(0.1562j\omega + 1)} \tag{10-26}$$

The polar locus for this equation has been added to Fig. 10-4. It may be seen that the desired resonance peak of 1.3 was not achieved. From

the curve, $M_p > 1.5$.   The reason for this error lies in the original estimate (from Fig. 10-4) that a phase lead of 30° at $\omega = 5$ would accomplish the desired result.   To obtain the desired performance, this estimate
would have to be revised, and the calculations repeated.

The second method requires development of the algebra up to Eq.
(10-14).   Then a new variable is defined as

$$u = \omega\tau'_m \tag{10-27}$$

Upon substitution of this in Eq. (10-14),

$$\frac{\theta_c}{E} = \frac{K'}{j\omega(j\omega\tau'_m + 1)} = \frac{K'\tau'_m}{ju(ju + 1)} \tag{10-28}$$

Setting the numerator of this equation to unity and plotting results in
Fig. 10-5.   The gain is then set for an M of 1.3, and it is found that the

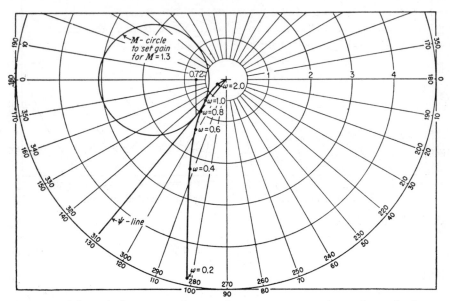

FIG. 10-5. Dimensionless approach to tachometer compensation, using polar locus.

required gain is 1.39.   Therefore, from Eq. (10-28),

$$K'\tau'_m = 1.39 \tag{10-29}$$

But

$$K' = 15$$

therefore

$$\tau'_m = \frac{1.39}{15} = 0.0926 \tag{10-30}$$

From Eq. (10-14),

$$\tau'_m = \frac{\tau_m}{1 + K_1 K_m K_t}$$

Thus

$$0.0926 = \frac{0.5}{1 + 0.262 K_t}$$

and

$$K_t = \frac{(0.5/0.0962) - 1}{0.262} = \frac{5.4 - 1}{0.262} = 16.8 \qquad (10\text{-}31)$$

Finally, from Eq. (10-25),

$$\frac{K}{1 + K_1 K_m K_t} = 1.0$$

$$K = 1 + K_1 K_m K_t = 1 + (0.262)(16.8) = 5.4 \qquad (10\text{-}32)$$

Thus all the parameters are evaluated directly without the need for trial-and-error procedures.

10-5. Design of Compensation on the Inverse Polar Plot. The inverse transfer function of the system may be used instead of the direct transfer function. To obtain the inverse transfer function, Eq. (10-13) is inverted, giving

$$\frac{E}{\theta_C} = \frac{j\omega(j\omega\tau_m + 1)}{KK_s K_1 K_m} + \frac{j\omega K_t}{KK_s} \qquad (10\text{-}33)$$

Inspection of Eq. (10-33) shows that the inverse transfer function of the compensated system is the vector sum of two terms. The first term is the reciprocal of the uncompensated transfer function [Eq. (10-11)] divided by the gain of the isolating amplifier. The second term is due to the tachometer, but is divided by the gain of the isolating amplifier and the synchro sensitivity. It is seen that both terms are divided by KK_s, and inspection of Fig. 10-3c shows that these terms are the transfer functions of the elements outside the compensation loop.

In this case, the system gain is to be maintained at 15; this is accomplished by adjusting K, the gain of the isolating amplifier. It is therefore desirable to arrange the system equation so that K appears as a factor. This is shown in Eq. (10-34):

$$\frac{E}{\theta_C} = \frac{1}{K} \left[\frac{j\omega(j\omega\tau_m + 1)}{K_s K_1 K_m} + \frac{j\omega K_t}{K_s} \right] \qquad (10\text{-}34)$$

Inserting the known numerical values, this becomes

$$\frac{E}{\theta_C} = \frac{1}{K} [0.0667 j\omega(0.5 j\omega + 1) + 0.0175 j\omega K_t] \qquad (10\text{-}35)$$

There are two independent adjustments in Eq. (10-34), K and K_t. These are to be set so that the system gain is 15 and the resonance peak is 1.3.   The adjustment K_t is part of a frequency dependent term, and thus will reshape the locus, while K merely adjusts the gain.   It is true that K_t also affects the gain, but this is a secondary effect.   The general procedure used to obtain the desired results must be trial and error. The locus is reshaped by arbitrarily selecting a value for K_t.   The gain is set by graphical methods to give $M_p = 1.3$, and the resulting value is checked with the equation to see if the system gain of 15 obtains.   This is repeated until the problem is solved, or at least until a system gain of more than 15 is obtained.

The procedure used in this case is detailed below:

1. Plot the first frequency dependent term of Eq. (10-35), i. e., the term representing the uncompensated system.

2. Add an inverse M circle for $M = 1.3$, and draw the ψ line.

3. By inspection of the plot, estimate the desired effect of the tachometer term at some value of ω.   Use this estimate to select a tentative value for K_t.

4. Plot the tachometer term.

5. Add the two terms vectorially.

6. Use the ψ line for $M = 1.3$, and construct an inverse M circle to set the gain.

7. Read off the value of K from the plot.

8. Use Eq. (10-14) for the system gain, and the values of K and K_t as determined, to see if the gain requirement of 15 has been satisfied.

9. If the result is not satisfactory, the procedure must be repeated, starting with a new value for K_t.

10-6. Design of Compensation on the Inverse Polar Plot (Continued). Returning to the problem of designing the compensation, the procedure of Sec. 10-5 is carried out:

1. The plot of the first term in Eq. (10-35) is shown in Fig. 10-6.

2. An M^{-1} circle for $M = 1.3$ has been added to Fig. 10-6, as has the ψ line.

3. Inspection of the inverse locus of the uncompensated system in Fig. 10-6 indicates that the response peak is considerably greater than 1.3.   The locus of the tachometer term is a straight line along the positive 90° axis, so that when added to the uncompensated locus it tends to move the locus out of the M circle.   This is in the desired direction, i. e., the nature of the tachometer effect is what is wanted, but the required magnitude of such a shift must be estimated.

If the magnitude of the compensator vector is selected so as just to move the locus out of the M circle, it would not be possible to increase the gain without exceeding $M_p = 1.3$.   This would not be satisfactory, because the addition of the compensation vector increases the length of each KG^{-1} vector, which corresponds to a decrease in system gain.   Thus a system gain of 15 would not be attained. From the gain-adjustment procedure previously discussed, it is seen that the center of the M^{-1} circle must be moved to the left to increase the gain. Thus the locus must be raised considerably by the compensation. As a first estimate, the point

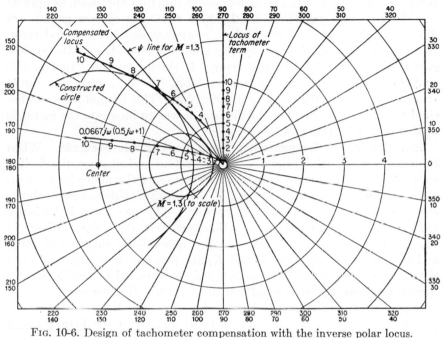

FIG. 10-6. Design of tachometer compensation with the inverse polar locus.

$\omega = 6$ should be moved above the ψ line, and an assumed length for the compensation vector is 1.2 at $\omega = 6$. Thus,

$$0.0175\omega K_t = 0.1050K_t = 1.2$$

$$K_t = \frac{1.2}{0.105} = 11.45$$

and the tachometer term in Eq. (10-35) becomes $0.2j\omega$.

4. The tachometer term is plotted on Fig. 10-6.
5. The compensated locus is shown on Fig. 10-6.
6. The constructed M^{-1} circle is shown on Fig. 10-6.
7. The center of the constructed circle is at 3.0, and therefore $K = 3.0$.
8. From Eq. (10-14), the system gain is

$$K' = \frac{KK_sK_1K_m}{1 + K_1K_mK_t}$$

where $K_sK_1K_m = 15$ and $K_1K_m = 0.262$. Substituting the numerical values,

$$K' = 11.25$$

Thus the desired system gain of 15 has not been attained, and another trial must be made. A larger value of K_t should be selected. Completion of the problem is left to the student.

One basic difference should be noted between the direct-transfer-function approach and the inverse-transfer-function approach, as applied to this particular problem. In the first case, the system gain is set directly, and the desired value of M is approached by trial and error. In the second case, M is set by the gain adjustment, and the system gain is approached by trial and error. It should be noted that in this simple case the definition of a new variable, $u = \omega \tau_m$, leads to a direct solution from either the direct or inverse plot. This has not been emphasized because the purpose of the discussion was to illustrate the methods needed on the inverse plot.

10-7. Design of Compensation Using Logarithmic Methods. When feedback compensation is used to adjust system performance, the decibel vs. phase-angle plot of the *loop transfer function* of the minor loop is usually a convenient starting place, and it will be used to design the tachometer loop of the system under discussion. The procedure is basically trial and error, but it has some advantage over the polar methods in that the performance of the minor loop is more thoroughly investigated, and the effects of adjusting K and K_t are perhaps more apparent. In the following procedure the steps outlined are intended as a guide; in any specific problem, deviations and additions are usually necessary.

In general, the procedure to be used is:

1. Consider only the subordinate loop, and write the loop transfer function.

2. Plot the loop transfer function and a number of M and N contours on decibel vs. phase-angle coordinates.

3. Adjust the gain of the loop transfer function, usually to some preselected value of M.

4. From the intersections of the locus with the M and N contours, determine the loop function $KGAF/(1 + KGAF)$. Plot this on decibel vs. log ω coordinates.

5. Obtain the frequency-response curve of the minor loop by multiplying the curve of step 4 by $1/AF$, using the decibel vs. log ω plot.

6. Combine the curve obtained in step 5 with the transfer-function curves of the components external to the minor loop. Plot the result on the decibel vs. phase-angle plot.

7. Set the system gain to obtain some selected M_p.

8. Check the steady-state performance.

In applying the above procedure, certain of the manipulations are peculiar to the problem. Where this is so, an effort is made to point out the reason.

1. From Fig. 10-3a, the loop transfer function of the minor loop is

$$KGAF = \frac{K_1 K_m K_t j\omega}{j\omega(j\omega\tau_m + 1)} = \frac{K_1 K_m K_t}{j\omega\tau_m + 1} = \frac{K_L}{j\omega\tau_m + 1} \qquad (10\text{-}36)$$

Since the gain is to be set in a later step, it is convenient to let $K_L = 1.0$. Then

$$KGAF = \frac{1}{j\omega\tau_m + 1} \qquad (10\text{-}37)$$

2. The locus of Eq. (10-37) is plotted on Fig. 10-7. It should be noted that the M values are expressed in decibels, i. e., as the log of the magni-

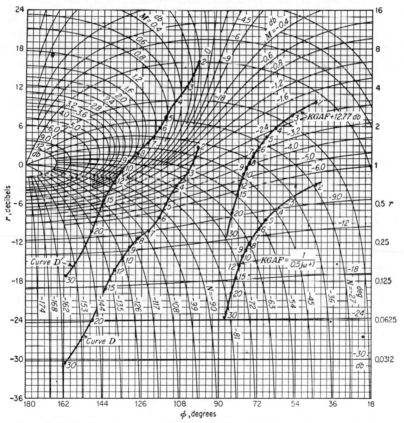

Fig. 10-7. Tachometer compensation on the decibel vs. phase-angle plot.

tude of θ_C/θ_R instead of the ratio ($M = 1.3$, etc.). This is a more convenient notation because the values of the intercepts with the contours are to be plotted as logarithmic curves in a later step.

3. In this step the main problem is to select the value of M to which the gain is to be set. For this system the phase angle of the loop transfer

function is never more negative than $-90°$, and thus can never intersect any M contour as great as or greater than $M = 0$ db. This is not a common situation. The main purpose of selecting a value for M for the minor loop is to prevent excessive resonances which usually are possible if the minor-loop gain is high. Since such resonances are not possible in this case, there is no point in selecting a value for M, and some other criterion must be determined and used to set the gain of the subordinate loop.

In general, setting the minor-loop gain sets the product KA of the main and feedback component gains, but does not set the individual gains K and A. It is then theoretically possible to use any arbitrary values for K and A, provided that their product is an acceptable gain and provided also that when the loop is closed the resulting frequency response is acceptable. Practically, there may be other limitations on the gain constants; there may be a maximum or a minimum possible gain for a given component; or the gain of a specific component may be fixed either by its physical nature or by some performance requirement of the system or process.

In this problem the gain K has two factors, K_1 and K_m. Of these, K_m is physically not readily variable; K_1 could be varied, but since it has not been varied in the preceding sections it will be kept constant here, and the product K_1K_m will be defined as in Eq. (10-21):

$$K_1K_m = 0.262 \qquad (10\text{-}21)$$

Thus, in this problem, setting the minor-loop gain is equivalent to selecting the gain of the feedback component, i. e., to selecting the value of K_t. Ultimately, the selection of K_t is a guess, but the guess may be guided by considering the over-all problem.

The purpose of the tachometric feedback is to provide damping, i. e., to permit high system gain without excessive overshoot. Since the uncompensated system is badly underdamped (see Fig. 10-4), a fairly large value of K_t will probably be needed; but the term "large" does not indicate the order of magnitude. If the effectiveness of the tachometer is investigated with the help of the equations, a preliminary choice for K_t may be made. The loop transfer function is given in Eq. (10-36), and the ratio of the feedback signal to the input of the minor loop is

$$\frac{KGAF}{1 + KGAF} = \frac{K_1K_mK_t}{j\omega\tau_m + 1 + K_1K_mK_t} \qquad (10\text{-}38)$$

If $K_t \gg 1.0$, so that $K_1K_mK_t \gg |j\omega\tau_m + 1|$, then Eq. (10-38) reduces to

$$\frac{KGAF}{1 + KGAF} = 1.0 \qquad (10\text{-}39)$$

The minor-loop frequency response is then

$$\frac{KG}{1 + KGAF} = \frac{1}{AF} \times \frac{KG}{1 + KGAF} = \frac{1}{j\omega K_t} \qquad (10\text{-}40)$$

and the system transfer function is

$$K_s G_s = \frac{KK_s}{j\omega K_t} = \frac{K_x}{j\omega} \qquad (10\text{-}41)$$

where $K_x = KK_s/K_t$.

Equation (10-41) represents a system with a constant phase angle of $-90°$. Therefore, regardless of the value of K_x, the phase margin would be 90°, and the system would always be overdamped. Thus it is seen that too high a value for K_t is possible.

If K_t is not made very large, then all terms in Eq. (10-38) must be retained, and the frequency-response function of the minor loop becomes

$$\frac{KG}{1 + KGAF} = \frac{1}{j\omega K_t} \times \frac{K_1 K_m K_t}{j\omega\tau_m + 1 + K_1 K_m K_t} = \frac{K_1 K_m}{j\omega(j\omega\tau_m + 1 + K_1 K_m K_t)} \qquad (10\text{-}42)$$

The transfer function of the system is

$$K_s G_s = \frac{KK_s K_1 K_m}{j\omega(j\omega\tau_m + 1 + K_1 K_m K_t)} \qquad (10\text{-}43)$$

This equation, of course, is the same as Eq. (10-13), but a somewhat different analysis is applied here. Note that the phase lag of the system transfer function may be controlled (at one frequency) by the selection of K_t. Referring again to Fig. 10-4 for the uncompensated locus, it is seen that the resonant frequency, uncompensated, is about $\omega = 5.0$. Since phase-lead compensation increases the resonant frequency, $\omega = 9$ is arbitrarily selected as a desirable value to use in setting the system phase angle. Also, since $M = 1.3$ is desired, the system phase angle at $\omega = 9$ should be approximately $-130°$, and therefore at $\omega = 9$,

$$\underline{/j\omega\tau_m + 1 + K_1 K_m K_t} = 40° \qquad (10\text{-}44)$$

Inserting numerical values,

$$\tan 40° = \frac{\omega\tau_m}{1 + K_1 K_m K_t} = 0.839 = \frac{4.5}{1 + 0.262 K_t}$$

$$K_t = 16.65$$

In Fig. 10-7, the locus $KGAF$ was plotted for a gain constant

$$K_1 K_m K_t = 1.0$$

since it was known that gain adjustment would be required. Having determined a value of $K_t = 16.65$, the gain for $KGAF$ becomes

$$K_1 K_m K_t = (0.262)(16.65) = 4.35$$

and

$$20 \log_{10} 4.35 = 12.77 \text{ db}$$

Thus the $KGAF$ locus in Fig. 10-7 must be raised through 12.77 db, as shown.

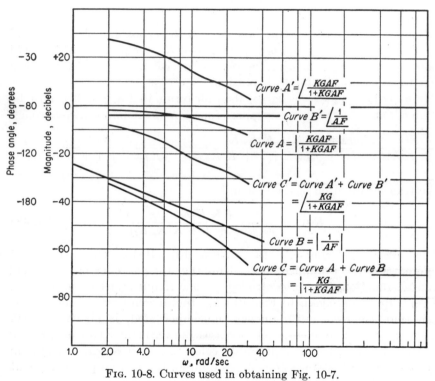

FIG. 10-8. Curves used in obtaining Fig. 10-7.

4. The locus of the intersections of the $KGAF + 12.77$ db curve with the M and N contours in Fig. 10-7 is shown in curves A and A' in Fig. 10-8.

5. The reciprocal of the feedback transfer function is

$$\frac{1}{AF} = \frac{1}{j\omega K_t} = \frac{1}{16.65 j\omega} \tag{10-45}$$

On decibel vs. log ω coordinates, Eq. (10-45) is a straight line of -6 db/octave slope, going through 0 db at $\omega = 1/16.65 = 0.06$. The phase angle is constant at $-90°$. These curves are shown as B and B' in Fig. 10-8. Curves A and B are added to get curve C, and A' and B' are added to get C'.

6. In this case the only components external to the minor loop are the

isolating amplifier and the synchros. K_s is known to be 57.3, and K is to be determined. Thus the transfer-function curves of these components need not be plotted. Curve C in Fig. 10-8 can be combined with KK_s simply by adding some number of decibels. The values for curves C and C' are given in Table 10-1. A column, D, has been added to include

TABLE 10-1

ω	C, db	C', deg	D, db
2	-32.5	-100	2.66
3	-36.5	-105	1.34
4	-39.5	-110	-3.34
5	-41.5	-115	-6.34
6	-43.5	-118	-8.34
7	-45.5	-123	-10.34
8	-46.5	-128	-11.34
9	-48.0	-132	-12.84
10	-49.5	-135	-14.34
12	-51.5	-139	-16.34
15	-54.5	-143	-19.34
20	-59	-149	-23.84
30	-66	-161	-30.84

the effect of K_s which is an addition of 35.16 db. The effect of K is to be determined later by gain adjustment. The resulting curve is plotted in Fig. 10-7 and is labeled D.

7. The gain is adjusted by moving D vertically upward and parallel to itself. Since the desired resonance peak is at $M = 1.3$, the new location is made tangent to the $M = 2$ db contour, because this corresponds to $M = 1.26$. This is shown in Fig. 10-7 also, and it is seen that the gain adjustment required was $+13.5$ db. Note that $\omega_r = 9$.

8. Curve D' of Fig. 10-7 is replotted on decibel vs. log ω coordinates, as in Fig. 10-9, to check the system gain. Asymptotes are constructed, and the -6 db/octave asymptote extrapolates to intercept the 0-db axis at $\omega = 13.2$, which means that the system gain is 13.2, and the required gain of 15 has not been obtained.

10-8. Summary of Tachometric-feedback Illustration. In the preceding sections the effect of a tachometric feedback loop was investigated. Attempts were made to design the feedback, i. e., select the gain constant of the feedback path, K_t, so that a specified M_p and a specified system gain could be obtained simultaneously. Various methods were used: polar plots of the direct transfer function, polar plots of the inverse

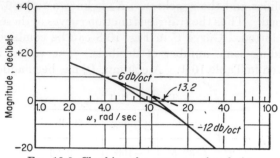

FIG. 10-9. Checking the compensation design.

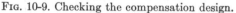

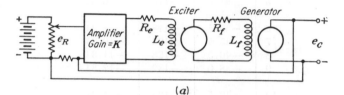

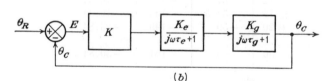

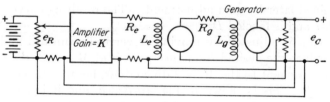

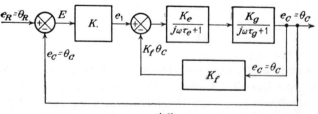

FIG. 10-10. Schematic and block diagrams for uncompensated and compensated voltage-regulated generator. (*a*) Generator regulated by a feedback loop. (*b*) Block diagram. (*c*) Compensation by direct feedback. (*d*) Block diagram.

transfer function, and logarithmic plots. The methods involved trial-and-error procedures and graphical manipulations. Most of the computed illustrations did not obtain the desired result, but each result indicated clearly what should be done in making a second trial.

10-9. Compensation of a Voltage-regulated Generator by Direct Feedback. Figure 10-10a shows the schematic diagram of a generator which is regulated by a feedback loop. The block diagram for the system is

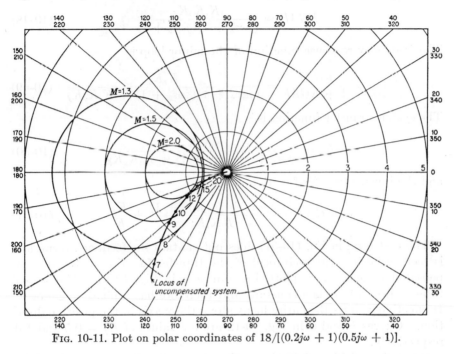

FIG. 10-11. Plot on polar coordinates of $18/[(0.2j\omega + 1)(0.5j\omega + 1)]$.

shown in Fig. 10-10b, and from this diagram the transfer function of the system is

$$\frac{\theta_C}{E} = \frac{e_o}{e_i - e_o} = \frac{KK_eK_g}{(j\omega\tau_e + 1)(j\omega\tau_g + 1)} \qquad (10\text{-}46)$$

Assuming that $K = 1.0$, $K_e = 30$, $K_g = 0.6$, $\tau_e = 0.2$, and $\tau_g = 0.5$, this becomes

$$\frac{\theta_C}{E} = \frac{e_o}{e_i - e_o} = \frac{18}{(0.2j\omega + 1)(0.5j\omega + 1)} \qquad (10\text{-}47)$$

A polar plot of Eq. (10-47) is shown in Fig. 10-11 with M circles added.

Inspection of Fig. 10-11 shows that the system is appreciably underdamped. The resonance peak is about $M_p = 2.0$. In the following section it will be shown that the resonance peak can be decreased by means of a minor feedback loop. No attempt is made to set and meet specifications. The illustration involves analysis only, i. e., the purpose is to show what the effect of the minor loop is, and how the effect may be computed from the inverse polar plot.

10-10. Analysis of a Compensated System with Inverse Polar Loci. If a minor feedback loop is added to the system, as shown in Fig. 10-10c, the block diagram is altered, as shown in Fig. 10-10d. The loop transfer function for the minor loop is

$$KGAF = \frac{K_e K_g K_f}{(j\omega\tau_e + 1)(j\omega\tau_g + 1)} \tag{10-48}$$

The frequency-response function of the minor loop is

$$\frac{1}{AF} \times \frac{KGAF}{1 + KGAF} = \frac{K_e K_g}{(j\omega\tau_e + 1)(j\omega\tau_g + 1) + K_e K_g K_f} \tag{10-49}$$

The system transfer function is

$$K_s G_s = \frac{KK_e K_g}{(j\omega\tau_e + 1)(j\omega\tau_g + 1) + K_e K_g K_f} \tag{10-50}$$

and the inverse transfer function is

$$(K_s G_s)^{-1} = \frac{(j\omega\tau_e + 1)(j\omega\tau_g + 1)}{KK_e K_g} + \frac{K_f}{K} \tag{10-51}$$

The first term in Eq. (10-51) does not contain the feedback term, and is seen to be just the reciprocal of the transfer function of the uncompensated system. It is plotted as curve A in Fig. 10-12. The second term in Eq. (10-51) is a constant and therefore has a phase angle of $0°$. It effectively shifts the entire locus along the x axis in the positive direction. Curves B and C in Fig. 10-12 are for values of $K_f = 0.5$ and 1.0, respectively.

Inspection of Fig. 10-12 shows that increasing the magnitude of the feedback, K_f, decreases the resonance peak and increases the resonant frequency. Thus the use of feedback definitely adjusts the transient performance of the system. Figure 10-12 does not indicate the effect of the compensation on the steady-state performance. This may be determined by using Eq. (10-50) and letting $j\omega$ approach zero; then for full feedback ($K_f = 1.0$),

$$K_s G_s(j\omega \to 0) = \frac{KK_e K_g}{1 + K_e K_g K_f} = \frac{18}{1 + 18} = 0.947$$

Thus the use of full feedback decreases the system gain considerably and makes steady-state errors large.

There are two reasons why the steady-state performance is so adversely affected by the feedback. The first reason is that essentially all the gain is enclosed by the minor loop. The second is that the minor loop feeds back the low frequencies as well as the high, and actually only high-frequency feedback is needed to control the transient performance. If more of the gain is external to the minor loop, the feedback is less effective in controlling the transient performance, but it does not affect the steady-state performance as adversely. This may be seen qualitatively from Eq. (10-51) and Fig. 10-12. Assume that the amplifier gain, K, is doubled, and the exciter gain, K_e, is halved. This leaves the uncompensated system gain the same, and curve A in Fig. 10-12 is unchanged;

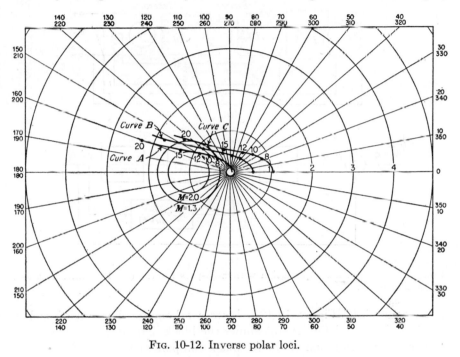

Fig. 10-12. Inverse polar loci.

however, for full feedback, the effect of the compensation is halved [see Eq. (10-51)] so that curve B in Fig. 10-12 corresponds to maximum compensation, rather than curve C, and it is readily seen that the transient performance is not as greatly improved. The steady-state performance is slightly better, however.

$$K_sG_s(j\omega \to 0) = \frac{KK_eK_g}{1 + K_eK_gK_f} = \frac{18}{1 + 9} = 1.8$$

The improvement in the steady-state performance is not great, and good transient compensation with better steady-state performance can be obtained by inserting a filter network in the feedback path.

It would be possible to repeat the studies using logarithmic coordinates. In this case, however, the inverse polar loci give a very clear picture of the effect of the compensation, and so logarithmic methods will not be used.

10-11. Feedback Compensation Using a High-pass Filter. Since the use of direct feedback impairs the steady-state performance of the voltage regulator, and since at least a portion of the difficulty lies in the fact that the direct-feedback connection passes low frequencies, the logical procedure is to place a high-pass filter in the feedback path to block the

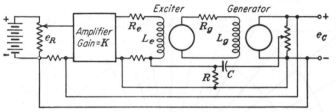

(a)

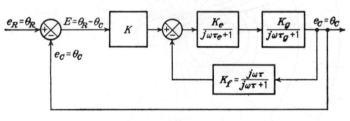

(b)

FIG. 10-13. Feedback compensation with high-pass filter. (a) Schematic diagram. (b) Block diagram.

low frequencies. Figure 10-13a shows a schematic diagram of such a feedback loop, and Fig. 10-13b shows the block diagram.

The transfer function of the feedback component is

$$AF = K_f \frac{j\omega\tau}{1 + j\omega\tau} \tag{10-52}$$

where K_f is the fraction of the output voltage fed back, and $\tau = RC$. The loop transfer function is

$$KGAF = \frac{K_e K_g K_f j\omega\tau}{(j\omega\tau_e + 1)(j\omega\tau_g + 1)(j\omega\tau + 1)} \tag{10-53}$$

The frequency-response function of the minor loop is

$$\frac{1}{AF} \times \frac{KGAF}{1 + KGAF} = \frac{K_e K_g(j\omega\tau + 1)}{(j\omega\tau_e + 1)(j\omega\tau_g + 1)(j\omega\tau + 1) + K_e K_g K_f j\omega\tau} \tag{10-54}$$

The system transfer function is

$$K_s G_s = \frac{KK_eK_g(j\omega\tau + 1)}{(j\omega\tau_e + 1)(j\omega\tau_g + 1)(j\omega\tau + 1) + K_eK_gK_f j\omega\tau} \quad (10\text{-}55)$$

and the inverse transfer function is

$$(K_s G_s)^{-1} = \frac{(j\omega\tau_e + 1)(j\omega\tau_g + 1)}{KK_eK_g} + \frac{K_f j\omega\tau}{K(j\omega\tau + 1)} \quad (10\text{-}56)$$

It may be seen that the inverse transfer function of Eq. (10-56) consists of two additive terms. The first term is the inverse transfer function of the uncompensated system, and the second term is the transfer function of the feedback path divided by the gain constant of the amplifier which is external to the minor loop. Thus the effect of the compensator is separated from the equation of the uncompensated system, and it is possible to study the effect of the compensation.

10-12. Analysis of the Effect of the Feedback Filter with Inverse Polar Loci. To simplify the computations, and to permit comparisons with preceding sections, the constants of the uncompensated system are assumed to be the same as in Eq. (10-47). If full feedback is used $(K_f = 1.0)$, then Eq. (10-56) becomes

$$(K_s G_s)^{-1} = \frac{(0.2j\omega + 1)(0.5j\omega + 1)}{18} + \frac{j\omega\tau}{j\omega\tau + 1} \quad (10\text{-}57)$$

The inverse polar curve of the first term in Eq. (10-57) is therefore the same as curve A in Fig. 10-12, and is reproduced as curve A in Fig. 10-14.

The choice of a value of τ is a trial-and-error procedure based on inspection of the uncompensated-system locus. It may also be desirable to use less than full feedback. To select a value for τ, it should first be noted that the polar locus of the compensator is a semicircle in the first quadrant, with its center on the positive real axis. The low-frequency end of the locus is at the origin, and at $\omega = \infty$ the locus intercepts the positive real axis at a value depending on the magnitude of the gain constant K_f/K. The value of τ determines the location of the individual frequency points on this locus. The compensation vector at any frequency is thus located in the first quadrant, and when added to the uncompensated locus will effectively rotate the inverse locus in a clockwise direction. This moves the compensated locus out of the region of high values of M, decreasing the resonance peak.

Since it is desired to move the entire locus out of the $M = 1.3$ circle, the compensation vector must have appreciable length at the lowest frequency which must be shifted. At higher frequencies the length of the compensation vector increases, but its phase angle decreases, and it is necessary to select τ so that sufficient displacement of the locus is obtained at high frequencies also.   In this illustration three values of τ are selected:

$$\tau = \tfrac{1}{10} = 0.1 \qquad \tau = \tfrac{1}{12} = 0.0832 \qquad \tau = \tfrac{1}{15} = 0.0665$$

These values correspond to three of the frequencies which lie within the $M = 1.3$ circle.

Curve B in Fig. 10-14 is a plot of the compensator locus for $\tau = 0.1$. Plots for the other values of τ could not be added because they fall identically on curve B but with a different frequency distribution.   Curve C

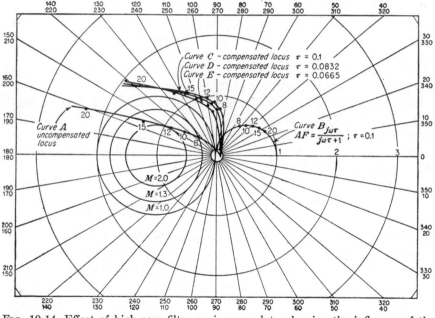

FIG. 10-14. Effect of high-pass filter on inverse plots, showing the influence of the time constant.

shows the compensated locus for $\tau = 0.1$, and curves D and E show the resulting loci for $\tau = 0.0832$ and $\tau = 0.0665$, respectively.

Inspection of these curves shows that any of the selected τs will damp the system so that the resonance peak is less than 1.3; in fact, it is seen that M is less than 1.0.   It might be possible to obtain a resonance peak of 1.3 by selecting a still smaller time constant, but it seems obvious that the same effect can be obtained by feeding back a smaller signal.   This is investigated in Fig. 10-15, where three values of K_f are used and τ is kept constant at $\tau = 0.0665$.

The curves of Fig. 10-15 show that a reduction in the magnitude of the feedback signal is quite effective in producing the desired M_p of 1.3. A feedback gain of $K_f = 0.5$ together with the time constant $\tau = 0.0665$

gives very nearly the desired result. Further changes in K_f and τ would permit closer adjustment and some variation in the resonant frequency.

10-13. Summary of Polar-loci Studies. It has been shown in Secs. 10-8 through 10-12 that the performance of a servomechanism may be controlled by feeding back a signal from the output to some point in the main amplification channel. If direct feedback is used, the only variable is the magnitude of the signal fed back. Polar plots of the inverse transfer function permit ready interpretation of the effects of such feedback.

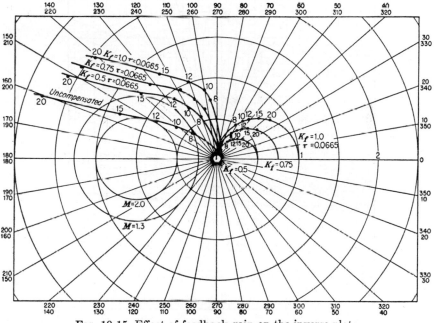

FIG. 10-15. Effect of feedback gain on the inverse plots.

Filter networks may be placed in the feedback path to obtain better system performance. The use of a high-pass filter has been investigated. Polar plots of the inverse transfer functions clearly show the effects of such a filter, and the system is readily adjusted to the desired performance.

10-14. Decibel vs. Phase-angle Coordinates Used in Feedback Compensation. When feedback compensation is used, and also when a filter is placed in the feedback path, the feedback gain and the time constants of the filter may be determined by the use of a decibel vs. phase-angle plot with M and N contours. The selection of the signal to be fed back, the location at which it is to be fed into the main loop, and the type of filter to be used are determined by preliminary studies or by physical reasoning and experience. In the following paragraphs, the system of

Fig. 10-13 is studied with a decibel vs. phase-angle plot rather than the inverse polar plot so that the student may see the manipulations involved.

1. The equation of the subordinate loop of Fig. 10-13 is

$$KGAF = \frac{K_e K_g K_f j\omega\tau}{(j\omega\tau_e + 1)(j\omega\tau_g + 1)(j\omega\tau + 1)} \qquad (10\text{-}58)$$

2. In order to plot the loop-transfer-function curve, the gain constant $K_e K_g K_f$ is arbitrarily set at 18, which is the value of $K_e K_g$, so that

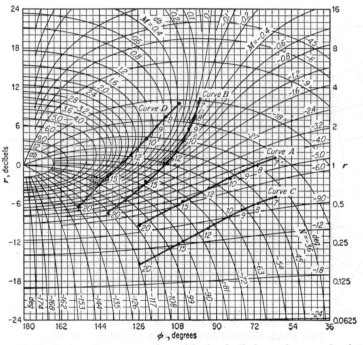

Fig. 10-16. Design of compensation with the decibel vs. phase-angle plot.

$K_f = 1.0$. It is necessary to select a value for the time constant τ (or several values may be used). This selection is essentially a guess which is guided by experience and by the known characteristics of the uncompensated system and the compensator. In this illustration a value $\tau = 0.06$ is chosen. The equation to be plotted is

$$KGAF = \frac{1.08 j\omega}{(0.2 j\omega + 1)(0.5 j\omega + 1)(0.06 j\omega + 1)} \qquad (10\text{-}59)$$

The decibel vs. phase-angle plot is shown in Fig. 10-16.

3. The intercepts of the loop-transfer-function locus with the M and N contours are plotted on decibel vs. log ω coordinates in Fig. 10-17.

4. The magnitude and phase curves for the inverse transfer function of the feedback component ($1/AF$) are added to Fig. 10-17.

5. The curves of step 3 and step 4 are added to give the curve for the closed-loop frequency response which is

$$\frac{1}{AF} \times \frac{KGAF}{1 + KGAF}$$

6. The curve of step 5 is replotted on the decibel vs. phase-angle plot of Fig. 10-16 as curve B. No gain adjustment or other modification is needed in this case, since the only component external to the minor loop is the amplifier with gain $K = 1.0$.

The transfer-function curve of the system (in Fig. 10-16) is seen to be entirely outside the $M = 0$ db contour for the frequencies plotted. This

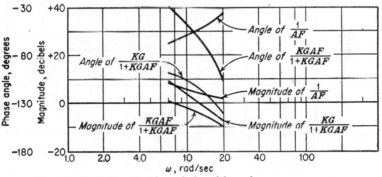

FIG. 10-17. Determination of closed-loop frequency response.

result is comparable to the curves in Fig. 10-13, which is to be expected since the systems are nearly identical.

Thus far the logarithmic methods have been used merely to duplicate the results obtained by one of the inverse polar curves. Having obtained one set of curves, however, it is now possible to analyze the effects of the feedback gain and the time constant. This is done in the following sections.

10-15. Effect of Varying the Feedback Gain. To analyze the effect of varying the feedback-gain constant, the decibel vs. log ω curves of Fig 10-17 are most convenient. It may be shown qualitatively that decreasing the feedback gain decreases the system phase margin and thus increases M_p and the speed of response. (Quantitative computations involve trial and error, of course.)

That a decrease in the feedback gain decreases the phase margin may be seen from the following reasoning:

1. The system magnitude curve is obtained on Fig. 10-17 by adding the decibel curves for $1/AF$ and $KGAF/(1 + KGAF)$. If the feedback

gain is decreased, the magnitude of $1/AF$ is increased; if the gain is halved, the magnitude of $1/AF$ is raised by 6 db.   If the term $KGAF/(1 + KGAF)$ is not affected by this change, the system magnitude curve will be raised by 6 db, moving the gain crossover to a higher frequency and certainly decreasing the phase margin.

2. It is obvious that decreasing the feedback gain also affects the $KGAF/(1 + KGAF)$ term.   However, both the numerator and the denominator are changed, and the net result is that the curve is lowered, but by a smaller amount than the $1/AF$ term is raised.   Thus the gain crossover is moved to a higher frequency.

3. The phase angle of the system is also affected by the feedback-gain change.   There is no change in the phase of the $1/AF$ term, but the

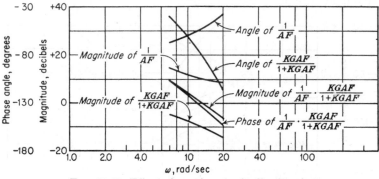

Fig. 10-18. Effect of varying the feedback gain.

phase of the $KGAF/(1 + KGAF)$ term is made more negative at all frequencies.   Thus the system phase-angle curve is made more negative, and this also decreases the phase margin.

To illustrate the effect, the feedback gain is reduced to $K_f = 0.5$ and the curves are recomputed.   The loop-transfer-function curve is lowered by 6 db.   This is shown by curve C in Fig. 10-16.   The intersections of curve C with the M and N contours are plotted as magnitude and phase curves in Fig. 10-18.   The phase and magnitude curves for the feedback term are then plotted, and the two sets of curves are added.   It is seen that the phase margin at the gain crossover has been reduced to about 48°.

The system-transfer-function curve has been replotted on Fig. 10-16 as curve D, using the data of Fig. 10-18.   It is seen that the resonance peak is now $M = 2.4$ db or $M = 1.35$.   The resonant frequency is approximately $\omega = 14$.   These results justify the statement that in this case decreasing the feedback gain increases M_p and the speed of response.

10-16. Effect of Varying the Feedback Time Constant.   Referring to the decibel vs. log ω plot of Fig. 10-18, changing the feedback time constant affects both the magnitude and the phase-angle curves.   If τ is increased, the curve for the phase of $1/AF$ is effectively moved parallel to itself to higher frequencies. The magnitude curve for $1/AF$ is lowered. Both of these effects tend to increase the phase margin of the system and decrease M_p. The magnitude and the phase curves for $KGAF/(1 + KGAF)$ are also affected, and the changes in these curves tend to counteract the changes in the $1/AF$ curves.

If the feedback time constant is decreased, the phase curve for $1/AF$ is shifted to lower frequencies. The magnitude of $1/AF$ is raised. This tends to decrease the phase margin and increase M_p. Again there are changes in the $KGAF/(1 + KGAF)$ locus which tend to counterbalance these effects. Verification of these statements is left to the student.

10-17. Summary. It has been shown that the transient and steady-state performances of servomechanisms may be controlled by minor feedback loops. The basic principle is the same as for series compensation, i. e., reshaping the transfer-function locus over a selected band of frequencies. The tools best suited to the calculation of feedback compensation are the inverse polar loci and the use of M and N contours on the decibel vs. phase-angle plot in conjunction with the decibel vs. log ω and phase-angle vs. log ω plots.

Several simple illustrations of feedback compensation have been worked out numerically. These illustrations were not intended to be practical cases, but were inserted to show the manipulations involved. The principles developed may be readily extended to the analysis and design of more complex systems.

PROBLEMS

10-1. Tachometer feedback is to be added to the system of Prob. 3-12, as shown in Fig. 10P-1.

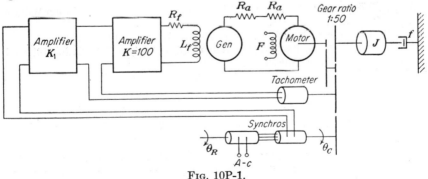

Fig. 10P-1.

a. Draw the block diagram, and derive the algebraic transfer function of the system.

b. From Prob. 3-12, insert the known parameter values.

c. Assuming $K_1 = 1$ and $K_t = 0.01$ volt/rpm, plot the polar-transfer-function locus.

10-2. Using the equation obtained in Prob. 10-1b, perform an inverse-polar-locus study and determine values for K_1 and K_t which permit an M_p of 1.5. Explain how the value of K_t may be obtained by physical adjustment of the system.

10-3. For the system of Prob. 10-1, determine values for K_1 and K_t which permit an M_p of 1.5. Use logarithmic methods.

10-4. A servomechanism has a block diagram and transfer functions as shown in Fig. 10P-2.

a. What are the loop transfer functions of the three loops?

b. Discuss the effects of varying K and K_1.

10-5. For the system of Fig. 10P-2, make an inverse-polar-locus study of the effect of variations in K on the transfer function across the innermost loop.

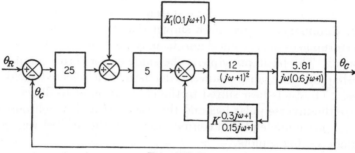

Fig. 10P-2.

10-6. Repeat Prob. 10-5, using logarithmic methods.

10-7. For the system of Fig. 10P-2, select two values of K (use the results of Prob. 10-5 or 10-6 if worked, otherwise select arbitrarily) and make an inverse-polar-locus study of the effect of varying K_1 on the system transfer function. Draw conclusions if possible.

10-8. Repeat Prob. 10-7, using logarithmic methods.

REFERENCES

BROWN, G. S., and D. P. CAMPBELL, "Principles of Servomechanisms," John Wiley & Sons, Inc., New York, 1948.

MARCY, H. T., Parallel Circuits in Servomechanisms, *Trans. AIEE*, 1946.

THALER, G. J., and R. G. BROWN, "Servomechanism Analysis," McGraw-Hill Book Company, Inc., New York, 1953.

CHAPTER 11

INTRODUCTION TO ADVANCED TOPICS—
LINEAR THEORY

11-1. Introduction. The purpose of this chapter is to describe, briefly and qualitatively, some of the topics in linear servomechanism theory which are too advanced for inclusion in the preceding chapters. For those interested in further study, a number of bibliographical references are noted.

11-2. Multiple-loop Systems. The treatment of feedback compensation given in Chap. 10 presents the fundamental aspects of the use of

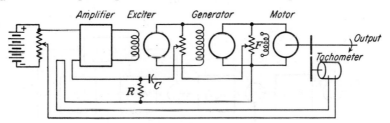

(a)

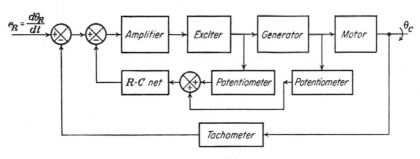

(b)

Fig. 11-1. Speed regulator with multiple feedback. (a) Schematic diagram of speed regulator. (b) Block diagram.

minor loops in improving system performance. Unfortunately, many systems are considerably more complicated than those treated in Chap. 10. As a simple illustration, consider the speed regulator of Fig. 11-1a and its block diagram as shown in Fig. 11-1b. There is actually only one minor loop, but in the design of this loop there are three parameters, the time constant of the RC network, and the setting of each of the potential dividers to determine. The problem may be solved by application of the methods indicated in Chap. 10, but it is considerably more complicated than are the simple feedback loops considered there.

Many systems utilize more than one feedback loop, and the block diagram may appear as in Fig. 11-2a. The A_1F_1 feedback component might be a tachometer providing velocity feedback for damping purposes. The

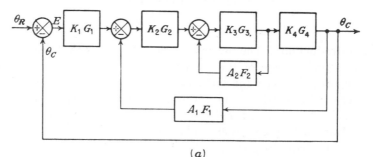

(a)

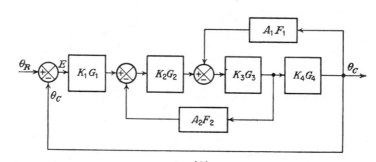

(b)

Fig. 11-2. Block diagrams of multiloop systems.   (a) Simple multiple-loop feedback. (b) Coupled minor loops.

A_2F_2 component might be inserted to compensate for a time lag (large time constant) in the forward component K_3G_3. Such compensation is normal, and the procedures involved are straightforward if not simple. However, the feedback arrangement at times assumes a configuration as in the block diagram of Fig. 11-2b. In this case the feedback loops are not independent, but are said to be "coupled." Mathematical procedures for handling such cases are not self-evident, and little concerning them is available in the literature.

Multiple loops are commonly encountered in the control of aircraft. One of the control systems which may be used in aircraft guided from the ground is shown in the simplified block diagram of Fig. 11-3. Note that there are three minor loops, feeding back position, velocity, and acceleration. Many control systems are considerably more complicated than this illustration.

11-3. Sampled-data Systems. The information supplied to closed-loop control systems is not always a continuous function of time, but may be intermittent or discontinuous data. For example, in some schemes for the remote control of aircraft or guided missiles, a radio transmitter in the controlled device sends to the control center the required information as to acceleration, velocity, altitude, etc. These quantities are measured continuously, but they cannot be transmitted simultaneously. Therefore a switching system is used, and the various signals are transmitted in a fixed sequence. It may be assumed that there are N signals to be transmitted, and for a fixed switching cycle of over-all

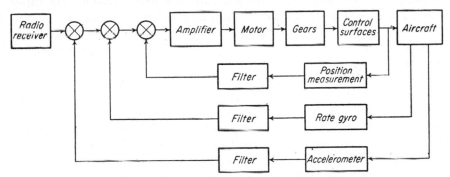

Fig. 11-3. Block diagram of part of an aircraft control system.

duration, D, the time allotted to each signal is D/N. Then the acceleration signal (for example) is transmitted for a time interval D/N, and for the remainder of the switching cycle, of duration $[(N-1)/N]D$, the control center receives no additional information about the acceleration.

At the control center each signal from the controlled aircraft is evaluated by a computer. In many cases, the signal may be fed into the computer by a servo; in other cases, the computer circuits contain servos which must operate on this data. The servo itself may be completely linear, but the command signal is discontinuous. The output of the servo, however, is to be a continuous signal, and this poses a number of interesting problems, among which are:

1. How can the servo system be designed to give a continuous output which closely approximates the original continuous signal (in the controlled aircraft) when the actual input to the servo is only a number of samples of this signal?

2. What influence has the sampling rate (number of samples per second) on the servo performance?

3. What criteria should be used for the quality of the servo performance?

4. Does the discontinuous input signal affect system stability?

There are many other examples of sampled-data systems. In the case of radar tracking of targets, the data supplied by the radar signal have a sampling rate which depends on the scanning rate of the radar antenna. Since the servo drive on the gun mount and the radar-antenna servo drive both operate from this data, they are sampled-data servo systems. In other cases, servo systems receive their command signal from digital computers, the output of which is inherently discontinuous, so that such servo systems are sampled-data systems.

Most of the previously cited examples are concerned with servo systems in which the discontinuous data are external to the closed loop. In such cases the servo system itself can be a linear system. In other cases, however, the discontinuous data may originate inside the loop in the error channel; such circumstances arise when the error signal must be modulated and pulse modulation is used. The servo system itself is then nonlinear.

11-4. Criteria for Best Performance. The primary function of a servomechanism is to drive its output in accordance with a command, or input, signal. In the ideal case the output should exactly duplicate the input. Since it is physically impossible to build a servo which exactly duplicates any command, the quality of performance obtained is evaluated on the basis of more or less arbitrary criteria. The criteria used in this text (which are those most commonly associated with linear servo theory) may be summarized as follows: The best servo is that system which responds to a step-displacement input by driving its output into approximate correspondence with the input in the shortest time compatible with a specified maximum permissible overshoot. In this text, the criteria have not been applied to a comparative study of different systems, but rather to the study of the optimum adjustment and compensation of a given system.

It should be recognized that the command signal to a servomechanism will seldom be a step displacement, and therefore the transient response to an actual input will not resemble the response to a step function. Nevertheless, the response to an actual input can be estimated fairly well from a knowledge of the response to a step function, if the input signal is continuous. If the input signal is not continuous, as in sampled-data systems, the step-function response of the system is not as useful as might be desired. Furthermore, if the actual input signal is not solely the command signal, but has unwanted signals (noise) combined with it, an ideal servo would follow the noise signal as well as the command, which is undesirable. For such cases, the criterion stressed in this text is not necessarily a desirable one; what is wanted is a criterion that permits a design method resulting in a servo which follows the actual command and is not greatly affected by the noise.

The root-mean-square (rms) error criterion is one which gives satisfactory results for systems designed to operate in the presence of noise, etc. It is not necessarily a better criterion than that previously stated, since neither criterion is suitable for all applications, but the rms error criterion seems much better suited to the design of systems where there is noise in the input signal or in the amplification channel. In brief, the rms error criterion states that the best servo is that system which minimizes the rms error. Expressed mathematically, this means that the best servo is obtained when

$$\sqrt{\overline{E^2}} = \sqrt{\lim_{T \to \infty} \frac{1}{2T} \int_{-T}^{T} E^2(t)\, dt} \qquad (11\text{-}1)$$

becomes a minimum.

For this concept to be useful, it is necessary to develop suitable equations for the command signal, the noise, and the servo-system components. It must also be possible to evaluate the integrals without excessive labor, and it must be possible to determine the minimum in terms of the variable system parameters in order to determine the proper adjustments for optimum operation. This has been done,[*] but a detailed discussion is beyond the scope of this chapter.

A crude explanation of the meaning of the criterion is this: Some compromise must be made between the sensitivity of the servo to the command signal and its sensitivity to noise. Of course, the noise should be filtered out as much as possible, but complete elimination is usually not practical. The problem then is to design the servo to follow the command and ignore the noise. Some of this is done naturally, since most servos are inherently low-pass filters, and the noise is likely to predominate at higher frequencies. However, a compensation filter is required to minimize the effect of lower-frequency noise. The type of filter desired is selected, the system equations (together with the command- and noise-signal equations) are formulated, and the rms error is evaluated in terms of known numbers and the unknown filter parameters. Further manipulation determines a set of filter parameters which make the rms error minimum, and these define the best servo. Note that the nature of the criterion discriminates very heavily against *large* errors, since the magnitude of the error is squared in the evaluation, and the minimum obtained for $\sqrt{\overline{E^2}}$ will be large if any E is large. Note also that the

---

[*] See James, H. M., N. B. Nichols, and R. S. Phillips, "Theory of Servomechanisms," Chap. 7, McGraw-Hill Book Company, Inc., New York, 1947.

criterion is not concerned with the time distribution of the error, but only the magnitude. Neither of these conditions is necessarily desirable in all servo systems. A large error is often permissible at times if it is eliminated quickly enough, as at the beginning of a transient disturbance, while relatively small, but appreciable, errors may be objectionable under other conditions. This merely indicates that the rms error criterion is not suitable for all applications; there is no question but that it is suitable in many cases.

11-5. Combined Frequency-domain–Time-domain Analysis and Design. In the design of servomechanisms, the ultimate criterion for performance is normally the transient (time) response, yet most design procedures use frequency-domain methods. The reason for this, of course, lies in the fact that calculations in the time domain require solution of the differential equation, and satisfactory simple design procedures do not obtain. The transient response is of such great importance, however, that considerable work has been done to find short methods for computing the roots of higher-order equations, and a number of papers have been written on correlations between transient response and frequency response.

Ideally, the designer would like to work in the time domain, since this would provide direct control over the transient response. The direct approach to such a design method would be to choose the roots of the system characteristic equation, and design the components to produce these roots. No satisfactory way to do this has been found thus far. Several methods which approximate this direct approach have been devised. These methods utilize the fact that the roots of the characteristic equation are related to the poles and zeros of the closed-loop frequency-response equation. If the designer works with the poles and zeros, he has readily available both the frequency response and the transient response, either being obtained by relatively simple calculations.

One method, developed by John G. Truxal, is summarized briefly in this section. A second, the *root-locus method* developed by Walter Evans, is summarized in the following section.

Most servomechanisms are designed to be slightly underdamped systems. The characteristic equation of any underdamped system has at least one pair of complex conjugate roots with negative real parts, and the frequency response has an identical pair of poles. Because of this, the designer may approximate the transient response of the system by selecting a pair of poles. The imaginary part of the pole is selected with due consideration of the specified speed of response or band width, and the overshoots are controlled by selecting the real part of the pole to provide the required damping. (Note that any pair of complex conjugate poles represents a quadratic equation, and the damping factor, ζ, is the ratio of minus the real part of the pole to the imaginary part, i. e., if the poles are $s_1 = -\sigma + j\omega$ and $s_2 = -\sigma - j\omega$, then $\zeta = \sigma/\omega$.)

In addition to the transient performance, the steady-state performance must be set. This may be done by inserting a zero or a dipole (zero and pole close together) on the negative real axis. The location of this zero or dipole essentially sets the loop gain, and it also has some effect on the transient response and the band width.

It is necessary, of course, that the components needed to produce the poles and zeros be physically realizable. In order to satisfy this condition, additional poles may be required; these are usually placed far out on the negative real axis.

From the poles and zeros thus determined, the designer readily obtains the closed-loop frequency-response equation and can determine from it both the frequency-response curves and transient curves to check against specifications. He will also know, in general, the transfer-function equations of certain components inside the loop which are specified parts of the system. The remaining problem, then, is to determine what must be added to the system to produce the postulated poles and zeros in the frequency-response equation. Normally, either series (cascaded) elements, feedback elements, or parallel (feed-forward) elements may be used. The designer must make a choice in this respect. Then the transfer functions of these components may be derived from the known equations. Finally, physical devices (filters, etc.) which have the required transfer functions must be designed.

The preceding paragraphs are a very brief and qualitative summary of Truxal's work. The mathematical justification for the location of poles and zeros as well as mathematical and graphical methods for use in design are contained in the original work.*

11-6. The Root-locus Method. The roots of the characteristic equation of a closed-loop system can be found from the loop transfer function of the system. The root-locus method provides a simple graphical method for determining these roots, while preserving relationships with the system frequency response. The plots also show clearly the effects of adjustments, and indicate what is needed in the way of system compensation. Only a brief introduction is presented here; more detailed discussions are available in the literature.

To apply the root-locus method, it is necessary to use transfer functions expressed as functions of the complex variable $s = \sigma + j\omega$, rather than the imaginary variable $j\omega$ used in most of this text. However, any transfer function used in this text may be converted to the proper form

---

* See Truxal, John G., Servomechanism Synthesis through Pole-zero Configurations, Massachusetts Institute of Technology, Research Laboratory of Electronics, *Report* 162.

simply by substituting s for $j\omega$. Further to simplify the algebra used here, it is assumed that the feedback is unity, so that the direct transfer function is also the loop transfer function. Then the system-function equation of a closed-loop system (also called the system function) is

$$\frac{\theta_C}{\theta_R}(s) = \frac{KG(s)}{1 + KG(s)} \tag{11-2}$$

The poles of Eq. (11-2) are those values of s which make $(\theta_C/\theta_R)(s)$ infinite. They are also the roots of the characteristic equation. To find these poles, note that the system function becomes infinite when

$$KG(s) + 1 = 0 \tag{11-3}$$

This equation may be solved graphically on the $s = \sigma + j\omega$ plane. To illustrate, assume that the system transfer function is

$$\frac{\theta_C}{E}(s) = KG(s) = \frac{K_1(s + 1/\tau_1)}{s(s + 1/\tau_a)(s + 1/\tau_b)} \tag{11-4}$$

[In Eq. (11-4) the factored terms are written in the form $s + 1/\tau$ for convenience.]

s can be represented as a vector. Therefore Eq. (11-3) is considered a vector equation, and is satisfied by values of s which produce a transfer-function vector of unit length with a phase angle of exactly 180°. These values may be determined by constructing the various $KG(s)$ vectors on the $s = \sigma + j\omega$ plane, as shown in Fig. 11-4a. The poles of the transfer function of Eq. (11-4) are 0, $-(1/\tau_a)$, and $-(1/\tau_b)$, and are shown by dots. The zero of Eq. (11-4) is $-(1/\tau_1)$ and is shown with an x. These points are used as references to set up the transfer-function vector, and ultimately to locate the roots of the frequency-response equation. The transfer-function vector, i. e., the value of the transfer function for a given value of s, may be found for any value of s, as shown in Fig. 11-4a. Any point is located on the plane arbitrarily, and vectors are drawn from each of the reference points to this point. These are the vectors s, $s + 1/\tau_a$, etc., as labeled. The angles associated with these terms are indicated on the figure. Each vector thus has a magnitude and a phase angle, and may be used to evaluate

$$\frac{s + 1/\tau_1}{s(s + 1/\tau_a)(s + 1/\tau_b)} = \frac{|s + 1/\tau_1|}{|s|\,|s + 1/\tau_a|\,|s + 1/\tau_b|}\underline{/-\Phi_1 - \Phi_2 + \Phi_3 - \Phi_4} \tag{11-5}$$

The evaluation is performed by measuring the vector lengths and angles and inserting in Eq. (11-5). This can be done for any point on the s plane. Note that this evaluation does not contain the parameter K_1 of the transfer function.

The only points on the s plane which are of interest are those for which the net phase angle [as in Eq. (11-5)] is 180°, because only these points can possibly make $KG(s) = -1$. The locus of all such points is called the root locus, because the roots of the system function are specific points on this locus. There are various ways in which the root locus

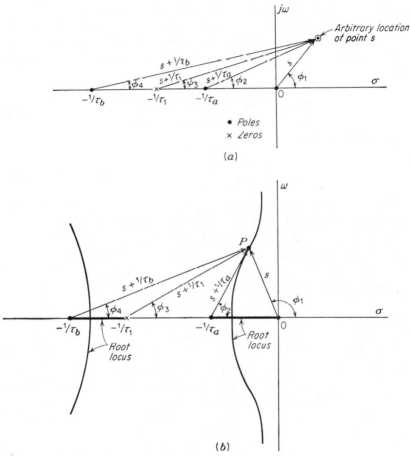

(a)

(b)

Fig. 11-4. (a) The vector factors of $KG(s)$ on the s plane. (b) The root locus for the pole and zero configuration of (a).

may be determined; in many cases, the approximate locus is easily found by inspection. The root locus for the pole-zero configuration of Fig. 11-4a is shown in Fig. 11-4b, (this locus is a sketch determined by inspection and is not accurate).

Since the roots of the system function are known to lie on the root locus, they may be found by trial and error, as follows:

1. Select a point on the root locus, such as point p in Fig. 11-4b.
2. Draw the vectors as shown.
3. Measure the lengths of these vectors and form the magnitude product, as in Eq. (11-5).
4. The result of step 3 is a negative number because the phase angle is 180°, and the magnitude determined by step 3, when multiplied by the parameter K_1, must be equal to 1.0 if the point p is a root.
5. This procedure is repeated until all roots are found, the number of roots required being known from the order of the transfer function.

Assume that these roots are thus determined.   The system function is then

$$\frac{\theta_c}{\theta_R}(s) = \frac{s\left(s + \frac{1}{\tau_a}\right)\left(s + \frac{1}{\tau_b}\right) KG(s)}{(s + r_1)(s + r_2)(s + r_3)} \tag{11-6}$$

The output function is

$$\theta_c(s) = \frac{s\left(s + \frac{1}{\tau_a}\right)\left(s + \frac{1}{\tau_b}\right) KG(s)}{(s + r_1)(s + r_2)(s + r_3)} \theta_R(s) \tag{11-7}$$

The frequency-response curves may be computed from Eq. (11-6), or from the graphical plot, and the solution to the differential equation is obtained by taking the inverse Laplace transform of Eq. (11-7).   The details of these procedures are beyond the scope of this text.

From the preceding discussion it may be seen that the location of the roots on the root locus depends on the value of the gain constant.   From basic principles it is known that the system is stable unless one or more roots lie in the right-hand half of the plane or on the imaginary axis. It is also known that the damping of a given pair of complex roots depends on the ratio of minus the real part of the root to the imaginary part. Thus, for a given system, stability and transient performance may be determined by inspection of the root location on the plot, and the mathematical computation of the frequency response and transient response is thus avoided.   Conversely, the gain required for a specified transient performance may be computed by arbitrarily placing the complex roots on the root locus in such a location that the transient requirements are met.   Then the gain constant required to produce the root location may be computed from step 4 of the procedure outlined for finding the roots. If more roots exist, their location would also be changed and should be computed.

In many cases the root locus associated with a given system does not permit roots which provide the desired transient performance, and in other cases roots which appear satisfactory cannot be used because the gain required does not permit proper steady-state operation.   In such cases the root locus itself must be reshaped.   This reshaping requires the introduction of additional poles and zeros, corresponding physically to compensation devices. The methods used in these cases are beyond the scope of this text.

REFERENCES

Brown, R. G., and G. J. Murphy, An Approximate Transfer Function for the Analysis and Design of Pulsed Servos, *Trans. AIEE (Applications and Industry)*, January, 1953.

Chu, Yaohan, Feedback Control Systems with Dead Time or Distributed Lag, *Trans. AIEE (Applications and Industry)*, November, 1952.

Chu, Yaohan, Synthesis of Feedback Control Systems by Phase Angle Loci, *Trans. AIEE (Applications and Industry)*, November, 1952.

Chu, Yaohan, Frequency and Transient Response of Feedback Control Systems, *Trans. AIEE (Applications and Industry)*, May, 1953.

Evans, W. R., Control System Synthesis by Root Locus Method, *Trans. AIEE*, 1950.

James, H. M., N. B. Nichols, and R. S. Phillips, "Theory of Servomechanisms," McGraw-Hill Book Company, Inc., New York, 1947.

Linvill, W. K., Analysis and Design of Sampled-data Control Systems, Thesis, Massachusetts Institute of Technology, 1949.

Mulligan, J. H., The Effect of Pole and Zero Location on the Transient Response of Linear Dynamic Systems, *Proc. IRE*, May, 1949.

Ragazzini, J. R., and L. A. Zadeh, The Analysis of Sampled-data Systems, *Trans. AIEE (Applications and Industry)*, November, 1952.

Truxal, J. G., Servomechanism Synthesis through Pole-zero Configurations, Massachusetts Institute of Technology, Research Laboratory of Electronics, *Report* 162.

CHAPTER 12

INTRODUCTION TO ADVANCED TOPICS— NONLINEAR SYSTEMS

12-1. Introduction. The bulk of the mathematical theory pertaining to servomechanisms is linear theory; that is, it postulates a system which can be described by a linear differential equation. Unfortunately, truly linear systems do not exist, and the results of linear calculations are inevitably in error. Many servomechanisms, however, operate in such a fashion that the assumption of linearity gives a close approximation to actual performance. In many other cases, the existing nonlinearities are not excessive, and a linear analysis provides a fairly good first approximation, final adjustments and compensation being obtained experimentally. In addition, there are many reasons why nonlinearities may be deliberately inserted in a closed-loop system.

Simple and accurate methods for the analysis and design of nonlinear systems are not available at present. Mathematical tools are gradually being developed to overcome this deficiency, and an analogue computer is extremely helpful. Such tools as are available are primarily intended for analysis. Design procedures employing these tools usually require, in addition, a good deal of experience, basic physical reasoning, intuition, and trial-and-error methods.

In this chapter the basic nonlinearities which are normally encountered are described, as well as a few of the nonlinearities which are sometimes inserted deliberately, and two of the most promising methods of analysis are introduced.

12-2. Types of Nonlinearities. Most servomechanisms utilize some moving mechanical parts, and many incorporate gear trains. There is always some friction associated with such components, and a portion of this friction is "static" friction, or stiction. Stiction is that frictional force which prevents motion until the driving force exceeds some minimum value. It also causes a moving object to stop, or stick, when the velocity reaches some lower limit. When it occurs in servo systems, it has objectionable effects; for static-positioning systems, it permits some error to exist without corresponding motion of the output, or, if a new position is commanded, the system stops, or sticks, when the output is not quite in the desired position. For velocity-operated positioning systems, there is a minimum velocity of smooth operation; for lower velocities, the stiction alternately stops and releases the output, causing a jumpy or jittery motion which is unsatisfactory.

When a gear train is used, an effect similar to stiction is possible. If the gears are mounted so that their pitch circles intersect instead of being tangent, i. e., if the gears are aligned too tightly, they bind. This binding acts in exactly the same way as stiction, except that in the case of eccentricity the binding occurs only at certain points and varies in magnitude. Figure 12-1a shows the effect of coulomb* friction on the response of a servo system to a step-displacement input. Curve A shows the linear system response, and curves B, C, etc., are for increasing amounts of coulomb friction. In like manner, Fig. 12-1b shows the effect of coulomb friction on the velocity of the servo when responding to a step-displacement input.

If a gear train is too loosely aligned, if couplings and set screws are not tight, or if bearings have too much clearance or are worn, it is often possible to turn a drive shaft through an appreciable angle before any motion is obtained at the output. This effect is called backlash. When an error occurs, there is a time lag in the response owing to the fact that the drive must take up the backlash before torque can be applied to the load. This time lag corresponds to an additional phase lag in the transfer function, with the result that the system becomes less stable. The curves of Fig. 12-2 illustrate the effect of backlash on the output position and output velocity of a servo when it is subjected to a step-displacement input. Curve a shows the response of a linear system with no backlash. Curves b and c show that the presence of backlash produces an oscillation of longer duration, ending in a constant hunting about the steady-state position. Curve d shows that the presence of excessive backlash can make the system completely unstable.

When there is sufficient backlash to produce a condition of hunting (constant oscillation of fixed small amplitude), the systems tend to approach that state after any disturbance. Curve e shows that the hunting *decreases* to a constant amplitude after a large disturbance, and curve f shows that the oscillation *builds up* to a constant amplitude after a small disturbance.

Another common nonlinearity is saturation. Any physical component

---

* Coulomb friction is defined as a constant frictional drag which opposes motion but has a magnitude that is independent of velocity. It therefore causes a sticking effect, as shown in Fig. 12-1a. In practice, however, it is frequently found that the force required to initiate motion (overcome stiction) is somewhat greater than the force of coulomb friction. Therefore some slight distinction must be made between stiction and coulomb friction.

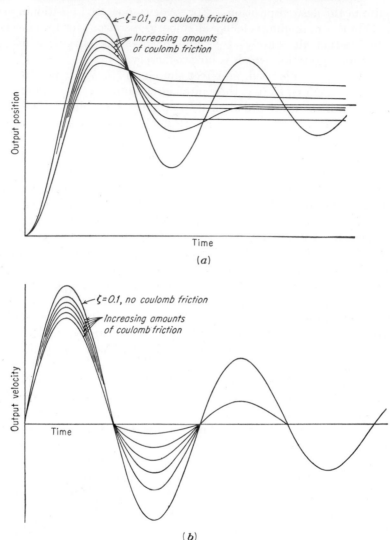

Fig. 12-1. (a) Effect of coulomb friction on the output position of a servomechanism when responding to a step-displacement input. (b) Effect of coulomb friction on the output velocity of a servomechanism when responding to a step-displacement input.

has a maximum possible output; in general, this is produced for some finite input. If the actual input is greater than this known input, the component is not able to produce a correspondingly greater output and is said to be saturated. Perhaps the most readily understood example is that of saturation in electronic amplifiers. The maximum voltage obtainable from an amplifier depends on the magnitude of the plate-supply voltage. If a given amplifier has a plate-supply voltage of 300 volts and an over-all gain of 50, one would expect the amplifier to saturate for an input signal of about 6 volts. Any input signal greater than 6 volts produces essentially the same output voltage, and so the amplifier is saturated for any input voltage above 6 volts. Similar phenomena occur in generators and motors. If an amplidyne generator is subjected to a variable-control field current, the output voltage of the generator is approximately proportional to the field current for normal small values of current. If larger values of field current are used, the magnetic circuit saturates; the output voltage does not increase as rapidly, and the generator is said to saturate.

Two types of saturation are found in motors, torque saturation and velocity saturation. There is a maximum torque available from a given motor. The application of large overvoltages does not increase this torque appreciably. Thus, if the system is subjected to a large command signal, the motor may be driven to maximum torque and it runs at maximum torque until the error has been sufficiently reduced to return the system to linear operation. (Note that linear theory requires a torque proportional to the error and does not consider the case of a maximum possible torque.) Velocity saturation in motors is a somewhat similar phenomenon. It is often encountered in two-phase motor servos. A two-phase motor has a maximum rotational velocity, and when used in servo systems it frequently works with a gear train having a large reduction ratio. A large command signal may require 20 or 30 revolutions of the motor shaft to regain correspondence. In a good servo, the two-phase motor accelerates to maximum velocity in just a few revolutions. Thus, for a large command signal, the motor runs at maximum velocity for an appreciable period and is said to be velocity-saturated. This is nonlinear operation, since a linear system either accelerates or decelerates during transient operation but has no period of constant-velocity operation.

Figure 12-3 shows the transient response of a velocity-saturated servo to a step-displacement input. Curves a and b are for different velocity limits. During velocity saturation the output should run at approximately constant velocity. On the position vs. time curve this should appear as a straight-line segment, i. e., a line of constant slope. It is rather difficult to note such an effect on the position curve, but the plots of velocity vs. time show the saturation clearly, since the oscillatory wave shape becomes approximately flat-topped during the saturation period.

Stiction, binding, backlash, and saturation may be called incidental nonlinearities because they are not deliberate design features, but occur either because of poor design, poor selection of components, poor assembly techniques, or because of limitations in the specifications which prohibit a truly linear design. In addition to these, there are a number of non-

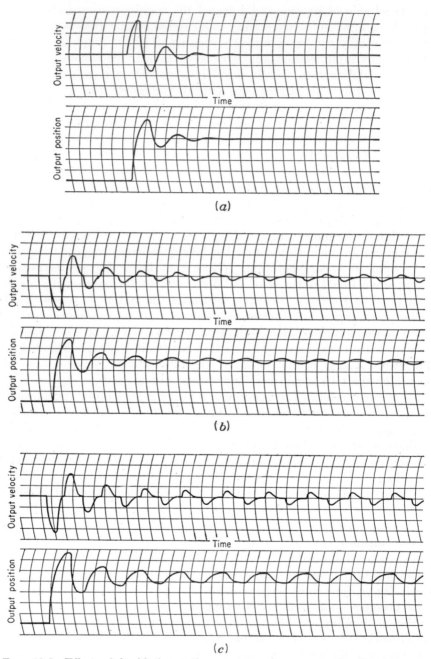

Fig. 12-2. Effect of backlash on the response of a servomechanism to a step-displacement input. (*a*) System without backlash. (*b*) System with some backlash. (*c*) With increased backlash. (*d*) Large amount of backlash, causing insta-

232

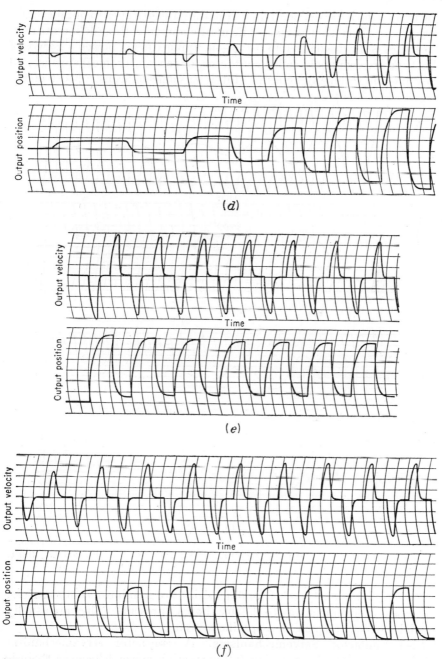

(d)

(e)

(f)

bility.   (e) Large amount of backlash and large disturbance; output decreases to a constant-amplitude oscillation.   (f) Large amount of backlash and small disturbance; output increases to a constant-amplitude oscillation.

linearities which are deliberately inserted by the designer to obtain better performance from the system.   The most common of these deliberate non-linearities is the discontinuous, or on-off, application of power.   Servos of this type are commonly called contactor, or relay, servomechanisms, and they include the many types of clutch servomechanisms.   Most of the

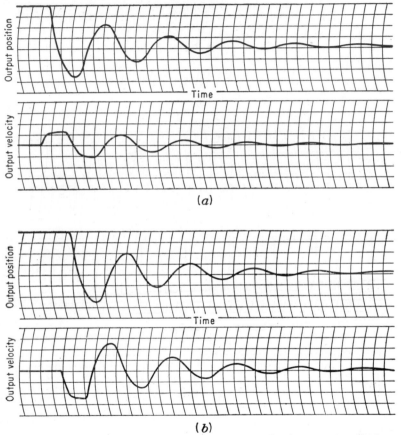

FIG. 12-3. Transient response of a second-order servomechanism to a step-displacement input, when operated so that velocity saturation occurs.   (a) With low velocity limit. (b) With different velocity limit.

remaining common types of nonlinearities are nonlinear compensators. There is no convenient way to classify these at present.   They are usually special devices designed for a specific system.

12-3. Contactor Servomechanisms. A contactor servomechanism controls its output by applying full corrective power whenever there is an error large enough to actuate the contact mechanism.   In the case of a true relay servo, the error closes a relay which applies full line voltage to a drive motor. For friction-clutch servos, the drive motor runs continuously at normal speed, and the error actuates a clutch which couples the motor to the load. If a magnetic fluid clutch is used, the coupling may be gradual but the action is still nonlinear.

In any of these cases, the servo system usually has fewer parts than an equivalent linear servo and thus is cheaper and often easier to maintain. The corrective action is usually faster, in the sense that greater accelerations and velocities are obtained. There are some definite performance deficiencies, however. If the error detector is made very sensitive, the system never reaches steady state but hunts (oscillates) continuously. This is not acceptable in many applications. To eliminate this hunting, the error detector may be made less sensitive by adjusting it to have a "dead zone," i. e., a range of values of small error for which the contactors remain open. This adjustment helps stability but decreases the static accuracy, since the exact value of the steady-state output is not known, but only the limits within which this output must lie.

An additional complication lies in the fact that contactor-type devices always have a "time lag" associated with them. Part of this time lag is due to inertia effects, i. e., the moving parts have inertia, and therefore motion does not begin instantaneously with the application of force. For electrically operated contacts, there is an additional time delay due to the inductance of the coil winding. When voltage is applied to the coil, a build-up of current takes time, and the contacts are not closed until the current reaches a definite value. Conversely, when the voltage is removed, the current does not drop to zero instantaneously, and consequently there is a delay in opening the contacts. For most relays the value of current required to close the contacts is different from the value of current at which they are opened. The time-lag effect, of course, is included in the total dead zone of the systems, and the fact that different currents are required for opening and closing means that the dead zone is not symmetrical about zero error. All these factors tend to make the servomechanism more oscillatory and also tend to decrease the steady-state accuracy.

An ideal relay servo may be defined as one which has inertia but no damping, and for which the relay responds instantaneously, i. e., has no dead zone and no time lag. For such a servo it is readily shown that the response to a step displacement is a constant-amplitude oscillation, the amplitude of this oscillation being twice that of the step disturbance. This is illustrated in Fig. 12-4a, which shows curves of position vs. time and velocity vs. time. Such a condition is not desirable, and the oscillations may be damped by adding a viscous friction damper. Mathematical analysis shows that the addition of such a damper causes a decrease in the amplitude of the oscillation but an increase in frequency.

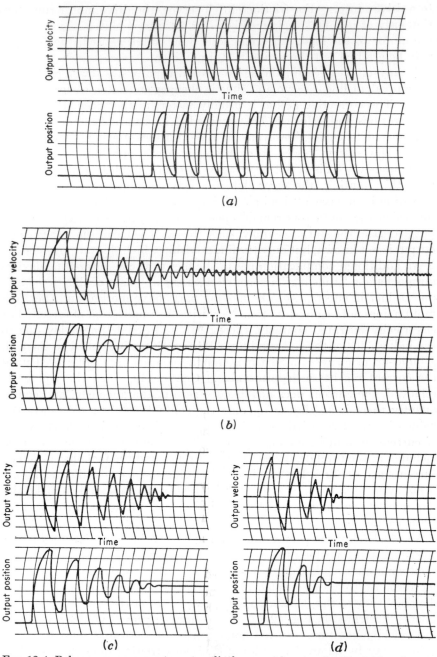

FIG. 12-4. Relay servo response to a step-displacement input. (a) Ideal relay, inertia load, no damping. (b) With viscous damping. (c) Ideal relay, inertia load, error-rate damping. (d) Greater amount of error-rate damping.

As a limit, the amplitude approaches zero and the frequency becomes infinite. This is illustrated in Fig. 12-4b.

The energy losses in the damper may be eliminated and a better transient performance obtained by using error-rate damping instead of viscous damping. The error-rate damper is used to throw the relay somewhat before the system reaches the correspondence point, thus applying full power to slow down the output and reducing the overshoot which follows. The effect of error-rate damping is illustrated in Fig. 12-4c and d.

12-4. The Phase-plane Approach to the Analysis of Nonlinear Systems. It is common engineering practice to analyze the performance of a device by studying curves that in some way describe the operation of the device. The curves used in the preceding chapters to analyze and design servomechanisms have been transient curves, transfer-function curves, and frequency-response curves. These have been used for linear systems only. In the case of nonlinear systems, such graphical representations need some modification. Transient curves, i. e., plots of position or velocity vs. time, are very laborious to calculate for nonlinear systems, and are not particularly helpful once obtained. A true transfer function does not exist for a nonlinear device, but a type of transfer function, known as a "describing function," may be derived and the basic methods of the transfer-function approach used with it. This is discussed in a later section.

Much useful information may be obtained if a plot is made of system velocity vs. system position. This is the so-called "phase-plane" plot. Such plots can be made of output velocity vs. output position, and Fig. 12-5 shows a family of these curves for a second-order servo with various amounts of damping. The curves are plotted for a step-displacement input. From Fig. 12-5, the maximum overshoot, the number of overshoots and undershoots, and the maximum velocity are readily determined. Calculation of the time associated with the overshoots, etc., is possible, but is beyond the scope of this text.

If a phase-plane plot is made of output position vs. output velocity, the result is applicable only to a step-displacement input, since the output position becomes very large if a step-velocity input is used. For this reason, it is more common to use a plot of error rate vs. error, since a closed-loop system reduces the error to zero or to some small constant for any normal input. Thus the phase-plane plot of error rate vs. error is interpretable for a number of inputs.

The calculation of phase-plane plots is not an easy matter. There are at least four methods by which the plot may be obtained:

1. Write the system differential equation, define a change in variable, and express velocity as a function of position. Integrate this equation and plot the resulting solution.

2. Write the differential equation for the system and obtain time solutions for the velocity and for the position. Eliminate the time variable by substituting one equation in the other.

3. Obtain the differential equation relating position to velocity as in method 1, but do not integrate; instead, solve the equation for the iso-

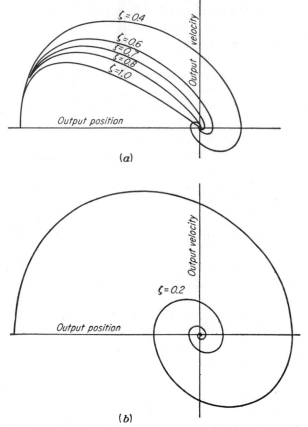

FIG. 12-5. (a) Phase-plane plots for a linear second-order viscous-damped servomechanism. (b) Phase-plane plot for a linear second-order viscous-damped servomechanism.

clines (loci of constant slope of the phase-plane curve) and use a graphical construction to obtain the phase-plane curve from the isoclines.

4. Set up the system, either physically or in an analogue computer, and obtain the phase-plane curves with an X-Y function plotter, or obtain position vs. time and velocity vs. time curves and obtain the phase-plane plot from the time curves.

Any of the methods are readily applicable to linear systems. The first and second methods may be used with nonlinear systems if the nonlinear

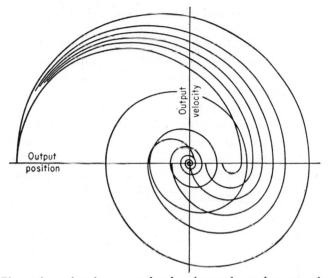

FIG. 12-6. Phase-plane plots for a second-order viscous-damped servomechanism with various amounts of coulomb friction.

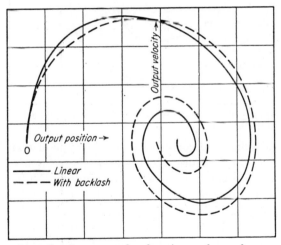

FIG. 12-7. Phase-plane plot for a second-order viscous-damped servomechanism with backlash.

differential equations can be solved. The third method probably applies to a larger number of nonlinear systems, and the analogue-computer method is limited only by the ability to simulate the nonlinearity.

Figures 12-6 to 12-9 are phase-plane plots of output position vs. output velocity showing the effects of coulomb friction, backlash, and velocity saturation. Such curves show clearly the effect of the nonlinearity on system performance, and therefore are valuable for purposes of analysis.

In design work certain additional factors make the phase-plane approach helpful; for example, the velocity-saturation limits and torque-saturation limits for a given system may be represented by straight lines on the phase plane. The use of such special techniques is discussed in the literature, but is beyond the scope of this text.

In development work the phase plane offers some interesting possibilities. To illustrate this point, consider Figs. 12-10 through 12-14, all of which refer to a relay servo with ideal relay. Figure 12-10 shows the phase-plane response of an undamped system to step-displacement inputs

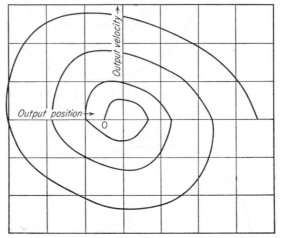

Fig. 12-8. Phase-plane plot of a second-order viscous-damped servomechanism with sufficient backlash to cause instability.

of various amplitudes, and corresponds to the type of transient response shown in Fig. 12-4a. Figure 12-11 shows the response of a viscous-damped relay servo to a step-displacement input. Note that the relay reversal is indicated by the sharp break in the curve, and that this occurs when the output position goes through the desired steady-state value.

Figures 12-12 to 12-14 show the response of an error-rate-damped relay servo to a step-displacement input, and are arranged in the order of increasing damping. Note that the relay no longer reverses at the desired steady-state position, but rather it reverses before this point is reached. Furthermore, the amount by which this reversal anticipates the desired position is proportional to the velocity, so that the locus of the reversal points is a straight line. As the damping increases, the number of overshoots and the magnitude of the overshoots both decrease as expected; this is accompanied by an increase in the angle between the velocity axis and the locus of relay-reversal points.

Observation of these facts might suggest the investigation of a non-linear locus of relay reversals such as that shown in Fig. 12-14. Such nonlinear anticipation has been studied* and the result has been a marked improvement in system performance; in fact, such nonlinear compensation provides an optimum system, as may be proved mathematically.

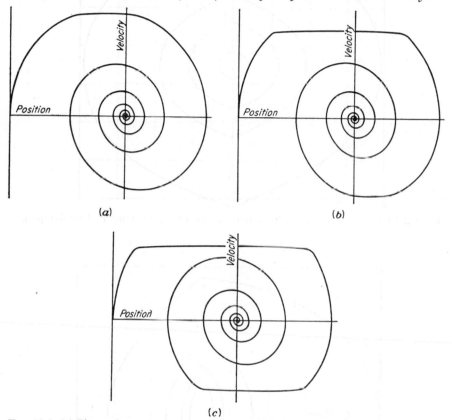

(a)   (b)

(c)

Fig. 12-9. (a) Phase-plane plot of a second-order viscous-damped servomechanism with velocity saturation at a fairly high velocity. (b) Phase-plane plot of a second-order viscous-damped servomechanism with velocity saturation at a medium velocity. (c) Phase-plane plot of a second-order viscous-damped servomechanism with velocity saturation at a low velocity.

12-5. Describing Functions and Their Use. Linear servomechanism theory uses transfer functions to describe the characteristics of linear components. When a component is nonlinear, its characteristics cannot be described by a true transfer function. In the case of most nonlinear components, it is possible to write the differential equation describing

* The author does not mean to imply that the development of nonlinear compensation for relay servos was actually prompted by a series of curves such as those discusse l.

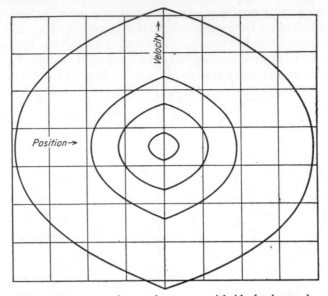

FIG. 12-10. Phase-plane curves for a relay servo with ideal relay and no damping.

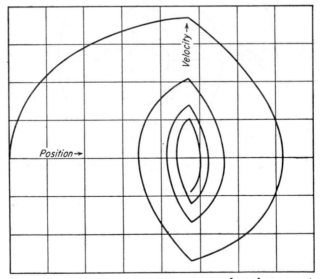

FIG. 12-11. Phase-plane plot for the output response of a relay servo to a step-displacement input; ideal relay and viscous damping.

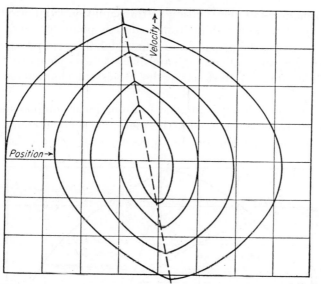

FIG. 12-12. Phase-plane plot for the output response of a relay servo to a step-displacement input; ideal relay and error-rate damping.

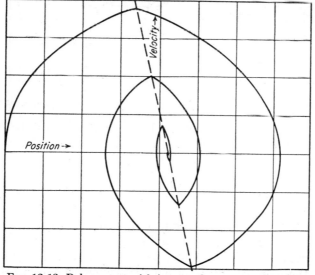

FIG. 12-13. Relay servo with increased error-rate damping.

their performance, but the solution of this equation is laborious and the results are seldom worthwhile from a design point of view. What is desired is a means of applying the sinusoidal frequency-response techniques, and the most satisfactory approach to this seems to be the use of a *describing function* to describe the important characteristics of the nonlinearity.

When a sinusoidal input is applied to a nonlinear component, the output is not a pure sine wave. Furthermore, for a given component, the output wave shape depends on the frequency of the sinusoidal input and

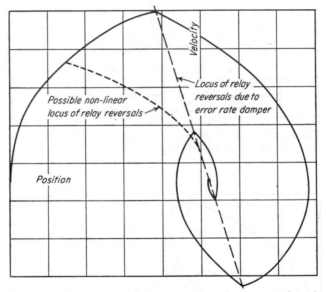

Velocity

Locus of relay
reversals due to
error rate damper

Possible non-linear
locus of relay reversals

Position

FIG. 12-14. Relay servo with large amount of error-rate damping.

also on the amplitude of the input. The output wave can be treated by Fourier analysis and described as a fundamental harmonic with various higher harmonics. The fundamental frequency is obviously that of the input sine wave, but its amplitude and phase may be different. A *describing function* may be defined as a function relating the fundamental frequency of the output to the input frequency for all positive frequencies and for all practical values of input amplitude. Such a function obviously does not describe the nonlinear component completely, and its use in the analysis and design of nonlinear servomechanisms is justified only because of the physical nature of normal servos, which, in brief, is that of a low-pass filter. In simple terms, the fundamental frequency in the nonsinusoidal output is usually larger in amplitude than any higher harmonic, and the servo system filters out the higher harmonics anyway; thus a good approximation may be obtained by using the fundamental fre-

quency in the Fourier series for the output wave as a means of describing the characteristics of the nonlinear component.

The derivation and application of specific describing functions are beyond the scope of this text, but describing functions for relays, backlash, hysteresis, saturation, dead space, and other common nonlinearities may be found in the literature. The procedure used in applying such describing functions is reasonably simple; they are used in the transfer-function equation in the same manner as any other transfer function, and the "appropriate" curves are plotted and interpreted.

The curves to be used in conjunction with describing functions are, basically, the same curves used in the analysis and design of linear systems. There are a few additional complications, however. When a describing function is used, the resulting system transfer function gives a family of curves rather than a single locus, because the describing function itself depends on the *amplitude* of the signal as well as its frequency, and a separate transfer-function curve is obtained for each amplitude of input signal. It is possible to plot a family of polar transfer-function curves and check stability and transient performance by relating these curves to the $-1 + j0$ point. This, however, is unnecessarily laborious in most cases. It is normally possible to draw a polar transfer-function locus for a unit amplitude signal. Then draw a second locus determined from the describing function which is a locus of stability points. Analysis and design then proceed from an interpretation of these two curves

REFERENCES

EKLUND, M. H., D. M. OLSON, and T. M. STOUT, Optimum Adjustment of Saturated Servomechanism, University of Washington, Electrical E Dept., *Report* 12, January, 1953.

GRIEF, H. D., Describing Function Method of Servomechanism Ana Most Commonly Encountered Nonlinearities, *Trans. AIEE Industry*), September, 1953.

HAAS, V. B., Jr., Coulomb Friction in Feedback Control S (*Applications and Industry*), May, 1953.

HAZEN, H. L., Theory of Servomechanisms, *J. Franklin I*

HOPKIN, A. M., A Phase Plane Approach to the Comp mechanisms, *Trans. AIEE*, vol. 70, 1951.

HUREWICZ, W., and N. B. NICHOLS, Servos with *Reports* 535, 592.

JOHNSON, E. C., Analysis of Feedback Contr *Trans. AIEE* (*Applications and Indust*

KOCHENBURGER, R., Limiting in Feedbac *tions and Industry*), July, 1953.

KOCHENBURGER, R. J., A Frequency ing Contactor Servomechanis

LEVINSON, E., Some Saturatio (*Applications and Industry*),

MARCY, H. T., M. YACHTER, and J. ZAUDERER, Instrument Inaccuracies in Feedback Control Systems with Particular Reference to Backlash, *Trans. AIEE*, 1949.

McDONALD, D., Non-linear Techniques for Improving Servomechanism Performance, *Proc. Natl. Electronics Conf.*, vol. 6, Chicago, 1950.

McDONALD, D., Multiple Modes of Operation for Continuous Servomechanisms, *Rev. Sci. Instruments*, vol. 23, 1952.

McDONALD, D., Basic Research in Non-linear Mechanics as Applied to Servomechanisms, *Cook Research Lab. Report* T16-1, Chicago, 1952.

NEISWANDER, R. S., and R. H. MacNEAL, Optimization of Non-linear Control Systems by Means of Non-linear Feedbacks, *Trans. AIEE (Applications and Industry)*, September, 1953.

STOUT, T. M., A Study of Some Nearly Optimum Servomechanisms, University of Washington, Electrical Engineering Dept., *Report* 10, 1952.

TUSTIN, A., The Effects of Backlash and Speed Dependent Friction on the Stability of Closed Cycle Control Systems, *J. Inst. Elec. Engrs. (London)*, 1947, part IIa.

TUSTIN, A., A Method of Analyzing the Effect of Certain Kinds of Non-linearity in Closed Cycle Control Systems, *J. Inst. Elec. Engrs. (London)*, 1947, part IIa.

WEISS, H. K., Analysis of Relay Servomechanisms, *J. Aeronaut. Sci.*, 1946.

APPENDIX I

TABLES OF NUMERICAL DATA

TABLE I-1
M-CIRCLE DATA FOR POLAR PLOTS

M	Center	Radius	$\psi = \sin^{-1} 1/M,$ deg
0.5	0.333	0.67	....
0.6	0.56	0.94	....
0.7	0.96	1.37	....
0.8	1.77	2.22	....
0.9	4.26	4.74	....
1.0	∞	∞	90
1.1	-5.77	5.24	65
1.2	-3.27	2.73	56.5
1.3	-2.45	1.88	50
1.4	-2.04	1.46	46
1 5	-1.80	1.20	42
1.6	-1.64	1.03	39
1.7	-1.53	0.90	36
1.8	-1.47	0.84	34
1.9	-1.38	0.73	32
2.0	-1.33	0.67	30
2.5	-1.19	0.48	23.5
3.0	-1.12	0.38	21
3.5	-1.10	0.34	16.6
4.0	-1.07	0.266	14.5
4.5	-1.05	0.234	12.8
5.0	-1.04	0.208	11.5

TABLE I-2

N-CIRCLE DATA FOR POLAR PLOTS

(All centers at $x = -\frac{1}{2}$)

Phase angle N, deg	Center y coordinate	Radius	Phase angle N, deg	Center y coordinate	Radius
0	∞	∞	− 70	−0.18	0.531
− 5	−5.73	5.75	− 75	−0.134	0.518
−10	−2.84	2.88	− 80	−0.087	0.508
−15	−1.84	1.90	− 90	0.000	0.500
−20	−1.37	1.46	−100	0.087	0.506
−25	−1.07	1.17	−110	0.18	0.531
−30	−0.866	1.00	−120	0.29	0.577
−35	−0.714	0.872	−130	0.42	0.656
−40	−0.596	0.775	−140	0.596	0.775
−45	−0.5	0.707	−150	0.866	1.000
−50	−0.42	0.656	−160	1.37	1.46
−55	−0.35	0.61	−170	2.84	2.88
−60	−0.29	0.577	−180	∞	∞
−65	−0.223	0.548			

TABLE I-3

CONVERSION FROM M IN DECIBELS TO M RATIO

M, db	M ratio	M, db	M ratio	M, db	M ratio
60	1000.0	5	1.78	− 4.0	0.63
50	316.2	4	1.588	− 5.0	0.562
40	100.00	3	1.412	− 6.0	0.500
35	56.23	2	1.26	− 8.0	0.398
30	31.62	1	1.12	− 9.0	0.354
25	17.78	0.5	1.06	−10.0	0.316
20	10.0	0.0	1.00	−12.0	0.251
15	5.623	−0.5	0.945	−15.0	0.178
12	3.99	−1.0	0.894	−18.0	0.125
9	2.82	−2.0	0.795	−20.0	0.100
6	2.00	−3.0	0.707		

TABLE I-4
DATA FOR M CONTOURS

Phase angle, deg	$M = 1.0$ db, decibels	Phase angle, deg	$M = 1.0$ db, decibels
−180	19.2	−120	2.6
−170	19.1	−125	0.6
−160	18.5	−130	−0.8
−150	17.9	−140	−2.7
−140	16.5	−150	−4.2
−130	14.5	−160	−4.8
−125	13.0	−170	−5.3
−120	10.6	−180	−5.6
−117	6.5		

TABLE I-4
DATA FOR M CONTOURS

Phase angle, deg	$M = 2$ db	Phase angle, deg	$M = 3$ db	Phase angle, deg	$M = 4$ db
−180	13.7	−180	10.7	−180	8.6
−170	13.5	−170	10.4	−170	8.3
−160	13.0	−160	9.7	−160	7.8
−150	12.0	−150	8.3	−150	6.3
−140	10.5	−145	7.7	−145	5.0
−130	7.2	−140	6.6	−141	2.2
−128	4.5	−135	3.0	−145	−0.6
−130	1.5	−140	−0.6	−150	−2.0
−140	−1.8	−145	−1.9	−160	−3.3
−150	−3.4	−150	−2.7	−170	−3.9
−160	−4.3	−160	−4.0	−180	−4.2
−170	−4.8	−170	−4.4		
−180	−5.1	−180	−4.8		

TABLE I-4
DATA FOR M CONTOURS

Phase angle, deg	$M = 5$ db	Phase angle, deg	$M = 9$ db	Phase angle, deg	$M = 6$ db	Phase angle, deg	$M = 12$ db
−180	7.0	−180	3.8	−180	6.0	−180	2.5
−170	6.8	−175	3.7	−170	5.7	−175	2.3
−160	6.0	−170	3.5	−160	4.8	−170	1.9
−155	5.3	−165	2.8	−155	3.9	−166	0.2
−150	4.0	−160	1.5	−150	1.0	−170	−1.2
−147	1.2	−159	0.8	−155	−1.5	−175	−1.8
−150	−0.7	−160	−0.2	−160	−2.3	−180	−1.9
−155	−2.2	−165	−1.6	−170	−3.4		
−160	−2.7	−170	−2.2	−180	−3.7		
−170	−3.5	−175	−2.4				
−180	−3.9	−180	−2.5				

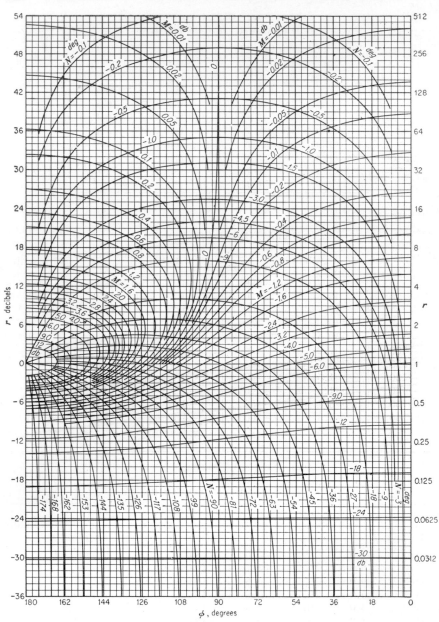

FIG. I-1. M-N-contour chart.

APPENDIX II

SERVO COMPONENTS

II-1. Introduction. Servomechanisms and other feedback control systems are used in so many fields of endeavor and have such a variety of physical natures that any attempt to list and describe all the components in use would require a complete book. Consequently, this appendix is restricted to a relatively small number of the components encountered in practice.

The components selected for inclusion are primarily those most commonly available in a college laboratory, since this text has been prepared for courses at the college level. The discussion is reasonably complete for those components which are standardized, but where considerable design variation is likely, only the general aspects are presented. A more detailed discussion of components is available in "Servomechanism Analysis" by Thaler and Brown (McGraw-Hill Book Company, Inc., New York, 1953), and references to the literature are made at appropriate points.

II-2. Error Detectors. In all feedback control systems some comparison is made between the output quantity (controlled variable) and the input quantity, or command signal. The device used to effect this comparison is commonly called an error detector, because it usually subtracts the two quantities being compared, thus producing a difference, or error, signal. In a true servomechanism, the quantities to be compared are normally mechanical positions, and three of the most commonly used error detectors are:

1. A synchro generator and control transformer
2. Two potentiometers
3. An E transformer

II-3. Synchros. The physical appearance of a synchro is similar to that of a small synchronous motor. Its stator is wound, having three coils with centers oriented at 120°. The rotor has only a single coil (except in the case of synchro differentials). This single coil is distributed in slots if the synchro is a control transformer, but is a concentrated winding on an H- or dumbbell-shaped rotor if the synchro is a generator or motor.

Synchros are never used singly except to generate test signals. They may be used in pairs, such as a synchro-generator–synchro-motor combination, or a synchro-generator–synchro-control-transformer combination. They may also be used in greater numbers, as in the case of two or more motors being driven by a single generator, or of a synchro differential unit used with two generators or a generator and a motor. The synchro motor and synchro differential are not discussed here, but the generator and control transformer are explained in the following paragraphs.

The synchro generator is a device used to produce a set of voltages which describe accurately the angular position of its shaft with respect to its stator. This is accomplished by exciting the rotor coil from a single-phase supply. The current in the rotor coil sets up an alternating magnetic field which induces a voltage in each of the three stator coils. The three induced voltages are in time phase, but their magnitudes depend on the orientation of the coils in the magnetic field.

If the shaft of the synchro is rotated, each of these voltages changes, and a plot of voltage vs. the angular position of the shaft shows that the variation of each voltage is sinusoidal. The maxima of these voltages are displaced 120° around the circumference of the synchro. The wave pattern is exactly that of a three-phase voltage supply, except that the abscissa is shaft position rather than time. Thus, any set of three coil voltages describes the angular position of the rotor shaft.

The synchro control transformer is a device designed to operate in conjunction with a synchro generator in such a way that it produces a single voltage which describes the angular difference in position between its shaft and that of the synchro generator. If the stator windings of a synchro control transformer are connected to the stator winding of a synchro generator, the voltages in the stator windings of the generator drive currents through the stator windings of the control transformer. These currents set up a single-phase magnetic field in the rotor of the control transformer. If the two machines are identical in construction, the magnetic field produced in the control transformer is identical with that in the generator.

In general, the magnetic field in the control transformer induces a voltage in the rotor winding. However, if the rotor winding is properly designed, there are two angular positions of the rotor shaft for which the induced voltage in the rotor is zero, and these positions are separated by 180°. Either of these positions may be used as a reference, i. e., when the control-transformer shaft is so oriented that there is no voltage across the rotor terminals, the generator and rotor are said to be "zeroed." If the shaft of either machine is moved, a voltage appears at the terminals of the rotor of the control transformer. For small angles, up to 10° or 15°, the magnitude of this voltage is directly proportional to the displacement, or "error," between the shafts, and the synchro-generator–control-transformer combination may be considered a *linear* error detector.

An error detector must not only produce a signal proportional to the magnitude of the error, but it must also indicate the sense, or direction, of the error. The synchro-generator–control-transformer combination does this by a phase reversal of the voltage; that is, the voltage produced by a clockwise displacement of either shaft is 180° out of phase with the voltage produced by a counterclockwise rotation of that shaft.

In order to use the synchro-generator–control-transformer combination as a position error detector, it is necessary that proper zero alignment be obtained by adjustment. Either the generator or the control transformer may be shafted to the output, and the other unit used as an input; the reference adjustment may be made at either unit.

The controller into which the error voltage is fed must be phase-sensitive, i. e., it must be capable of reversing its output when the phase of the error voltage reverses. Finally, the error signal must be fed into the controller in proper phase, i. e., in such a manner that the output produced by the system tends to reduce the error.

In some applications a servomechanism using synchro error detectors may be required to operate at constant or nearly constant velocity. Under such conditions the rotor-induced voltage contains a component due to the velocity of the rotor. This component of voltage is not related to the position error. It is in time quadrature with the true error voltage and is commonly called a "speed voltage." Because it is in time quadrature with the error voltage, it normally does not contribute directly to the operating characteristics of the system, but it may cause saturation in some components in the controller, with consequent impaired performance.

It should be noted that the synchro-generator–control-transformer combination is also a transducer, in that it subtracts two mechanical-shaft positions and converts this difference into an electrical voltage. Consequently, there is a conversion factor associated with this change. This factor is known as the synchro-sensitivity constant and is normally expressed in volts-per-radian error. It is a necessary factor in computing the system gain.

II-4. Potentiometers as Error Detectors. Two potentiometers may be connected, as in Fig. II-1, and used to produce a voltage proportional to the angular position between the potentiometer shafts. The voltage may be either a-c or d-c, as desired. Note that, if the two pickoff brushes are at the same percentage travel from one end of the potentiometers, there is zero potential difference between them. Displacement of either shaft produces an error voltage proportional to the percentage displacement. If a d-c voltage is used, the polarity of the voltage depends on the direction of displacement, and if an a-c voltage is used, there is a 180° phase change about the null point, as in the case of synchros.

Certain factors must be considered in the selection and use of potentiometers for error detectors. Wire-wound potentiometers are usually preferred because they can be made with greater linearity and because their characteristics do not change appreciably with time. Good mechanical design is important in reducing friction drag and must also be considered in terms of the operating life of the potentiometer. Wire size determines the ultimate accuracy available, since the voltage variation is not continuous but changes in discrete incremental steps as the pickoff brush moves from wire to wire. The mechanical travel of a potentiometer is limited. If stops are used in the potentiometer, the brush arm may be bent or broken by overshooting. When stops are not used, mechanical damage is avoided but overshooting may cause loss of synchronization or calibration. Where the load shaft must rotate through more than one revolution, helical potentiometers may be used. This permits extended travel but, in general, decreases the error-detector sensitivity, i. e., the error voltage per unit angular displacement between shafts.

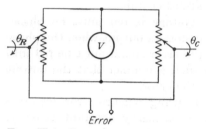

FIG. II-1. Potentiometer error detector.

Note that the connections shown in the circuit of Fig. II-1 are not necessarily ideal. The error detector may be set up and used exactly as shown, but certain other factors must then be considered. The error voltage would normally be fed into an electronic amplifier. If typical amplifier design is used, one of the input terminals will be grounded. If this is so, the voltage supplying the potentiometers cannot be grounded. Since circuit design varies considerably, no additional comments are made here.

II-5. The E Transformer. When small angular displacements are to be measured, and it is desired to eliminate frictional effects, an E transformer is a useful error detector. Devices of this type are often used in gyroscopes, and a sketch is shown in Fig. II-2. The transformer is a laminated-iron structure shaped like a letter E, as shown. A coil is wound on each leg, and the coils on the outside legs should be identical. An alternating voltage is applied to the coil on the center leg, and it sets up a magnetic field which passes through the air gap to the keeper bar and back to the outside legs. To use the device, the E magnet and the keeper bar must be fastened to the two members between which the dis-

placement is to occur, and the keeper bar must be lined up mechanically
to be parallel to the faces of the E-magnet fingers.   The amount of air
gap permissible depends on the design of the E transformer.   Additional
alignment is required to center the keeper bar when the system is at
zero error.

The operation of the E transformer is as follows: When the keeper is
parallel and centered, the magnetic-field pattern is symmetrical about
the center leg, and so the voltages induced in the two end coils are
identical.   The coils are then connected bucking, so that the error voltage is zero.   The mechanical displacement must be such as to move the
keeper across the face of the E mag-
net while maintaining the parallel
relationship.   Such motion increases
the reluctance of the air gap over one
end pole, thus reducing the induced
voltage in the coil on that pole.   The
two induced voltages are then different in magnitude; hence they do not
cancel out, and a net error voltage is
obtained.   Directional sensitivity is
obtained by a 180° phase shift at the
null point.   By proper design the
magnitude of the error voltage is made

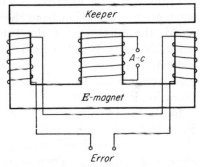

Fig. II-2. E transformer for position error detection.

directly proportional to the displacement for a limited range of travel.

II-6. Servo Amplifiers.   Quite a large number and variety of amplify-
ing devices are used as servo amplifiers.   These include rotating amplifiers such as the amplidyne, Rototrol, and Regulex; hydraulic amplifiers;
magnetic amplifiers; and many types of electronic amplifiers.   A detailed
discussion of these is impractical here,* and the following brief remarks
are limited to electronic amplifiers.

Electronic amplifiers built for servo applications may be classified
roughly as d-c or a-c amplifiers.   In general, they are essentially the
same as amplifiers built for any instrumentation or audio work.   The
d-c amplifiers normally need an output with reversible polarity and must
accept input signals of reversible polarity.   These requirements may
result in a few circuit modifications, but otherwise the design procedures
follow standard practices.   The a-c amplifiers normally are designed for
single-frequency operation, usually at 60 cycles or 400 cycles.   Their
pass band seldom exceeds about 15 per cent plus or minus about the
carrier frequency, and the frequency-response characteristics are readily
specified to be essentially constant gain and constant (but not necessarily

* See Thaler, G. J., and R. G. Brown, "Servomechanism Analysis," McGraw-Hill
Book Company, Inc., New York, 1953.

zero) phase shift over this pass band. These specifications are easily met with normal amplifier design techniques. The only additional specification might be that of phase sensitivity, i. e., the output must reverse in phase when the input phase reverses. This is easily accomplished.

One way to obtain phase sensitivity is to apply an alternating-plate voltage. The usual procedure is to use two output tubes connected to the a-c plate supply so that both tube plates are driven positive simultaneously. The grids, on the other hand, are fed 180° out of phase. For an input signal of given phase, the grid and plate of one tube are driven positive, while in the other tube the plate is driven positive and the grid is driven negative. The plate current from one tube is thus much greater than that from the other. For a 180° reversal of the input signal, the operation of the tubes interchanges, thus providing phase sensitivity if a suitable load circuit is used. When operated in this fashion, the output wave shape is not a good sine wave. However, most servo loads are essentially low-pass filters so that nearly linear operation is obtained.

In some applications the error detector provides a low-level d-c signal. Since high-gain d-c amplifiers often are troublesome, a chopper, or synchronous vibrating switch, may be used to convert the d-c signal to alternating current. Then a normal a-c amplifier may be used to raise the level. If the servo load requires alternating current, no other modifications are necessary. If the servo load requires d-c power, then the output of the a-c amplifier must be rectified. Normal rectifier circuits may be used, but they may produce undesired attenuation. A second chopper is often employed as a rectifier by synchronizing it to chop as the a-c voltage goes through zero, thus inverting the negative half wave. When so used, the chopper is usually located in a low-current stage since the contacts normally cannot handle more than a few milliamperes. Power amplification is then handled in a single d-c stage.

II-7. Compensation of A-C Servos. As is clearly shown in the text, transient-performance difficulties may be compensated for by introducing a device which produces a phase lead at the higher frequencies in the pass band of the servo, but the attenuation accompanying this phase lead is normally undesirable and must be counteracted by a gain increase. Steady-state-performance errors may be compensated for by introducing a phase-lag device in which the desired characteristic is attenuation at high frequencies, the attendant phase lag being an undesirable feature which must be accepted by the system.

These features are general, applying to both d-c and a-c servos, and the desired effect may be obtained by introducing cascaded elements in the main transmission channel or by feedback devices. The illustrations in the text were restricted to d-c systems, and only simple filter networks

were used. Various other networks for d-c servo compensation are discussed in the literature, but they are beyond the scope of this text. In
the case of a-c servos, the basic compensation problem is the same, but
the circuits used are necessarily somewhat different.

If a sinusoidal command signal is applied to an a-c servo, the voltage
wave shape in the error channel is that of a modulated wave; more specifically, it is that of a suppressed-carrier modulated wave. In terms of
physical reasoning, a phase-lead compensator should produce phase shift
in the envelope of the wave, not in the carrier. For phase-lag compensation, additional attenuation should be inserted for high-frequency command signals. The mathematical equations for the suppressed-carrier
modulated signal describe it in terms
of sideband frequencies. In terms
of sidebands, phase-lead compensation is accomplished by producing
phase shift at the upper sideband
frequencies, and steady-state errors
require attenuation of the upper
sideband frequencies.

A simple and effective method for
accomplishing this is to demodulate
(rectify) the error signal, obtain the
desired compensation with a d-c
filter network, and then remodulate.
A convenient and satisfactory way
to do this is with two choppers; one
rectifies the a-c signal by chopping
at the zero-voltage point, and the
second chopper converts the signal

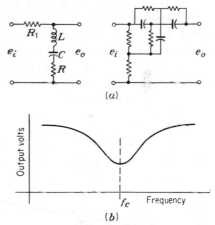

(a)

(b)

Fig. II-3. A-C phase-lead networks.
(a) Resonant and parallel T notch
filters. (b) Frequency-response curve
of a notch filter.

back to a-c after it has passed through the d-c filter. Although this
method is effective, it is expensive; in addition, choppers may not be
permissible in some applications. It is therefore desirable to attain the
same result with a network which will operate directly on the a-c error
signal.

Little work has been done on a-c networks for steady-state error compensation, but a-c phase-lead compensation networks have been devised.
The networks used for such compensation are in general single-frequency
rejection filters or "notch" filters. They are designed so that the rejected
frequency is the a-c carrier frequency, but they must have a bypass
channel which permits passage of some voltage at that frequency in order
to provide synchronization. Two networks capable of the desired performance are shown in Fig. II-3a. Their general frequency-response
characteristics are shown in Fig. II-3b.

The exact transfer function of these notch filters is easily derived in terms of the general frequency variable, ω. However, the transfer function must be expressed in terms of the signal, or data, frequency, ω_d, in order to be useful in analysis and design. In general, the exact transfer function in terms of the data frequency is cumbersome, and an approximation is made by assuming that the notch has straight-line sides, as shown in Fig. II-4, and that these straight lines intersect at the carrier frequency. With this assumption, it can be shown that the approximate transfer function is

$$KG = A + j\omega B$$

where A = bypass output
$\qquad B$ = slope of notch Y/X

In practice, the notch is not shaped as assumed, but it may be calculated or measured readily and a straight-line approximation drawn. Normal procedure is to draw the straight-line approximation from the bottom of the notch to the half-power point, i. e., the point on the notch curve for which the voltage is $\sqrt{2}$ times the voltage at the bottom of the notch.

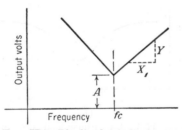

FIG. II-4. Idealized notch characteristics.

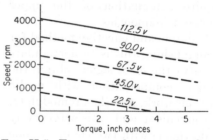

FIG. II-5. Torque-speed curves of a d-c shunt motor.

II-8. Electric Servo Motors. The only two types of motors to be discussed in this section are the d-c shunt motor and the two-phase induction motor. Conventional single-phase, three-phase, and series motors may be used in servo applications, but normally they are used in nonlinear applications, i. e., either they are controlled through relays, or they operate at constant speed and are connected to the load through a clutch of some sort. Occasionally a field-controlled d-c motor is used (constant armature current), but this is not discussed here.

The d-c shunt motor as used in most servo applications has a constant voltage applied to its field circuit, and is controlled by varying the voltage applied to its armature. The approximate transfer function of a d-c shunt motor has been derived in Chap. 4. Name-plate data on a small d-c shunt-connected servomotor might be as follows:

$$\begin{array}{ll} \text{110 volts d-c} & \text{0.22 amp} \\ \text{4,000 rpm} & \frac{1}{60} \text{ hp} \end{array}$$

The moment of inertia, J, of the motor armature is needed if the transfer function or time constant of the motor is wanted, as is also a torque-speed curve. If this information is obtained from the manufacturer or is measured, and the torque-speed curve is as given in Fig. II-5, the desired information may be computed as follows:

1. Note that the torque-speed curve is a straight line in the range of values plotted. For reduced armature voltages, the corresponding curves would be parallel straight lines with spacings proportional to the voltage, as indicated by the broken-line curves.

2. The equation of this family of curves is

$$T = PV + \frac{\partial T}{\partial \omega}\omega$$

where T = motor torque
V = voltage
P = a constant, with dimensions of torque/voltage
ω = speed, rpm

The constant P is the rate of change of torque with respect to voltage. It is a constant only because the curves are straight parallel lines, and it may be evaluated from the curves in several ways, one of which is

$$P = \frac{\text{stalled torque at any voltage}}{\text{voltage producing that torque}}$$

Thus, from the curves, the numerical value of P in this case is

$$P = \frac{3.85}{22.5} = 0.172 \text{ oz-in./volt}$$

The partial derivative of torque with respect to speed is also a constant in this case because the curves are straight lines and the partial derivative is simply the slope of the curve. In this case

$$-\frac{\partial T}{\partial \omega} = \frac{5.3}{1,150} = 0.0046 \text{ oz-in./rpm}$$

3. From steps 1 and 2, the motor transfer function may be determined approximately, provided it is permissible to neglect bearing and brush friction. With this assumption,

$$J\frac{d^2\theta_C}{dt^2} = T = PV + \frac{\partial T}{\partial \omega}\omega = PV + \frac{\partial T}{\partial \omega}\frac{d\theta_C}{dt}$$

From which

$$\frac{\theta_C}{V} = \frac{-\dfrac{P}{\partial T/\partial \omega}}{j\omega\left(j\omega\dfrac{J}{-\partial T/\partial \omega} + 1\right)} = \frac{0.172/0.0046}{j\omega\left(\dfrac{J}{0.0046}j\omega + 1\right)}$$

$$\frac{\theta_C}{V} = \frac{37.4}{j\omega(217.5Jj\omega + 1)}$$

But from Eq. (4-50) the approximate transfer function is

$$\frac{\theta_c}{V} = \frac{1/K_e}{j\omega(j\omega\tau_m + 1)}$$

Thus

$$\frac{1}{K_e} = 37.4$$

and

$$\tau_m = 217.5J$$

If J is known, then the approximate transfer function of the motor is determined.

Rewriting the differential equation,

$$J\frac{d^2\theta_c}{dt^2} - \frac{\partial T}{\partial \omega}\frac{d\theta_c}{dt} = PV$$

it is seen that $-\partial T/\partial \omega$ is the coefficient of the first-derivative term. It is therefore called the damping coefficient of the motor, and by proper conversion may be expressed in foot-pounds per radian per second.

The two-phase induction servomotor has a squirrel-cage rotor specially designed for low inertia. The shaft is usually mounted in ball bearings. The stator is generally wound with multiple poles, six or eight poles being common, and of course there are two coils which are in space and time quadrature. The rotor is normally a high-resistance type to provide large starting torques, and consequently the motor runs with considerable slip. In a well-designed two-phase servomotor, there is no tendency to single phase, i. e., the rotor stops almost instantly if the control phase is deenergized.

Unlike a d-c motor, a two-phase motor may be operated under stall conditions without appreciable ill effect; consequently torque-speed characteristics, when available, cover the entire range of speeds from full speed to stall. Normal operation in a servo system is in the speed range near stall conditions, and in this range the torque-speed curve is essentially a straight line. The family of curves for various control-field voltages is a set of straight and nearly parallel lines in this region of normal operation. As a first approximation, therefore, the torque-speed curves of a two-phase motor may be considered as straight parallel lines similar to the d-c motor characteristics of Fig. II-5. As a result, the equations previously derived for the d-c motor apply also to the two-phase motor, and the damping constant of the two-phase motor is approximately the slope of the torque-speed curve. The approximate time constant is the rotor inertia divided by the damping constant.

Figure II-6 is a family of measured torque-speed curves for a two-phase motor. It is seen that the curves are not straight lines, nor are the curves parallel. Consequently the two-phase motor is a nonlinear device. Its time constant is actually a function of the control voltage, and so is its damping coefficient, and the linear approximation gives accurate results only when the motor is operated within a specified speed and voltage range.

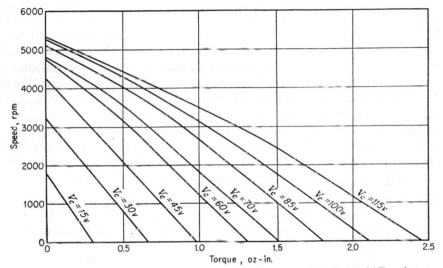

Fig. II-6. Torque-speed curves for a two-phase motor, Kearfott R-111-2AB, reference field at 115 volts, 400 cycles.

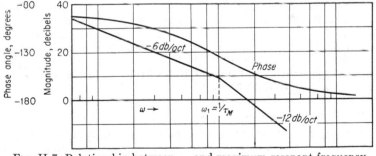

Fig. II-7. Relationship between τ_m and maximum resonant frequency.

II-9. Estimation of System Performance from the Motor Time Constant.
If the time constant of a motor is obtained from the torque-speed characteristics (or by other means), it may be said that the highest resonant frequency obtainable in a closed-loop servo using that motor is approximately equal to the reciprocal of the motor time constant. This statement may be justified by the following reasoning:

Assume that the closed-loop system using the motor will have no additional time constants, and that a resonance peak $M_p = 2.0$ is the maximum desirable. Then a phase margin of 30° would be necessary, and the decibel vs. log ω plot for the system would be as given in Fig. II-7. For a system represented by the asymptotes of Fig. II-7 it can be shown that the natural frequency* is the frequency at which the -12 db/octave asymptote intercepts the 0-db axis. The resonant frequency is somewhat lower than the natural frequency and thus is nearly at $\omega_1 = 1/\tau_m$. However, when the motor is used in a closed-loop system, it is loaded with the inertia of a gear train, the output measuring device, and the load inertia. These inertias tend to make the combined motor-load time constant a larger number than the motor time constant, and this effectively *reduces* the natural frequency and the resonant frequency. Thus it is seen that the reciprocal of the motor time constant is a reasonable approximation for the highest probable resonant frequency. The use of a phase-lead compensator can increase the resonant frequency somewhat, and if a value of $M_p > 2.0$ is acceptable some increase in resonant frequency is obtainable.

REFERENCES

ATTURA, G. M., Effects of Carrier Shifts on Derivative Networks from A-C Servomechanisms, *Trans. AIEE*, 1951.

BLACKBURN, J. F., "Components Handbook," McGraw-Hill Book Company, Inc., New York, 1949.

CHESTNUT, H., Electrical Accuracy of Selsyn Generator-control Transformer System, *Trans. AIEE*, 1946.

CHESTNUT, H., Obtaining Attenuation-frequency Characteristics for Servomechanisms, *Gen. Elec. Rev.*, December, 1947.

EDWARDS, R. S., Selecting Electric Servomotors, *Machine Design*, January, 1949.

NEWTON, G. C., What Size Motor?, *Machine Design*, November, 1950.

SOBSZYK, A., Carrier Frequency Servomechanisms, *J. Franklin Inst.*, 1948.

TSCHUDI, E. W., Transfer Functions of *RC* and *RL* Equalizer Networks, *Electronics*, May, 1949.

TUTTLE, W. M., Bridged T and Parallel T Null Circuits for Measurements at Radio Frequencies, *Proc. IRE*, 1940.

WHITE, C. F., Transfer Characteristics of a Bridged Parallel T Network, *Naval Research Lab. Rept.* R-3167.

* See Thaler, G. J., and R. G. Brown, "Servomechanism Analysis," p. 255, McGraw-Hill Book Company, Inc., New York, 1953.

APPENDIX III

AN INTRODUCTION TO THE
LAPLACE TRANSFORMATION

III-1. Introduction. The Laplace transformation is at present the most popular form of operational calculus. It has many uses which are beyond the scope of this introductory treatment, the purpose of which is to present the fundamental theorems and their application to servomechanism analysis.

From a practical engineering point of view, the Laplace transformation is a simple mathematical means of changing a differential equation expressed in terms of the time variable, t, into an algebraic equation expressed in terms of the variable s. The advantage of this lies in the following facts:

1. The resulting algebraic equation is readily manipulated, using the normal laws of algebra.

2. Boundary conditions and forcing functions, which are sometimes difficult to handle in solving differential equations, are inserted automatically in the process of applying the Laplace transformation.

Once the algebraic manipulation has been completed, the result may be utilized in one of two ways:

1. The equation may be converted back to the time domain, thus obtaining the solution of the differential equation.

2. Useful information may be obtained from the algebraic equation, usually by inserting convenient values for the variable, s, and plotting curves.

Both of these applications of the Laplace transformation will be illustrated and explained in later sections.

III-2. Basic Definitions. The variable s used in the Laplace transformation is a complex variable

$$s = \sigma + j\omega$$

where σ is a real number, and ω is an angular velocity with dimensions of radians per second. The formal relationship between the time variable, t, and the complex variable, s (as established in the Laplace transformation), is defined by the equation

$$F(s) = \int_0^\infty f(t)e^{-st}\, dt$$

This relationship states that an expression in the real variable, t [expressed by the term $f(t)$ in the equation], may be transformed into an expression in the complex variable, s [symbolized by $F(s)$ in the equation], by forming the product $f(t)e^{-st}$ and integrating this product between the limits $t = 0$ and $t = \infty$. There are restrictions on the continuity of $f(t)$ which are not discussed here, and also the real part of the complex variable must be large enough to assure that the integral converges. If these conditions are met, the function of time, $f(t)$, may be transformed into a function of the complex variable, $F(s)$, by performing the indicated integration.

III-3. Transforms of Special Functions.   In this section a number of common direct transforms are indicated symbolically. The actual integration is not performed, and it is suggested that the student check those with which he is not familiar.

1. Let $f(t)$ be $u(t) = 1$.   Then

$$F(s) = \int_0^\infty u(t)e^{-st}\, dt = \frac{1}{s}$$

2. Let $f(t)$ be A, a constant.   Then

$$F(s) = \int_0^\infty Ae^{-st}\, dt = \frac{A}{s}$$

3. Let $f(t)$ be t.   Then

$$F(s) = \int_0^\infty te^{-st}\, dt = \frac{1}{s^2}$$

4. Let $f(t)$ be t^2.   Then

$$F(s) = \int_0^\infty t^2 e^{-st}\, dt = \frac{2}{s^3}$$

5. Let $f(t)$ be t^n.   Then

$$F(s) = \int_0^\infty t^n e^{-st}\, dt = \frac{n}{s^{n+1}}$$

6. Let $f(t)$ be $\sin \omega t$.   Then

$$F(s) = \int_0^\infty \sin \omega t\, e^{-st}\, dt = \frac{\omega}{s^2 + \omega^2}$$

7. Let $f(t)$ be $\cos \omega t$.   Then

$$F(s) = \int_0^\infty \cos \omega t\, e^{-st}\, dt = \frac{s}{s^2 + \omega^2}$$

8. Let $f(t)$ be $e^{-\alpha t}$. Then

$$F(s) = \int_0^\infty e^{-\alpha t} e^{-st} \, dt = \frac{1}{s + \alpha}$$

9. Let $f(t)$ be $e^{-\alpha t} \sin \omega t$. Then

$$F(s) = \int_0^\infty e^{-\alpha t} \sin \omega t \, e^{-st} \, dt = \frac{\omega}{(s + \alpha)^2 + \omega^2}$$

III-4. Important Laplace-transformation Theorems. The following theorems are presented because they are needed in the solutions of transient problems and servo problems. They are stated without much auxiliary comment since they are referred to where they are applied later in this appendix, and the explanations made with the application are deemed sufficient.

Real Differentiation Theorem. The equations of the systems to be studied will, in general, contain various derivatives. It is therefore necessary that these terms be transformed. This may be accomplished in the following manner:

THEOREM: To find the Laplace transform of a derivative $df(t)/dt$, it is first required that both $f(t)$ and its derivative be $\mathcal{L}$ transformable. Then, if the transform of $f(t)$ is $F(s)$,

$$\mathcal{L}\left[\frac{df(t)}{dt}\right] = sF(s) - f(0+)$$

PROOF: Let $df(t)/dt$ be symbolized as $f'(t)$. It is known that

$$F(s) = \int_0^\infty f(t) e^{-st} \, dt$$

Let $u = f(t)$ and $dv = e^{-st} \, dt$. Then, integrating by parts,

$$\int u \, dv = uv - \int v \, du$$

$$\int_0^\infty f(t) e^{-st} \, dt = \frac{f(t) e^{-st}}{s}\bigg|_0^\infty - \int_0^\infty -\frac{1}{s} e^{-st} f'(t) \, dt$$

$$F(s) = \frac{f(0+)}{s} + \frac{1}{s} \int_0^\infty f'(t) e^{-st} \, dt$$

from which

$$\int_0^\infty f'(t) e^{-st} \, dt = sF(s) - f(0+)$$

and the left-hand term is, by definition, the Laplace transformation of $f'(t)$. The term $f(0+)$ is the constant obtained by evaluating the function $f(t)$ as t approaches zero from positive values.

It may be shown in like manner that the Laplace transform of the nth derivative is given by

$$\left[\frac{d^n f(t)}{dt^n}\right] = s^n F(s) - \sum_1^n \frac{d^{k-1} f(t)}{dt^{k-1}} (0+) s^{n-k}$$

In the above equation, for the case where $k = 1$, $d^0 f(t)/dt^0 \triangleq f(t)$.

Real Integration Theorem. For many practical systems, the equations contain an integral term. It is therefore necessary to transform such terms, and the Laplace transform of an integral may be found from:

THEOREM: To find the Laplace transform of an integral term, $\int f(t)\, dt$, it is necessary that both $f(t)$ and $\int f(t)\, dt$ be transformable. Then, symbolizing the integral by $f^{-1}(t)$, the Laplace transform of the integral is:

$$\mathcal{L}\left[\int f(t)\, dt\right] = \frac{F(s)}{s} + \frac{f^{-1}(0+)}{s}$$

PROOF: $\int_0^\infty f(t)e^{-st}\, dt = F(s)$. Let $u = e^{-st}$ and $dv = f(t)\, dt$. Integrating by parts,

$$\int u\, dv = uv - \int v\, du$$

$$\int_0^\infty f(t)e^{-st}\, dt = e^{-st} \int f(t)\, dt \bigg|_0^\infty + s\int_0^\infty \left[\int f(t)\, dt\right] e^{-st}\, dt$$

$$F(s) = -f^{-1}(0+) + s\int_0^\infty \left[\int f(t)\, dt\right] e^{-st}\, dt$$

$$\int_0^\infty \left[\int f(t)\, dt\right] e^{-st}\, dt = \frac{F(s)}{s} + \frac{f^{-1}(0+)}{s}$$

In the above equation, the left-hand term is the Laplace transform of $\int f(t)\, dt$. The term $f^{-1}(0+)$ is by definition the value of $\int f(t)\, dt$ evaluated as t approaches zero from positive values.

Expressions for the Laplace transform of terms involving multiple integrals may be derived in like manner. Since such terms are not encountered in the remainder of this text, the result is not presented here.

Initial-value Theorem. In some cases, after the transformed equation has been obtained and manipulated, it is desired to check the behavior of the function of time in the region near $t = 0$. This can always be done by making the inverse transformation, but considerable labor is usually involved in this process. It is possible (and much simpler) to check the initial value of the variable by merely substituting a number in the transformed equation.

THEOREM: If the Laplace transform of $f(t)$ is $F(s)$ (a known expression), and if the two additional conditions are met,

1. $df(t)/dt$ is $\mathcal{L}$ transformable.
2. The limit of $sF(s)$ exists as s approaches infinity.   Then

$$\lim_{s \to \infty} sF(s) = \lim_{t \to 0} f(t)$$

PROOF: It has been shown that

$$\int_0^\infty f'(t)e^{-st}\, dt = sF(s) - f(0+)$$

Let $s \to \infty$; then

$$\lim_{s \to \infty} \int_0^\infty f'(t)e^{-st}\, dt = \lim_{s \to \infty} [sF(s) - f(0+)]$$
$$0 = \lim_{s \to \infty} sF(s) - \lim_{s \to \infty} f(0+)$$
$$\lim_{s \to \infty} sF(s) = \lim_{s \to \infty} f(0+)$$

The right-hand side of this equation is not a function of s, and therefore is not affected by letting s vary.   By definition,

$$f(0+) = \lim_{t \to 0} f(t) \qquad \text{Q.E.D.}$$

Final-value Theorem.   When studying transients, the final steady-state value is often of considerable importance.   For example, if a servomechanism system is being analyzed from the transient point of view, it is a worthwhile precaution to check the final steady-state condition first, provided this is possible.   The reason for this is that the final steady-state performance must be as specified or the servo system is not satisfactory, in which case it is useless to complete the transient analysis.

When using the Laplace transformation, it is possible to check the final steady-state value of the time performance simply by multiplying the transformed equation by s and substituting a numerical value for $s(s = 0)$.   This procedure is the result of the final-value theorem which may be stated as follows:

THEOREM: If the Laplace transform of $f(t)$ is $F(s)$, and if certain conditions are satisfied,

1. $f(t)$ and $df(t)/dt$ must be $\mathcal{L}$ transformable.
2. $s\bar{F}(s)$ must be analytic on the axis of imaginaries and in the whole of the right half-plane; then

$$\lim_{s \to 0} sF(s) = \lim_{t \to \infty} f(t)$$

PROOF: By definition,

$$\int_0^\infty f(t)e^{-st}\, dt = F(s)$$

and it has been shown that

$$\int_0^\infty f'(t)e^{-st}\, dt = sF(s) - f(0+)$$

Letting s approach zero,

$$\lim_{s \to 0} \int_0^\infty f'(t)e^{-st}\, dt = \lim_{s \to 0} [sF(s) - f(0+)]$$

Taking this limit on the left-hand side only,

$$\int_0^\infty f'(t)\, dt = \lim_{s \to 0} [sF(s) - f(0+)]$$

But

$$\int_0^\infty f'(t)\, dt = \lim_{t \to \infty} \int_0^t f'(\tau)\, d\tau = \lim_{t \to \infty} [f(t) - f(0+)]$$

Thus

$$\lim_{t \to \infty} [f(t) - f(0+)] = \lim_{s \to 0} [sF(s) - f(0+)]$$

From which,

$$\lim_{t \to \infty} f(t) = \lim_{s \to 0} sF(s)$$

Real Translation. By definition of the Laplace integral, the transformed function is zero for values of the independent variable which are less than zero, i. e., the integral $\int_0^\infty f(t)e^{-st}\, dt$ states that t is to be considered as having only positive values. It is therefore possible to move, or translate, the origin of the coordinate system along the real axis by the simple expedient of defining the variable as $\tau = t \mp t_1$. This has various applications and is particularly useful in studying transients which involve several successive switching operations.

THEOREM: If $f(t)$ is $\mathcal{L}$ transformable and has the transform $F(s)$, and if t_1 is a real positive number, then

$$\mathcal{L}f(t - t_1) = e^{-t_1 s}F(s)$$

where $f(t - t_1) = 0$ for $0 < t < t_1$, and

$$\mathcal{L}[f(t + t_1)] = e^{t_1 s}F(s)$$

where $f(t + t_1) = 0$ for $-t_1 < t < 0$.

PROOF: The Laplace transform integral has the general form

$$\int_0^\infty f(\tau)e^{-s\tau}\, d\tau = F(s)$$

If

$$\tau = t - t_1$$

then

$$\int_0^\infty [f(t - t_1)e^{-s(t-t_1)}]\, dt = F(s)$$

or

$$e^{st_1} \int_{t_1}^\infty f(t - t_1)e^{-st}\, dt = F(s)$$

Multiply both sides by e^{-st_1}, and

$$\int_{t_1}^{\infty} f(t - t_1)e^{-st}\, dt = e^{-st_1}F(s)$$

If $f(t - t_1) = 0$ for $0 < t < t_1$, then the lower limit of the integration can be changed from t_1 to 0.

$$\int_{0}^{\infty} f(t - t_1)e^{-st}\, dt = e^{-st_1}F(s)$$

Transform of an Impulse—Transfer Function. A pulse may be defined as a function which has a finite unidirectional amplitude and a finite, but incremental, duration. If the duration of the pulse is made to approach zero while the amplitude of the pulse is increased, so as to keep the area under the curve constant, then the limit which is approached is said to be an *impulse.* Furthermore, it is convenient in the derivation of the transform to consider that the area under the pulse curve is unity; then the impulse derived by the limiting process may be called "unit impulse."

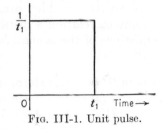

Fig. III-1. Unit pulse.

The actual shape of the pulse curve is not important mathematically because, in general, the same limit is approached, i. e., the resulting impulse is the same. For the purposes of this text, consider the flat-topped pulse in Fig. III-1. The area enclosed is unity; thus this may be considered a unit pulse. It may be considered as the difference of two step functions, so that the time equation of the pulse is

$$f(t) = \frac{u(t)}{t_1} - \frac{u(t - t_1)}{t_1}$$

The Laplace transform of this function is

$$F(s) = \frac{1}{st_1} - \frac{e^{-st_1}}{st_1}$$

Inspection shows that if t_1 approaches zero, both terms become indeterminate. Further investigation shows that

$$\lim_{t_1 \to 0}\left[\frac{1 - e^{-t_1 s}}{t_1 s}\right] = \lim_{t_1 \to 0} e^{-t_1 s} = 1.0$$

Therefore, the Laplace transform of a unit impulse is

$$\mathcal{L}\left[\lim \frac{u(t) - u(t - t_1)}{t_1}\right] \overset{\Delta}{=} \mathcal{L}u_1(t) = 1.0$$

The unit impulse, of itself, is not used extensively in this text. It is important in the interpretation of the real convolution integral (which is discussed later) and in the definition of transfer functions.

The concept of a transfer function arises from the basic principles governing the transfer of energy. If a disturbance, or "forcing function," is applied at some point in a physical system, the effect of this disturbance is noticeable at other points in the system. The specific reaction of the system at any chosen point is called the *response* of the system to the disturbance. In order that a response be obtainable, there must be a transfer of energy from the location of the disturbance to the location of the response, and any suitable function which describes this transfer in terms of the system parameters may be called a transfer function.

In using the Laplace transformation to study physical systems, particularly those which are linear systems with lumped parameters, the equations relating a disturbance and a response are normally algebraic equations of the general form

$$H(s) = G(s)F(s)$$

where $H(s)$ = transform of system response

$F(s)$ = transform of disturbance or "forcing function"

$G(s)$ = transform involving parameters of system (called either the "system function" or the "transfer function")

It is readily seen that if the disturbance is a unit impulse, $u_1(t)$, then the forcing function is $F(s) = \mathcal{L}u_1(t) = 1$, and the above equation becomes

$$H(s) = G(s)$$

This leads to the basic definition of a transfer function:

The *transfer function* of a physical system is the Laplace transform of the response of that system to a unit impulse.

An equivalent (and more commonly used) definition is obtained by rearranging the basic relationship.

$$G(s) = \frac{H(s)}{F(s)}$$

This leads to the definition:

A *transfer function* is the ratio of the Laplace transform of the response of a system (to any input) to the Laplace transform of the forcing function which causes that response.

Transfer functions are utilized more often in steady-state sinusoidal analysis than they are in transient analysis, but they can be very useful in setting up the characteristic equation of some rather complex systems and are used for this purpose later in the text.

III-5. Methods of Finding Inverse Transforms. *Complex Integration.* The basic mathematical equation defining the time function corresponding to a given transformed function is the complex integral

$$\frac{1}{2\pi j} \int_{c-j\infty}^{c+j\infty} F(s)e^{-st}\, ds\ (=) f(t)$$

Actual evaluation of this integral for most practical cases involves excessive labor, and it is not used in this text.

Table of Transforms. Laplace transforms are normally obtained by application of the direct Laplace integral. Once obtained, they may be tabulated with the $f(t)$ from which they are derived and may be used just as integral tables are used in calculus.

Use of such tables is by far the most common method for obtaining the inverse transform. In general, too extensive a table is not practical, and most texts list only the more commonly encountered forms. Complicated forms are then reduced to simpler expressions by the partial fraction expansion or are handled by one of the methods presented later.

The Partial Fraction Expansion. In general, the transformed equation takes the algebraic form of a ratio of two polynomials: $H(s) = A(s)/B(s)$, where $A(s)$ is of lower order than $B(s)$. If $B(s)$ can be factored or its roots found in some other fashion, the function may be written as

$$\frac{A(s)}{B(s)} = \frac{A(s)}{s^n(s-s_1)(s-s_2)(s-s_3)\cdots}$$
$$= \frac{K_n}{s^n} + \frac{K_{n-1}}{s^{n-1}} + \cdots + \frac{K}{s} + \frac{K_a}{s-s_1} + \frac{K_b}{s-s_2}\cdots$$

where the series of additive terms is called the partial fraction expansion. If a common denominator is obtained for the partial fraction expression, and the numerator is collected in the usual way, then

$$\frac{A(s)}{B(s)} =$$
$$\frac{K_n(s-s_1)(s-s_2)\cdots + K_{n-1}s(s-s_1)(s-s_2)\cdots + K_{n-2}s^2(s-s_1)}{s^n(s-s_1)\cdots}$$

These expressions are defined to be equal. Their denominators are obviously identical, and therefore the numerators must be identical, term for term. Thus the coefficients, K_n, etc., in the partial fraction expansion may be evaluated by equating the coefficients of like powered terms in the two numerators and solving these equations simultaneously.

ILLUSTRATION: Let

$$F(s) = \frac{13s^2 + 16s + 4}{s(s-3)(s-4)}$$

The partial fraction expansion gives

$$\frac{13s^2 + 16s + 4}{s(s-3)(s-4)} = \frac{K_1}{s} + \frac{K_2}{s-3} + \frac{K_3}{s-4}$$
$$= \frac{K_1(s-3)(s-4) + K_2(s)(s-4) + K_3(s)(s-3)}{s(s-3)(s-4)}$$
$$= \frac{s^2(K_1 + K_2 + K_3) - s(7K_1 + 4K_2 + 3K_3) + 12K_1}{s(s-3)(s-4)}$$

Equating coefficients,

$$K_1 + K_2 + K_3 = 13$$
$$-7K_1 - 4K_2 - 3K_3 = 16$$
$$12K_1 = 4$$

from which

$$K_1 = \tfrac{1}{3}$$
$$K_2 = -169\tfrac{}{3}$$
$$K_3 = 207\tfrac{}{3}$$

Substituting these in the partial fraction expansion gives

$$F(s) = \frac{1}{3s} - \frac{169}{3(s-3)} + \frac{207}{3(s-4)}$$

and the inverse transform of each of these terms is readily obtained from the tables.

The Methods of Residues (Inversion Theorem). The theory of functions of a complex variable has developed a very simple and powerful method for inverting functions of a complex variable into functions of a real variable, i. e., for finding $f(t)$ from $F(s)$. The final result is known as the inversion theorem, and it utilizes the method of evaluating the residues of the function $F(s)$. A complete derivation of the results is desirable, but space limitations do not permit its presentation here. On the other hand, a mere statement of the final result does not seem satisfactory. Therefore, the derivation is outlined by presenting the most important relationships, and the reader is referred to a more complete text (such as Stanford Goldman's "Transformation Calculus and Electrical Transients," Prentice-Hall, Inc., New York, 1949) for the intermediate steps.

One approach to the derivation of the inversion theorem is to consider the unit step function as a contour integral. This leads to the relationship

$$u(t - t_1) = \frac{1}{2\pi j} \int_{\sigma-j\infty}^{\sigma+j\infty} \frac{e^{s(t-t_1)}}{s}\, ds$$

This expression may be used to determine the expression for a unit impulse as a contour integral, leading to the expression

$$u_1(t) = \lim_{\Delta t_1 \to 0} \frac{1}{2\pi j} \int_{\sigma-j\infty}^{\sigma+j\infty} \left(\frac{1 - e^{-s\Delta t_1}}{s\,\Delta t_1} \right) e^{-s(t-t_1)}\, ds$$

This expression is then used to consider a generalized function $f(t)$ as an infinite number of impulses, which leads to the expression

$$f(t) = \frac{1}{2\pi j} \int_{\sigma-j\infty}^{\sigma+j\infty} F(s)e^{st}\, ds$$

It may be shown by considering a contour on the complex plane that the above expression reduces to

$$f(t) = \frac{1}{2\pi j} \oint F(s)e^{st}\, ds$$

which is the mathematical expression for the inversion theorem.

Now, by definition, a residue is

$$R = \frac{1}{2\pi j} \oint F(z)\, dz$$

where z is a complex variable, and the path of integration is any closed path in the complex plane. In general, then, the time function may be obtained by determining the sum of the residues, i. e.,

$$f(t) = \Sigma R[F(s)e^{st}]$$

Residues exist at singular points, which are those values of the variable that make the function infinite. Thus, for any function which is in the form of a rational fraction, there is a residue for each root of the denominator. If the form of the function is

$$F(s) = \frac{A(s)}{(s - s_1)(s - s_2)(s - s_3)\,\cdots}$$

then the time function is obtained from

$$F(s)e^{st} = \frac{A(s)e^{st}}{(s - s_1)(s - s_2)(s - s_3)\,\cdots}$$

Thus

$$f(t) = \sum R[F(s)e^{st}] = \frac{A(s_1)e^{s_1 t}}{(s_1 - s_2)(s_1 - s_3)\,\cdots} + \frac{A(s_2)e^{s_2 t}}{(s_2 - s_1)(s_2 - s_3)\,\cdots}$$
$$+ \frac{A(s_3)e^{s_3 t}}{(s_3 - s_1)(s_3 - s_2)\,\cdots} + \cdots$$

If the denominator is not in factored form, but the poles are known, each of the terms in the summation may be determined from

$$\left. \frac{f(t)}{\text{at pole } s_1} = \frac{A(s)e^{st}}{(d/ds)B(s)} \right|_{s=s_1}$$

where $B(s)$ is the unfactored denominator, and the value $s = s_1$ must be inserted after differentiating.

Multiple-order Poles. Some functions may have multiple poles; for example,

$$F(s) = \frac{A(s)}{s^3(s - s_1)^2(s - s_2)}$$

At each multiple pole a single expression for the residue is obtained from

$$R = \frac{1}{(m-1)!} \frac{d^{m-1}}{ds^{m-1}} [(s - s_x)^m F(s)]_{s=s_x}$$

The above expression for the residue applies to both single and multiple poles, and to real as well as complex poles.   For complicated expressions the differentiation is laborious, but the desired result may be obtained without searching transform tables for a suitable transform pair.

EXAMPLES:

$$F(s) = \frac{1}{s(s-1)(s-3)}$$

$$f(t) = \frac{e^{st}}{(s-1)(s-3)}\Big|_{s=0} + \frac{e^{st}}{s(s-3)}\Big|_{s=1} + \frac{e^{st}}{s(s-1)}\Big|_{s=3}$$

$$= \frac{1}{3} + \frac{e^t}{-2} + \frac{e^{3t}}{6}$$

$$= 0.333 - 0.5e^t + 0.167e^{3t}$$

$$F(s) = \frac{s-4}{s^2(s-6)}$$

$$f(t) = \frac{d}{ds}\left(\frac{s-4}{s-6} e^{st}\right)\Big|_{s=0} + \frac{(s-4)e^{st}}{s^2}\Big|_{s=6}$$

$$= \frac{s-4}{s-6} te^{st} + \frac{e^{st}}{s-6} - \frac{s-4}{(s-6)^2} e^{st}\Big|_{s=0} + \frac{2e^{6t}}{36}$$

$$= \frac{2t}{3} - \frac{6}{36} + \frac{4}{36} + \frac{2e^{6t}}{36}$$

$$= \frac{2t}{3} - \frac{2}{36}(1 - e^{6t})$$

III-6. Applications of Laplace Transforms to Elementary Electric Circuits.

1. Consider the circuit of Fig. III-2a.   The differential equation of this circuit is

$$Eu(t) = iR + L\frac{di}{dt}$$

where $u(t)$ indicates that the closing of the switch creates a step function of applied voltage.   Multiplying through by the Laplace integral,

$$\int_0^\infty Eu(t)e^{-st} dt =$$

$$\int_0^\infty iRe^{-st} dt + \int_0^\infty L\frac{di}{dt} e^{-st} dt$$

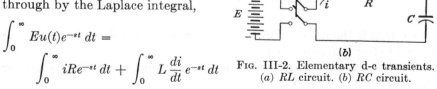

FIG. III-2. Elementary d-c transients. (a) RL circuit. (b) RC circuit.

Transforming term by term as indicated, the equation becomes

$$\frac{E}{s} = I(s)R + L[sI(s) - i(0+)]$$

where $i(0+)$ is the initial value of the current, which must be $i = 0$ because of the series inductance. Therefore

$$\frac{E}{s} = I(s)R + sLI(s)$$

Solving algebraically for $I(s)$,

$$I(s) = \frac{E}{s(sL + R)} = \frac{E/L}{s(s + R/L)}$$

To obtain i as a function of time, the inverse transformation must be determined. This is readily done with the help of a transform table, but the method of residues is applied here to illustrate its use.

$$i = s \frac{(E/L)e^{+st}}{s(s + R/L)} \bigg|_{s=0} + \left(s + \frac{R}{L}\right) \frac{(E/L)e^{+st}}{s(s + R/L)} \bigg|_{s=-(R/L)}$$

$$= \frac{E/L}{R/L} + \frac{(E/L)e^{-(Rt/L)}}{-R/L}$$

$$= \frac{E}{R} - \frac{E}{R} e^{-(Rt/L)} = \frac{E}{R} [1 - e^{-(Rt/L)}]$$

2. Consider the elementary resistance-capacitance circuit of Fig. III-2b. The differential equation of this circuit is

$$Eu(t) = iR + \frac{1}{C} \int i \, dt$$

This is transformed by using the methods applied to the RL circuit, and the result is

$$\frac{E}{s} = I(s)R + \left[\frac{I(s)}{sC} + \frac{i^{-1}(0+)}{sC}\right]$$

The initial value of the charge on the capacitor $[i^{-1}(0+)]$ may be any finite value, and here it is assumed to be zero. Then

$$\frac{E}{s} = I(s)R + \frac{I(s)}{sC}$$

Solving for $I(s)$,

$$I(s) = \frac{E}{s(R + 1/sC)} = \frac{E/R}{s + 1/CR}$$

The time solution may be obtained directly from transform 8 in Sec. III-3 and is

$$i = \frac{E}{R} e^{-(t/RC)}$$

III-7. Obtaining Transfer Functions with the Laplace Transform.

1. The fundamental definition of a transfer function is that the transfer function of a component is the response of that component to a unit-

impulse input.   Considering the circuit of Fig. III-3a, the output voltage, e_o, obtained from an input $u_1(t)$ is the transfer function of the network. The differential equation of the system is

$$u_1(t) = iR + \frac{1}{C_1} \int i \, dt$$

Transforming

$$1 = I(s)R + \frac{1}{C_1} \left[\frac{I(s)}{s} + \frac{i^{-1}(0+)}{s} \right]$$

Assuming no initial charge on C_1, this becomes

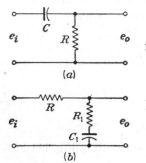

$$1 = I(s)R + \frac{I(s)}{sC_1}$$

from which

$$I(s) = \frac{1}{R + 1/sC_1} = \frac{sC_1}{sC_1R + 1}$$

But the transform of the output is

$$E_o(s) = I(s)R = \frac{sC_1R}{sC_1R + 1} = \frac{s\tau}{s\tau + 1}$$

(a)

(b)

FIG. III-3. Circuits to illustrate the derivation of transfer functions.

which is the transfer function of the network.

2. The second definition of a transfer function was given as the ratio of the transform of the output to the transform of the input for any arbitrary input.   To illustrate this, consider the circuit of Fig. III-3b, and assume an arbitrary input $e_i(t)$; then

$$e_i(t) = iR + iR_1 + \frac{1}{C_1} \int i \, dt$$

Also

$$e_o(t) = iR_1 + \frac{1}{C_1} \int i \, dt$$

Transforming,

$$E_i(s) = I(s)R + I(s)R_1 + \frac{1}{C_1} \left[\frac{I(s)}{s} + \frac{i^{-1}(0+)}{s} \right]$$

$$E_o(s) = I(s)R_1 + \frac{1}{C_1} \left[\frac{I(s)}{s} + \frac{i^{-1}(0+)}{s} \right]$$

Again assuming no initial charge on C_1, these equations become

$$E_i(s) = I(s) \left(R + R_1 + \frac{1}{sC_1} \right)$$

$$E_o(s) = I(s) \left(R_1 + \frac{1}{sC_1} \right)$$

The transfer function is

$$\frac{E_o(s)}{E_i(s)} = \frac{R_1 + 1/sC_1}{R + R_1 + 1/sC_1} = \frac{sC_1R_1 + 1}{sC_1(R + R_1) + 1} = \frac{s\tau_1 + 1}{s\tau_{12} + 1}$$

III-8. Application of the Laplace Transform to the Differential Equation of a Simple Servo System—The Use of the Final-value Theorem.

The servomechanism considered is the simple second-order servo of Fig. 3-4 in Chap. 3, and is described by the differential equation given in Eq. (3-4), which is

$$J\frac{d^2\theta_C}{dt^2} + f\frac{d\theta_C}{dt} + K\theta_C = K\theta_R$$

Assume that the input is a step-velocity function (ramp function). Then

$$\theta_R = \omega_R t$$

and the equation becomes

$$J\frac{d^2\theta_C}{dt^2} + f\frac{d\theta_C}{dt} = K\omega_R t$$

Transforming by application of the theorems developed earlier in this appendix,

$$J\left[s^2\Theta_C(s) - s\theta_C(0+) - \frac{d\theta_C}{dt}(0+) \right] + f[s\Theta_C(s) - \theta_C(0+)]$$

$$+ K\Theta_C(s) = \frac{K\omega_R}{s^2}$$

From physical reasoning,

$$\theta_C(0+) = 0$$

$$\frac{d\theta_C}{dt}(0+) = 0$$

Therefore

$$(Js^2 + fs + K)\Theta_C(s) = \frac{K\omega_R}{s^2}$$

and

$$\Theta_C(s) = \frac{K\omega_R}{s^2(Js^2 + fs + K)}$$

$$= \frac{\omega_R(K/J)}{s^2[s^2 + (f/J)s + K/J]}$$

The inverse transform may be taken to obtain $\theta_C(t)$, using residues or any other convenient method. This is left to the student as an exercise. The final-value theorem may be used to check the steady-state performance as follows:

Note that, at $t = \infty$, the output position corresponding to a constant-velocity input would be $\theta_C = \infty$, and thus it is not profitable to apply the final-value theorem to the expression for $\Theta_C(s)$. However, the steady-state error should be finite, and the final-value theorem may be applied to the equation for the error.   By definition,

$$E = \theta_R - \theta_C$$

Therefore

$$E(s) = \Theta_R(s) - \Theta_C(s)$$

Thus

$$(Js^2 + fs + K)[\Theta_R(s) - E(s)] = K\Theta_R(s)$$
$$(Js^2 + fs + K)E(s) = (Js^2 + fs + K)\Theta_R(s) - K\Theta_R(s)$$
$$= (Js^2 + fs)\Theta_R(s)$$
$$E(s) = \frac{Js^2 + fs}{Js^2 + fs + K}\Theta_R(s) = \frac{s(Js + f)}{Js^2 + fs + K} \times \frac{\omega_R}{s^2}$$
$$E(s) = \frac{Js + f}{s(Js^2 + fs + K)}\omega_R$$

To apply the final-value theorem, multiply both sides by s, and substitute $s = 0$.

$$\lim_{t \to \infty} E(t) = \lim_{s \to 0} sE(s) = \frac{Js + f}{Js^2 + fs + K}\omega_R \Big|_{s \to 0} = \frac{f}{K}\omega_R$$

Thus the steady-state error is

$$E_{ss} = \frac{f\omega_R}{K}$$

That this is the correct steady-state error may be verified from Eq. (3-15) in Chap. 3, where the steady-state error is seen to be

$$E_{ss} = \frac{2\zeta\omega_R}{\omega_n}$$

Substituting,

$$\zeta = \frac{f}{2\sqrt{KJ}}$$

$$\omega_n = \sqrt{\frac{K}{J}}$$

$$E_{ss} = \frac{2(f/2\sqrt{KJ})\omega_R}{\sqrt{K/J}}$$

$$= \frac{f\omega_R}{\sqrt{KJ}\sqrt{K/J}} = \frac{f\omega_R}{\sqrt{K^2}} = \frac{f\omega_R}{K} \qquad \text{Q.E.D.}$$

INDEX

M_p, 24, 92
Margin, gain, 89, 118, 119
 phase, 89, 116, 119
Maximum overshoot, 16, 18
Motor, counter-emf constant, 22
 d-c, 59, 258
 time constant of, 60, 66, 260, 261
 torque constant, 22
 torque-speed curves, 65, 258, 261
 two-phase, 65, 260
Multiple-loop systems, 217

N circles, 92
N contours, 96
Natural frequency, 31, 120
Networks, carrier-frequency, 257
 phase-lag, 168
 phase-lead, 149
Nyquist criterion for stability, 99
Nyquist diagrams, interpretation of, 99–
 104

Octave, 83
ω_n, 31, 120
ω_r, 24, 92
Open-loop systems, 2
Oscillation, transient, 19, 116
Overshoot, maximum or peak, 16, 18, 43,
 116

Paper-reel drive, tension control for, 3, 7
Partial fractions, 271
Peak overshoot, 16, 18, 43, 116
Performance requirements, 13, 125, 220
Phase-angle loci, 92, 96
Phase lag, 128
Phase lead, 128
Phase margin, 89, 116, 119
Phase plane, 237
Polar plot, of direct functions, 79
 of inverse functions, 93, 196, 197, 206,
  209
 stability determination from, 99
Poles of equations, 223
Position, step function of, 15, 24

Quadratic factors, 85

Ratio, damping, 31, 223
Real-differentiation theorem, 265
Real-integration theorem, 266
Real-translation theorem, 268
Reciprocal functions, 67
Relay servomechanisms, 126, 234
 with error-rate damping, 237, 240
 ideal, 235, 240
 with viscous damping, 236, 240
Residues, 272
Resonant frequency, 24, 92
Response, frequency, 24, 67, 69, 77, 92
 speed of, 16, 17, 24, 32
Response delay or lag, 229, 235
Response time, 16, 32
rms error criterion, 220
Root-locus method, 222, 223
Roots of equations, 104, 222
Routh's criterion, 104

s, complex variable, 223
Sampled-data systems, 219
Saturation, 229
 torque, 231
 velocity, 231
Sensing elements (*see* Error detectors)
Series compensation, 129, 144–182
Servomechanism, definition of, 1, 110
 design considerations, 19
 equations of, 21
 initial conditions, 28, 29
 performance criteria, 34, 37
 type 0, 110
 type 1, 112
 type 2, 115
Servomechanism systems, classification
 of, 110
Servomotors, d-c, 59, 258
 two-phase, 65, 260
Settling time, 16, 17
Speed of response, 16, 17, 24, 32
Speed-torque curves, 65, 258, 261
Stability, absolute, 98
 from logarithmic plots, 106
 Nyquist criterion for, 99
 from polar plots, 99
Stabilization (*see* Compensation)
Static friction, 228
Steady-state error, 19, 37, 110
Steady-state performance, from equa-
 tions, 109–116